A history of modern British geography

A history of modern British geography

T. W. Freeman

*Secretary, Commission on the History of Geographical Thought,
International Union of the History and Philosophy of Science,
International Geographical Union*

Emeritus Professor of Geography, Victoria University of Manchester

Longman
London and New York

Longman Group Limited London

*Associated companies, branches and representatives
throughout the world*

*Published in the United States of America
by Longman Inc., New York*

©Longman Group Limited 1980

First published 1980

British Library Cataloguing in Publication Data

Freeman, Thomas Walter
  A history of modern British geography.
  1. Geography – Great Britain – History
  I. Title
  910′.941   G98   79–41477

  ISBN 0–582–30030–4

Set in 10/11pt Comp/Set Times Roman
Printed in Great Britain by
Richard Clay (The Chaucer Press) Ltd, Bungay, Suffolk

Contents

List of maps and diagrams

Preface

Forty-three years of university teaching does not in itself produce wisdom, but at least it provides an opportunity of observing the development of a subject, the emergence of ideas, the response of geography to the challenge of war and peace, the eager arrival of new prophets, the achievements of some and the disappointment of others. In retirement it is possible to reflect on what has been seen in the working years, for there is no longer the concern for the progression of students from neat freshmen to picturesque graduates, for the routine of lectures, tutorials, examinations, field tours and ever more abundant meetings. The don's secret, withdrawn life of study and writing, so little known to the students and emulated by many of them only to a slight extent, can become more precious than ever.

To some extent the history of geography is a personal story, for geographers have reacted to the needs and challenge of their time in varied ways. In the archives of the Royal Geographical Society there is a letter from H. J. Mackinder to H. R. Mill dated 16 May 1915 saying that: 'You and I have taken somewhat different paths in Geography – you rather the scientific and I the literary', and twenty years later Mackinder wrote again saying that: 'It is indeed for both of us a glorious thing to have lived to see what I soberly believe is the beginning of the triumph of our youthful ideas (6 August 1935). Both in their different, though complementary, ways made a fine contribution to British geography and to education. In Mackinder's case, for example, much that he taught was passed on to others working in classrooms and many of his ideas stimulated others to write.

British geographers have been people varied in gifts, outlook and achievement, as a rapid reading of the bibliographical section of this book will show. Many of the earlier teachers in universities wished to provide a complete view of geography, to give it system and purpose, to lay effective foundations for later progress. They might have been surprised by conversation with teachers of the present age who explain that their major interest lies in the retail trade of cities (even of a single city), frost on motorways or intensive observation of one accessible glacier. Perhaps they would have had the imagination to realise that progress comes through detailed work, made possible only when the number of researchers has become considerable, if never adequate. Indeed, there is clear evidence that the modern pioneers, including Herbertson, Mill and Mackinder, were eager to encourage detailed work.

Geography as a study deals with the 'here and now' of human experience for individuals and for all the world. It is broader in scope than the understanding of any individual mind. In its progress its followers have found themselves led into paths they never expected to see, and if some people appear to have taken strange views, for example on racial qualities or world politics, their outlook may well have been a product of the ethos of their own times. Perhaps they are more conscious than many other academics of the relationship of their own studies to those of other specialists, even over-anxious to define their own field and at times obsessed by methodology. All this may be a sign of growth, but the future is rooted in the past and ideas may be more abiding than people, for though every age is new it is never as new as it is supposed to be.

Acknowledgement is due to various friends who have given encouragement and support over the years, and particularly to my wife and family for enduring life with a perpetually aspirant author. Helpful librarians have included those of the Royal Geographical Society and the University of Manchester. From 1975 to 1976 the Social Science Research Council gave a grant for the study of the history of geographical thought in Britain through which, with Miss M. Oughton as research associate, it was possible to collect material on British geographers and to plan the annual issue of *Geographers: Bibliographical Studies*, of which volume 1 appeared in 1977. This publication, international in scope, is one fruit of the work of the Commission on the History of Geographical Thought of the International Geographical Union and the International Union of the History and Philosophy of Science. It need hardly be said that the views expressed here are the author's own.

This book has been considered for many years, indeed ever since the British Association for the Advancement of Science, at its 1947 meeting in Dundee, gave a small grant to finance a committee to enquire into the modern revival of geography in Britain, of which J. N. L. Baker was the chairman and I was the secretary. British geographers are far less prone to celebrate anniversaries than their continental colleagues (with happy exceptions such as Sir Clements Markham who loved anniversaries and seized every opportunity of writing something as they came) but fortunately the Royal Geographical Society is publishing as a special volume a history of its 150 years of work in 1980. As I am the author of a 50,000 word contribution to that volume it should be noted that what has been written here differs in scope though naturally this book contains many references to the work of the country's major geographical society, the third oldest in the world.

To the author and no doubt to many others it is a source of

satisfaction to note that many young writers are interested in various aspects of the history of geographical thought, and are producing studies of individuals, of societies, of universities, of movements. This is not new, for the history of geographical thought has attracted writers in many periods and countries, all of whom have been conscious that their study has led them into wider fields of study and enquiry, for geography does not and cannot exist in isolation from concern for man and his world.

T. W. Freeman,
August 1979
1 Thurston Close,
Abingdon OX14 5RD

Acknowledgements

Grateful acknowledgement is made for permission to reproduce copyright material. Figure 12 has been redrawn from Sir Cyril Fox's map in *The Personality of Britain*, fourth edition, 1943, and is reproduced here by kind permission of the National Museum of Wales and the University of Wales Press Board. Figure 13, from C. B. Fawcett's *Provinces of England*, revised and reissued in 1960, appears by permission of Hutchinson and Co., who also agreed to the reproductions of figures 14, 15, and 16 from the fourth edition of T. W. Freeman, *Geography and Planning*, 1974. Permission to reproduce the letter from G. G. Chisholm to J. K. Wright was kindly given by the American Geographical Society, Broadway at 156th Street, New York.

Chapter 1

A century of progress

A hundred years ago the geographer of popular conception and widespread adulation was an explorer of pathless African jungles or Arctic snows, but now he might well be a mathematician handling quantities of statistical data and experimenting in computer-graphics, concerned more with calculus than cartography. Each in his own time has been conscious of an opportunity of exploring the world and explaining what he sees. The explorer was actuated partly by curiosity, for so much of the world was unknown and so much remained to be mapped. The modern quantitative geographer wants to explain and classify, to analyse the actual world of living experience, to show that there is pattern, order and sequence in so much that has happened, is happening and may conceivably happen.

Just as order and relationship in the world known in the 1880s fascinated the thoughtful people of a day when Darwin had opened a new vision of a scientifically integrated earth, so in our own time mathematical analysis may offer a vision of world patterns of development and movement. Their very complexity is a challenge, in fact a challenge so vast that some have said that every observed phenomenon is unique. And yet comparisons of like to like emerge as surely as contrasts emerge and many close analytical studies, for example of towns and cities, have shown that human enterprise may achieve similar results in varied physical, social and economic circumstances. Physical processes are even more amenable to mathematical analysis, for they are concerned with forces that may be far more accurately measured than the human aspirations that result in towns and cities. Fifty years ago one studied the diagrams of W. M. Davis which showed the possible evolution of landscapes, but the attractive illustrations and the elegantly expressed text left unanswered the question of exactly what force was possessed by winds, rivers and waves, especially under exceptional conditions, as moulders of the physical landscape. Far too much was inductive and far too little was demonstrated in the scientifically unequivocal language that mathematics appeared to provide. That sooner or later a cult of quantification should arise was only to be expected.

Even so, as more light and understanding is given of the world more will be wanted. It is surely an academic truism that any research of value will only have value if it opens a way to further research. The vast enterprise devoted to urban study in recent years has shown that there are all kinds of patterns in the lives of people which result in patterns of land use. And as these patterns have been expressed in models, there have been many people who, while recognising their value, have wanted to look more deeply and fundamentally into the living community of individual men and women. It is they who have made the world and they who can destroy it. Talk of environment means little unless it is conceived as something within the experience of any man, woman and child. Environment for people does not mean a mental rabbit burrow with convenient food in the farmer's grass and crops above it, but a complex, long-developed web of experiences into which we are born, in which we make our choices of new experiences through the years according to opportunity, education, enterprise, and – it may seem – chance. The vogue word of the day is 'perception', meaning our use of possibilities to create our own chosen environment. And there are fears that the apparent command of resources may be our undoing, that in using the resources of the world we may be so extravagantly selfish, even so scientifically unwise, that the whole basis of human existence will be destroyed. The 'environmentalist' has emerged as a person imbued with ideas of conserving rather than destroying the living world. It is not a new idea: indeed it was a commonplace in lecture rooms fifty years ago. But the right use of the world's resources is also an abiding human problem and the relationship between humanity and the physical world is a source of endless interest.

'Environment' as a word has had so many connotations among geographers that for many years it was avoided whenever possible, but in time it acquired new popularity through planners' constant discussion of environmental conditions. The whole trouble has been to define exactly what is meant by environment, for until recently it was often taken to be natural phenomena, though in fact what people normally experience is life in their home, workplace, local town or village, school and other places rather than natural conditions. Outdoor workers are a small minority of the population in modern industrial and commercial societies, though vastly more numerous in predominantly agricultural societies. A modern use of 'environment' as a term has developed through the study of perception, meaning the environment as an individual perceives it. Everyone clearly has his own mental map of the area in which he lives and works and finds his recreation. Estimates of the desirability of the environment will differ from one person to another, especially after any change of residence.

Since the Second World War there have been vast schemes of rebuilding cities, but steadily through the years it has been appreciated that replanning can only be successful if it meets human needs. But whose needs? At one and the same time the whole population and each individual are involved, for any community is made up of men, women and children with their distinct needs as persons as well as members of families. A New Town is built with the highest aspirations, expressed in fine schools with extensive playing fields, convenient shopping precincts with traffic-free pedestrian ways, suitable housing for families of different sizes, medical, social, entertainment and sporting facilities, public parks and open spaces. It should be the ideal environment, but there is abundant evidence that the residents may not think so. Even allowing for the natural human tendency to grumble and the fear of change that many people feel on a move from the familiar to the unfamiliar, there are clearly problems worthy of investigation in such communities. That many of them may be sociological, even psychological, should not deter the geographer from studying perception of the environment as one aspect of the problem. And this means, more and more, the urban environments in which an increasing proportion of the world's increasing population inevitably reside.

Fundamentally, there is a growing concern with the general wellbeing of the population. This is by no means as new as some modern writers suppose, for during the nineteenth century many revealing articles, books and government reports were written on the living conditions in London and provincial cities, but not by geographers. Medical men, clergy, philanthropists, Fabians, social statisticians and others saw that beyond their own comfortable circumstances there was another world riddled with disease and misery. Industrialists with enlightened views endeavoured to provide healthy conditions for the daily life of their workers, while housing trusts tackled the problem of building homes for artisans. Unfortunately, much of the work done in the nineteenth century is so rarely studied that some geographers appear to think that their concern with the well-being of the people is new. This, however, hardly matters, for one can only welcome such studies as those of the distribution of immigrant groups in British cities, especially if they are repeated at intervals as the newcomers become absorbed, to a varying degree, in the general population.

Such work may become of fascinating interest to a wide public, as in the case of Belfast where segregation of Catholic and Protestant communities has been studied by several urban geographers at Queen's University. Even if no such dramatic situation as the civil strife in Belfast appears (and fortunately it rarely does), there is always a problem in the emergence of a ghetto, populated by immigrants. French geographers have perhaps been more aware of the significance of migration throughout prehistoric and historic times than British geographers, and immigration is obviously a crucial concern in any study of the social geography of the United States and Canada. The geographer's demonstration of an existing situation will be all the more effective if based on detailed knowledge, and the hope of change may be all the greater if an emotional approach is avoided. When Patrick Geddes spoke of 'survey before action' he was speaking good sense for the national interest in problem areas, such as those experiencing industrial decline, has developed because people studied them carefully and presented their findings comprehensibly. With hindsight, geographers will probably feel that more could have been done, but it is often easier to recognise a receding rather than an advancing opportunity.

So far consideration has been given mainly to human problems, but physical geography, in the broadest sense, retains its attraction for academics. Far from losing significance it is gaining it, for geomorphologists in their studies of landscape evolution may be making a contribution to direct human problems such as land use, water supply, the location of roads, railways, houses or public buildings, the changes likely in a coastline, the silting of rivers and harbours and many more questions of a practical character that are familiar to rural and urban planners. Many geomorphological studies are directly related to climatic studies, some of which note the occasional incidence of unusual weather conditions such as the sudden heavy rainfall frequently experienced in some climates but less frequently in areas such as Great Britain. Such events may have dramatic landform effects like a change in the course of a river or a permanent deepening of its bed. Climatic study, always dependent largely on statistical data, has its obvious relevance to many immediate human concerns. With the intensification of farming, for example, the inevitably increased capitalisation may include provision for surface irrigation in some areas, notably eastern England where the rainfall in some years is inadequate for full vegetable and fruit production. Equally careful recording of late frosts in the spring has enabled fruit farmers to take appropriate precautions to save their budding crop. Motorways across the Pennines are frequently subject to hill fog, but have been so planned that the possibility of closure by snow is less than on their predecessors as main roads: though climatic hazards have been fully considered, the amount of possible detailed research has been limited by the lack of statistical data.

In recent years there has been a renewal of interest in vegetation and soils, much to be welcomed as these were neglected for many years though some excellent pioneer work was done in the late nineteenth century. This should be contributory to the work of the Land Use Survey initiated in 1959 by Alice Coleman, which includes an analysis of the moorland areas of Britain (p. 158). And all these enquiries, apart from any directly practical applications, will contribute to the interest of people using mountains, coasts, beaches, indeed any part of the countryside, as recreational areas. In the nineteenth century the Council of the Royal Geographical Society realised that many explorers saw very little of what, with more education, they might have observed and recorded. A century later one might comment that those who love outdoor recreation might well combine the physical satisfaction of mountaineering with observation of the geomorphology and vegetation. Fortunately, the National Parks now have literature available on their physical features, vegetation, fauna and agricultural use, and the success of exhibition centres and nature trails has shown that thousands of visitors are eager to learn.

Dual influences on the development of geography in Britain during the past 100 years have been the general advance in scientific enquiry and the social and political outlook of the time. Of these, the first was given impetus by the Darwinian view of the wholeness of the world, with all its living forms interlocking in mutual dependence, evolving, stagnating or decaying from the beginning of time. Archbishop Usher was manifestly wrong in thinking that it all began in 4004 B.C. The idea of environment developed from the natural world, and though there was a social element in the relation of all flora and fauna not only to the earth but also to other forms of life, the environment was seen first in physical rather than in social terms. Indeed it was almost with relief that many 'human' geographers of forty or fifty years ago turned to primitive societies, either prehistoric or contemporary, as among them it was far easier to see the direct relationship to environment than in the more sophisticated circumstances of contemporary living. Breadth of vision was characteristic of some geographers, notably of H. J. Fleure who related geography to a wide range of field sciences, and P. M. Roxby, who related it to the whole of human history in his teaching. Nor were they unique, for H. J. Mackinder was concerned with world political power, past, present and in a predictable future. They and many others were anxious to see life, and see it whole. But is this possible?

Veneration of the explorer was natural in the nineteenth century, for apart from the natural admiration for a heroic figure that exists at all times the explorer was regarded as a messenger of civilisation penetrating barbarism, the forerunner of trading and missionary activity and possibly also of territorial acquisition for the British Empire. For the geographer he was a man adding to the knowledge of a world only partially known. And he made maps. Year by year the Royal Geographical Society recorded the progress made by the Ordnance Survey in its home territory, and by the Admiralty in its famous coastal charts with their associated *Pilot* volumes. Excellent mapping firms, working at times in collaboration with the great German cartographers of the day, produced successive editions of atlases. Much of the early impetus for the training of geographers in universities was inspired by the wish to train intelligent explorers as well as to provide suitable teachers in schools. Textbooks of regional geography (much maligned at a later time) were valued as sources for an appreciation of other continents and countries, for knowledge of the world was regarded – quite reasonably – as part of a liberal education.

During the Second World War geographers showed that they could make a significant contribution to the national effort and geography shared in the post-war expansion of the universities. Part of the British contribution to the world advance of geographical study was made by exporting geographers to other countries, including the United States, Canada, Australia and New Zealand, as well as to Africa and other areas within the British Commonwealth. With vastly greater numbers of geographers in the universities and in government service, far more research resulting in publication was achieved and more specialisation became possible. This had its dangers, for just as the earlier aspirations to present broad views led to superficiality which, however brilliantly expressed, was still superficiality, so the new emphasis on specialisation might lead to narrowness of outlook. In urban geography, for example, concentration on a few (even a single) examples of towns, or even of part of one town, may give excessive emphasis to the unique rather than typical.

It may not be unfair to relate the zeal for quantification to the wish to establish some kind of general law, in fact a difficult task in any human distribution. In the handling of social data mathematical techniques have proved productive, though many might wish that the ultimate findings could be more elegantly – even comprehensibly – expressed. In the modern emphasis on perception one may see a return to respect for the views of individuals, just as in modern studies of regional economic development one may recognise an appreciation of the individuality of regions which, however imperfectly, earlier geographers were eager to discern. Fear of the future may be partly responsible for the current emphasis on conservation and there is no need to labour the point that short-term profit may result in long-term ruin. However much is known of the world, nobody can reliably assess the whole range of its resources or, at the moment of writing, know whether a world shortage of food and power is a temporary problem capable of quick solution or likely to be a blight on progress for many decades. Boundless optimism characterised the later Victorian period: who can be so hopeful now?

A hundred years ago the achievements of the time and the hopes of advance in a near future appeared to be limitless. Steadily the whole world was being explored by Europeans as Africa was partitioned, Canada settled, Australia and New Zealand colonised. China was penetrated by traders and Japan was entering a new phase of industrialisation of which little was known to Europeans. Not only was the whole world open to enterprise, but three nations of western Europe – Britain, France and Germany – were becoming Great Powers with imperial aspirations. Patiently the world was being mapped, and the new emphasis on the scientific unity of all creation was stimulating research on the relation of man and environment. Along with the spread of trade, likely to be beneficial to all it seemed, there was the prospect of the spread of education, medical services and Christianity 'o'er heathen lands afar' where 'thick darkness broodeth yet'. Having achieved a high level of civilisation, it was thought, western nations must share their rich heritage of learning and scientific achievement with those less fortunate. If Britain in the late twentieth century seems uncertain of its position in the world, no such attitude was apparent 100 years ago, nor for a considerable time afterwards. Apart from confessed imperialists, men of more liberal views thought that Britain could offer other nations great benefits: P. M. Roxby, for example, though sharply critical of many enterprises like the foundation of strategic bases in China, was anxious that Britain should subsidise educational and other beneficent institutions in China and regretted that his own people had been far less generous in such ways than the Americans. Just as in our own day there is an obvious rivalry between Russian and American influence in much of the world, so at an earlier time there was rivalry between Britain and other powers.

By the First World War geographers, though few in number, had drawn attention to many world problems. They had done more, for there was a growing interest in local survey, much fostered at Oxford, not as a rival enterprise to world study but as complementary to it. This was less spectacular than the presentation of the gradual settlement of Europe and the Mediterranean basin in the volumes by H. J. E Peake and H. J. Fleure issued as the 'Corridors of Time' (p. 113) or even the various attractively written papers of P. M. Roxby on China. But the British were only following the French of an earlier day as they studied their own land geographically, with considerable effect. Although they said little of the problems of old industrial areas plunged into economic darkness during the 1930s (when in fact the most useful reports were written by economists) there was in time a fuller appreciation of the human situation in such areas, which became of permanent interest after the Second World War. The help that could be given by geographers was apparent when the Barlow Report on the distribution of the industrial population (p. 139) appeared in 1940, but by 1945 circumstances had changed.

During the Second World War the publication of the Admiralty Handbooks (p. 143) showed the fruits of patient study and research in a series of volumes perhaps worthy of comparison with the *Géographie Universelle*. Certainly many people were induced to write down their knowledge who might have been reluctant to do so, or at least would have postponed doing so. Under pressure they were willing to 'publish and be damned', but far more good than harm came from the enterprise. Steadily the work of the Land Utilisation Survey went on and, as shown on pp. 144–5, became part of the foundation for the post-war replanning of Britain. In the years since the Second World War the progress of geography has been undoubted and it is easy to recognise both a concern with the whole world and with the parish. This is not new. Nor is the fascination of young geographers with a variety of problems, physical and human, in the environment new. Hope lies in the constant wish to try new methods, to evolve new techniques, in studying so vast, and so engrossing, a subject as the world and its constituent parts.

Geography has been a source of fascination to people from classical times, and the story told here deals only with one recent period in one part of the world. Even so, the material available is abundant for the literature is vast and scattered. Happily it is becoming more abundant year by year despite the immense increase in the cost of publication, felt keenly by the various geographical societies as well as by publishers. Perhaps one fortunate result is that papers in journals are now shorter and more incisive than in earlier years and that books are shorter. Authors have to avoid fascinating byways that they might wish to explore. Nevertheless, generalisations of the past have been questioned for progress has come by specialisation, by looking again at broad assumptions, by remembering that a hypothesis is never an established truth but only a stage in the long search for understanding. There have been, and still are, some attitudes unhelpful to progress. One of these is the assumption that a particular specialism is greater than all others, leading the researcher along the one golden road of progress. Another is the tendency, perhaps less prevalent now than in former years, to accept the views of one writer or teacher as the source of all geographical wisdom. A third is the failure to appreciate that geography is as inseparably intertwined with other subjects as they in turn are related to geography. That geographers are aware of these problems is undoubted, for at times it may seem that many are so concerned with methodology that advance in knowledge is promised rather than given. This may well be a reaction against much of the pragmatism of former years, especially the Victorian era, when the main emphasis was on fact until Mackinder and others, including some presidents of the Royal Geographical Society, saw that the problem lay in studying the relevance and the relationships of the information so plentifully supplied by travellers, explorers, cartographers, field scientists, oceanographers, military forces, statisticians, governments, traders and many others.

Sources for such a book as this are therefore endless. Some are particularly helpful, particularly the publications of the geographical societies, including the Royal Geographical of 1830, the Royal Scottish and Manchester societies of 1884, the Geographical Association of 1893. From 1934 there has been the large contribution to the subject of the Institute of British Geographers, not a society in the more technical sense. A distinguished contribution has also been made at the annual meetings of Section E (Geography) of the British Association from 1851. Many of the papers given there have been published later, particularly those of the presidents elected annually. Books have become more numerous in time, and the demand for good texts became insatiable once geography became a favoured school subject: of some half a million copies or more were sold. Behind all this progress there was a number of people, in fact not a great many, who saw opportunities for the advance of geography, many of them concerned in one way or another with education while others, such as the remarkable if generally mistaken medical, Dr Haviland, or the great biblical scholar George Adam Smith, saw the geographical aspects of their researches when few had any such ideas. That the expansion of knowledge of the world in the nineteenth century, combined with the vast accession of maps from Ordnance Surveys and cartographical firms naturally led to the emergence of geographers is hardly surprising.

Study of individual geographers is attracting an increasing number of people. Here a number are given a short summary treatment: the year of birth and death are given for individuals and a 'dagger' is shown for those given (very) short biographical treatment (at the end of the text) the first time they are mentioned, from Chapter 2 onwards. This method does not imply approval of the statement that 'geography is what geographers do', for the subject is greater than individuals and more abiding. To some it is of limitless scope and not the least fascinating part of the story lies in the emergence of ideas bearing varied academic fruit according to the quality of the seed and the skill of cultivation.

A hundred years ago

'Expansion' was the vogue word a century ago. Never had the world seemed more inviting, for steamships, railways, new roads and even telegraph lines were extending the known world year by year and both national surveys and cartographical firms were filling in the numerous blank areas on their maps. Expeditions of traders, sailors, missionaries, consular officials and even the sporting adventurers of the time were a source of fascinated interest to a wide public. Much of the interest lay in the revelations of strange customs that some explorers provided, but polar ice-caps, tropical forests, waterless deserts and towering mountains all appealed to human imagination, and those who courageously visited such places became heroes of the time just as astronauts did a century later. That explorers might be harbingers of political expansion, commercial development and missionary enterprise was clearly understood. And a discerning few realised that scientific advances would result from the observations of travellers both on land and sea. Charles Darwin (1809–82) had already published his *Origin of Species* in 1859, but whether or not one accepted his views the idea of relationship between all living forms both with the physical environment and with one another was not only challenging but to many people incontrovertible. Often the Victorian period is regarded as fusty and conventional, as in some ways it was, but it was also an exciting period for those looking out on a world of expanding horizons. It was a time when the young men could see visions and the old men could dream dreams.

The lure of Africa

Late in 1870, Dr David Livingstone wrote to a friend saying; 'Had I known all the hunger, hardship, toil and time required, I might have preferred a strait-waistcoat to undertaking the task: but, having taken it in hand, I could not bear to be beaten by it. . . . It is not without anxious care that I have stuck to my work with John Bullish tenacity.' When this and other letters were published by the Royal Geographical Society in 1874 Livingstone, who was born at Blantyre in Scotland on 19 March 1813 and died near the shores of Lake Bangweole in Africa on 4 May

1873, had been buried in Westminster Abbey at H. M. Government's expense. A long obituary notice by Sir Bartle Frere (1815-84) concluded by saying that:

As a whole, the work of his life will surely be held up in ages to come as one of singular nobleness of design, and of unflinching energy and self-sacrifice in execution. It will be long ere any one man will be able to open so large an extent of unknown land to civilized mankind. Yet longer, perhaps, ere we find a brighter example of a life of such contained and useful self-devotion to a noble cause (*Proc. R.G.S.* **18**, 1874: letters pp. 254-80; obituary pp. 497-512).

Apart from the hardships of African travel, Livingstone was often short of money and the Government of the day might, he noted, have been more generous. True, Lord Palmerston had sent a consul to offer help but this did not include, Livingstone notes, any kind of public honour or office that might have shown the Portuguese colonial officials that his work was approved in Westminster. Like many explorers Livingstone had his edges, but though 'a rough-hewn Scots doctor' he was a man of undeviating purpose who saw the great need of Africa as the suppression of the slave trade and the spread of the Gospel. 'Wherever English missionaries are established,' he notes, 'traders are welcomed and protected. We need native Christians to diffuse morality.'

Thrilled audiences assembled at the Royal Geographical Society, not infrequently with the Prince of Wales present, to hear the stories of exploration, especially in Africa. The Society ran into considerable trouble because it was unable to accommodate the thousands of members and guests who attended such gatherings, at which some of the lectures, notably one given by H. M. Stanley† (1841-1904) on 7 February 1878 which was a farrago of egoism and crudity, were followed by an adulatory vote of thanks by the Prince of Wales (*Proc. R.G.S.* **22**, 1877-8, pp. 408-10). Widespread reservations felt about the explorations of H. M. Stanley were due to several reasons, including first, the loss of Africans on the way through the indiscriminate use of force, and secondly, the excessively dramatic presentation of the results. Dr W. Kirk, who was Consul-General at Zanzibar, noted that some of Stanley's written material was 'exaggerated and inaccurate' (*Proc. R.G.S.* **22**, 1877-8, p. 454). Clearly, Stanley was not quite the type of man that most members of the Council of the Society normally met, though they admitted that 'they would have to search far in the history of geographical discovery before they would find a man equally successful as an active explorer and an intelligent observer,' as the President, Sir Rutherford Alcock (1809-97), graciously said in 1878.

Nothing is made more easily than cynical criticism of the passionate interest in exploration that characterised the 1870s. Undoubtedly it was in part an expression of the imperialism of the time, linked with a firm conviction in the value and necessity of trade for all peoples whether they wanted it or not, but it was also linked with a detestation of the brutality of life in Africa and other continents, especially where slave trading was rife. Horror stories of the conditions in such areas were plentifully given to the well-nourished audiences at the Royal Geographical Society, who were told not only of massacres and wholesale devastations of areas that could have been fertile and well populated, but also of places where 'the men wore not a vestige of clothing, and many of them had their bodies smeared with black, white and red paint, which gave them a most hideous appearance'. On another occasion a missionary bishop reported that 'most of the inhabitants were clad in native-made clothes, but some appeared in garments made of goat-skins, while a few wore scanty coverings of green leaves' (*Proc. R. G.S.* **21**, 1876–7, pp. 602–22). The view of the time was that Africa must be opened to civilising western influence and on 19 July 1877 a meeting attended by many explorers and others supported a resolution moved by the Archbishop of York on the suppression of the slave trade, 'an essential preliminary to which is a systematic effort, such as is now proposed, to obtain further information regarding the less-known regions of central Africa, and ascertain the best routes thereto from the coast' (*Proc. R.G.S.* **21**, 1876–7, p. 609). Shortly afterwards, a conference was held on the possibility of running an overland telegraph line from Khartoum to Kimberley, 2,826 miles. It was noted that a telegraph line from Adelaide to Port Darwin, 2,000 miles long, had been successfully erected across the Australian desert in two years from August 1870. Nothing, it was thought, was needed in Africa more than roads, with the hope that mission stations and outposts of empire might be established in suitable places from which further civilising work could be carried forward (*Proc. R.G.S.* **21**, 1876–7, pp. 616–22).

And there were frequent appeals to the spirit of adventure. One has not to look very far through the published material of the Royal Geographical Society a century ago (and very fascinating material it is to read) to discover statements such as that made by Rev. Horace Waller in 1872 who said that 'it was a matter of surprise to many, that with so many young men with large fortunes in England – men fond of exploring, of sports, and with glory enough to be obtained – so few were found to visit Africa' (*Proc. R. G.S.* **17**, 1873, pp. 33, 187–3). In short, the Grand Tour of the young and wealthy might well be replaced by exploration which, though admittedly dangerous, was at least interesting. Sir Bartle Frere, a passionate advocate of the suppression of the slave trade who had been to Zanzibar to study it at close quarters, devoted much of his presidential address in 1874 to the work of Livingstone (*Proc. R.G.S.* **18**, 1874, pp. 579–80) and to its possible further development. Explorers could benefit by geographical training and therefore an appeal was made to the universities of Oxford and Cambridge to recognise geography as a subject of study when resources permitted and in part to do this by establishing fellowships, including one in memory of Livingstone, 'the great traveller who continued in himself the character of Missionary, Geographer and Scientific Observer, and whose example might be thereby kept before the eyes of

English youths for generations to come' (*Proc. R.G.S.* **18**, 1874, pp. 451–2). This was only one of several appeals made to the universities (pp. 33–5) and it is clear that a fascinating story of university politics (not to be told here) lies behind the failure of such appeals. Much more interest lies in the efforts of the Royal Geographical Society to acquire government help for exploration. On this Sir Bartle Frere commented that 'every proposal for state assistance is scanned as if it were a proposal to rob the Treasury'. Nevertheless, much had been done by naval officers in Arctic exploration, and the Government had also made vast contributions to the advance of geography through mapping by the Ordnance Survey and the Admiralty's charting of waterways at home and abroad.

The relation of exploration to colonial expansion was a problem to which many people have given anxious thought. Sir Henry Rawlinson† (1810–95) in 1872 having deplored the futility of the Livingstone relief expedition under Lieutenant Dawson, who never went beyond Zanzibar on hearing that Stanley had found Livingstone, announced that a second expedition was to be sent 'to ascend the Congo and pre-occupy the Congo' before the Germans did so (*Proc. R.G.S.* **17**, 1872–3, pp. 8–9, 13; **19**, 1874–5, pp. 452–3). England, he noted proudly, had no reason to shrink from the honourable competition of other European nations in exploration either by sea or land 'although it might be wise to get there first and so avoid the risk of another Berlin arbitration on a disputed question of priority of discovery'. As it happened, two expeditions were sent out in 1872 to replace the abortive Dawson effort, of which one under Lieutenant W. G. Grandy found immense difficulties in the Congo, though the East–West expedition under Lieutenant V. Lovett Cameron† (1844–94) crossed Africa and sent back informative and entertaining despatches. Cameron finally reached the conclusion that 'the only thing that will do away with slavery is opening up Africa to legitimate commerce, and this can be best done by utilising the magnificent water-systems of the rivers of the interior' (*Proc. R.G.S.* **20**, 1875–6, p. 325). But who was to control Africa? In Cameron's despatches, the Portuguese were condemned repeatedly for their part in the slave trade, but the President, Sir Henry Rawlinson, in closing a meeting at which Cameron's letters were read (*Proc. R.G.S.* **20**, 1875–6, pp. 117–34), pointed out that his main contribution was not such revelations but his additions to the map of Africa:

the longitudes of many important points had been determined by a numerous series of lunar observations . . . as the previous knowledge of the longitudes of the interior of Africa was founded upon one single lunar observation obtained at Ujiji it would at once be apparent what an enormous difference Lieutenant Cameron's work had made. . . . The Royal Geographical Society was not instituted for the purpose of merely registering personal adventures or sensational journeys; they had a higher object in view, that of the advancement of pure, substantive, scientific Geography. . . .

Undoubtedly this attitude influenced the lukewarm reception given by the Royal Geographical Society to the 'International Commission of Exploration and Civilization of Central Africa' set up at a congress held in Brussels by the invitation of King Leopold of the Belgians in September 1875. H. M. Stanley had joined Leopold II in a scheme for the development of the Congo basin under an independent state with the King as personal ruler, in association with an international committee, on which Britain declined to be represented. On 12 March 1877 the Royal Geographical Society launched the African Exploration Fund for 'the exploration of the regions as yet unknown to civilised Europe, the attainment of accurate information as to climate, the physical features and resources of the country, the character of the inhabitants, the best routes of access, and all such other matters as may be instrumental in preparing the way for opening up Africa by peaceful means' (*Proc. R.G.S.* **21**, 1876–7, p. 21; **22**, 1877–8, pp. 12–28, 463–75). In the next year it was pointed out that although Britain had a long and distinguished record of African exploration, much of it fostered by the Royal Geographical Society, the Society could not compete with governments or even with missionary societies in expeditions on a large scale as it had neither the powers of the first nor the financial resources of the second. It could not, for example, expect to receive the equivalent of the grant-in-aid given to the German Geographical Society (Berlin) for exploration in the expectation that commerce would develop. Nor was the Society concerned with political matters as some governments undoubtedly were when they assisted expeditions. Finally, it was agreed to support an expedition under Alexander Keith Johnston† (1844–79) to explore the country between Dar-es-Salaam and the northern end of Lake Nyasa, where Mr E. D. Young, a naval officer, had in effect founded a colony around a mission station in 1875. Unfortunately, Keith Johnston died on 28 June 1879 within a month of leaving Dar-es-Salaam, but his young colleague Joseph Thomson (1858–95), then only twenty-one years of age, continued the expedition with marked success. Afterwards, however, the African Exploration Fund was wound up, partly because it had not evoked the public response that had been expected.

Although Africa attracted more attention during the 1870s than any other continent, many other explorations were in progress, of which a number were hazardous and even dangerous. Without doubt the great interest in Africa was due partly to the emotional appeal generated by the journeys of Livingstone, recorded by H. M. Stanley in journalistic despatches to the *Daily Telegraph*. The abolition of the slave trade was a matter of concern to many people and there was a widespread view that only the Christian religion could save Africa. Travellers expatiated on the boundless fertility of the continent and conjured up visions of a happy, smiling peasantry who would be well provided with roads, even in time railways, and so live in prosperity and health: in sickness they would be nursed in hospitals run by missionaries and others. Trade would flourish, and strife disappear. It was not an ignoble vision and in effect it was natural at a time when the European nations were seeking more raw materials and more outlets for their trade in manufactured goods. But whether many of the members of the Royal Geographical Society shared its official disclaimer with political and missionary aims is doubtful, for many of the speakers at meetings showed only too clearly their concern for the spread of British influence as a colonial power.

Exploration in other continents

Britain was very definitely a first-class power a century ago; and the concern with all the world undoubtedly seemed reasonable at the time. Throughout the 1870s the Royal Geographical Society published numerous papers on Persia, Afghanistan and the other areas marginal to the Indian subcontinent, some of which included suggestions for the building of roads and, as far as possible, railways between India and China. There were accounts of journeys in China and the possible future status of Japan was well forecast by Sir Henry Rawlinson in 1872, when introducing three papers from travellers. 'Until quite recently Japan was popularly supposed to be a barbarous country, but it has been suddenly found that she had become a competitor with the most advanced European nations in every branch of art and industry' (*Proc. R.G.S.* 17, 1872-3, p. 77). In the journals of the time, commercial activity appeared to be tacitly accepted as an inevitable duty of everyone in the world, whether they wished for it or not. Even the journeys in the Arctic, mentioned below, were justified partly, though not primarily, by the hope that in time it might be possible to run steamships from British ports to the mouth of the Yenesei. And possible world powers were watched with interest. Running through the 1870s there is frequent mention of the work of the famous Russian explorer, Colonel N. M. Prejevalsky (1839–88), partly through the translations of his articles given by Mr E. Delmar Morgan.

Fears that Russia might threaten India were explicable. Sir Rutherford Alcock (1809–97), in his presidential address of 1873 to the British Association expressed the opinion that the future of the Russian Empire was 'more a matter of physical geography than of politics or of policy if we look to determining causes' (British Association, 1873). Understandably, hemmed in by two seas frozen for several months a year, she had to look for warm-water ports, and what therefore would attract her more than the Chinese ports on the Pacific, or those on the Danube, the sunny Mediterranean and the Persian Gulf? It was as natural as the descent of a glacier to the valleys and as inevitable. Sir Rutherford Alcock viewed with some misgiving the progress of Russia over central Asia as he feared that she would exclude all trade but her own. *The Times*, however, was given to pro-Russian sentiments for

it was one of the happiest coincidences of history, that just at the time when the natural course of commercial and political development brings central Asia into importance, there should exist in the eastern border of Europe an empire retaining sufficiently the character of a military absolutism to render it especially adapted for the conquest and control of these semi-barbarous communities.

There was a time, Sir Rutherford Alcock shrewdly notes, when the Mongols controlled the Old World from Poland to the China seas, but 'the successors and descendants of those same Mongols and Tartars have another tale to tell now'.

Political implications may easily be found in much of the geographical activity of the 1870s, but some investigations show clearly the scientific curiosity of the time. Of these the most interesting were the efforts to penetrate the Arctic (the Antarctic was a more remote prospect) and the world voyage of the *Challenger* for deep-sea research, but there was much more to interest geographers willing, as our precursors of a century ago undoubtedly were, to take a world view. Cautious expeditions ventured up the Fly river in New Guinea, with the fear of cannibalism constantly present, and J. Forrest with his brother had found that much of the Australian interior was a gently undulating desert, never likely to be settled and covered with the spinifex grass hated by all Australians including the patient Forrest brothers (*Proc. R.G.S.* **19**, 1874–5, p. 446). The vast accumulation of information on India was conscientiously noted: has it, in fact, ever attracted the researchers it deserves? More and more material was available and some commentators saw that its use could be of unlimited value in making a new and more inspired geography at a later time.

The entry to the Arctic

A British Arctic expedition in the 1870s was regarded largely as a matter of prestige, and oddly enough support for it came from August Petermann (1822–78) of Gotha who wrote to the Royal Geographical Society in 1874 saying that 'as a nation, we Germans are only now beginning to turn our attention to nautical matters. We have had no vessels, no means, and our Government has had to fight three great wars these ten years'. He goes on to say that expeditions had been sent to the Arctic from Austria, Sweden, Norway, Russia and America, but strangely enough England, formerly always taking the lead in these matters, was 'almost the only maritime power that has kept aloof' (*Proc. R.G.S.* **19**, 1874–5, p. 179). However, on 8 February 1875 a jubilant meeting was held at the Royal Geographical Society to announce that the Government was providing two ships, the *Alert* and the *Discovery* for an expedition under the supreme command of Captain G. S. Nares (1831–1915) (*Proc. R.G.S.* **19**, 1874–5, p. 206). This success was ascribed to the assistance of three influential men, of whom the first was Admiral Sherard Osborn, who expected valuable scientific results as well as much benefit to the naval personnel who went (and apparently very large

numbers were eager to go). The second friend was Sir Joseph D. Hooker†
(1817–1911), who in 1865 had sent a memorandum for the Linnean
Society pointing out the biological results that might be expected and in
1875 still gave his support while President of the Royal Society. The
third was Commander C. R. Markham† (1830–1916) who, having been
to Baffin Bay in 1873 in the *Arctic*, convinced everyone that steamships
could travel effectively in icy waters. It was proposed that the expedition
should be provided with all possible information on the Arctic in a
manual in which the geography and ethnology should be written by the
R.G.S. and the remainder by the Royal Society.

The expedition left in 1875 and returned a year later, having reached on
foot latitude 83°20′26″ and made many interesting observations,
notably on snow melting and freezing. North of 70°, evaporation in May
and June was followed by a rush of waters in July which broke up the
pack-ice, of which a small quantity escaped until the end of September,
when the frost cemented the ice together so that by the end of October
everything was frozen again (*Proc. R.G.S.* **19**, 1874–5, pp. 206–8; **21**,
1876–7, pp. 93–100). In 1878 C. R. Markham suggested that the next
objectives should be the completion of the discovery of Greenland, the
examination of the supposed lands north of Siberia and the further
exploration of Franz Josef Land. Material from various voyages made it
clear that the extent of ice varied from year to year, but though
Markham notes this he makes no comment on its possible climatic
significance, which in fact was only appreciated several decades later. In
1879, for example, it was noted that there was less ice than normally in
the seas around and beyond Spitsbergen, according to information
gathered by hunters of seals, bears and walruses from Norway (*Proc.
R.G.S.* New Series 2, 1880, p. 128; Markham, 1879). Other voyages, such
as those of the *Erebus* and the *Terror* under James Clark Ross (1800–82)
to the Antarctic, a purely scientific enterprise financed by the British
Government, had shown the possibilities of exploration which the
Royal Geographical Society warmly commended. It was clear that
scientific knowledge could be a by-product of adventurous travel,
missionary enterprise, military or naval activity, topographical and
marine survey, but naturally the Society viewed the *Challenger*
expedition with unusual enthusiasm.

The *Challenger* voyages

In December 1872 the *Challenger* sailed under the command of Captain
G. S. Nares with an abundant supply of instruments and apparatus for
the physical investigation of the seas. It finally returned in 1876, three
and a half years later. The findings were investigated at an office in
Edinburgh and published in fifty volumes of which the last appeared in
1895. Those on board included Sir Charles Wyville Thomson (1830–82)
who in 1870 became Professor of Natural History at Edinburgh

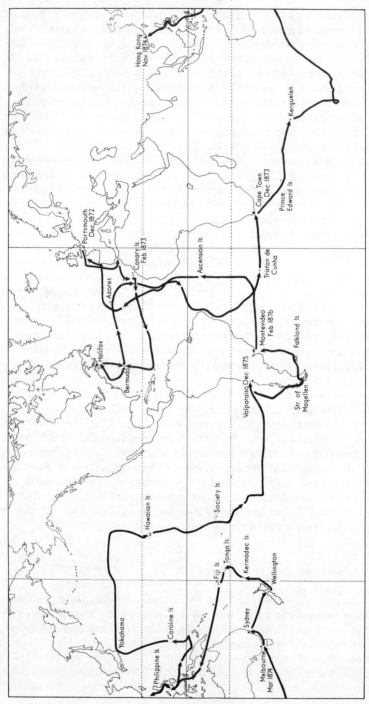

University. He had a wide grasp of botany, geology and zoology and from the return in 1876 he worked at the *Challenger* office until his death, when he was succeeded by Sir John Murray† (1841–1914), a Canadian-born Scot of rugged appearance and speech who made a considerable stir in the circumspect and correct atmosphere of Edinburgh learned society. Murray had been a member of the *Challenger* team, in which another notable figure was the chemist, John Young Buchanan† (1844–1925) whose work consisted mainly of the analysis of sea water from various depths. Initially the Atlantic was crossed to Bermuda, with a survey of the American coast to Halifax and a return to Bermuda so that the Gulf Stream was crossed twice on widely spaced tracks. From Bermuda the *Challenger* went to the Azores, Madeira, the Canary Islands, the Cape Verde Islands, to the coast of South America, Tristan da Cunha and finally to Cape Town, having covered 18,610 miles of ocean and made deep-sea soundings, temperature observations at various depths and many more observations, some of which were surprising. It appeared, for example, that below the level of 60–80 fathoms the water was colder at the equator than in the tropical and subtropical belt at 40°N.

The first, Atlantic, part of the voyage lasted for approximately one year, and in December 1873 the *Challenger* had a refit at Cape Town and left for Melbourne. The Antarctic Circle was crossed on 16 February 1874. Pack-ice was encountered at 65° 30′S and the surrounding sea-water was found to have a temperature of 28–29°, sufficiently warm to melt ice formed from salt water but not the bergs formed from fresh water. Melbourne was reached in March 1874, and after another refit at Sydney a tour of various Pacific islands and of the Great Barrier Reef followed. Finally the ship went northwards to reach Hong Kong on 16 November 1874 and an extensive survey of the western Pacific and the various relatively shallow seas led the party to Japan where hospitality was given at the government port of Yokoska. Very little of interest was found in the Inland Sea of Japan, but much of note emerged from the traverses of the Pacific which included a section from Yokohama between longtudes 35° and 38° to 156°W. Work was continued around the Hawaiian (Sandwich) Islands, after which the ocean was crossed to Valparaiso. The Pacific proved to have two layers of water, of which the

---

Fig. 1 The voyage of the *Challenger*.
This is reproduced from a map which appeared in the *Report on the Scientific Results of the Voyage of H.M.S. Challenger During the Years 1872–76: a summary of the scientific results, first part*, H.M.S.O. 1895, between pp. 72 and 73. The volume is described as 'prepared under the superintendence of the late Sir C. Wyville Thomson and now of John Murray'. On p. 104 it is noted that: 'The expedition was successful beyond the expectations of its promoters, and opened out a new era in the study of Oceanography.'

upper cooled rapidly from the surface downwards and the lower, of incomparably greater amount, extended to the bed of the ocean. The temperature change to this lower layer came at about 400–500 fathoms, at a temperature of about 40° F. It appeared, therefore, that the bottom-water of the Pacific Ocean was an extremely slow indraught from the southern seas with no northern source of consequence as the Behring Strait was only 40 fathoms deep and mainly occupied by a warm current from the Pacific into the Arctic seas. The equatorial current branched off into the Kuro Siwo which flowed to Japan, on its way striking against the Philippines and other islands. In the Atlantic the Gulf Stream, flowing along the American coasts, gave an even more marked flow of tropical waters.

On 10 December 1875 the *Challenger* reached Valparaiso and on 16 February 1876 Montevideo. The coldest water in the world, except in the Antarctic, was found at latitude 37°S in the Atlantic. In all, the *Challenger* travelled 68,890 miles and returned with specimens of water for physical and chemical examination from the ocean depths, faunal specimens from the ocean floor and from surface and intermediate levels, records of climatic phenomena encountered, and many obser-vations of flora and fauna made on islands and mainland areas while the ship was in port. Scientifically the results were of such enormous value that they laid the foundations of modern oceanography (*J.R.G.S.* **44**, 1874, clvi–clxii; **45**, 1875, clxi–clxiii; **46**, 1876, clxi–clxvii; **47**, 1877, clxii–clxiv; Mill, 1895a, 1951). The *Challenger* voyages demonstrated the unity of the world as a scientific phenomenon, on which much modern geographical theory has been based. The consequences for the student of physical geography were profound. From this time the relation between land masses and oceans became more certainly known than ever before and the ocean currents became effectively recognised with interesting results in the developing theories of climate and weather. Although the world distribution of flora and fauna has not perhaps received the attention that might profitably have been given to it, great stimulus was given to this work by the observations collected during this time. In short, the *Challenger* voyage gave scientific results that must have made all the less comfortable periods of the long tour seem of little account.

Exploration is not enough

As the 1870s came to an end nobody could doubt that the discoveries of the time, the new mapping of the Ordnance Survey and the Admiralty and the scientific results of the *Challenger* voyages had opened new doors to the geographer. More was known of the world than ever before and the natural curiosity of people about lands they had never seen could be more easily satisfied. But that was not enough, as the Royal Geographical Society was frequently reminded by various speakers. They therefore made two attempts to induce a more discriminating attitude among those interested in geography: the first through training of explorers, and the second through the education of pupils in schools and universities.

Explorers need many qualities, not least physical fitness and pertinacity but not infrequently private means as well. They also need to have a considerable appreciation of what they are looking for and this develops only through appropriate education for, contrary to the general belief, the power of observation is not instinctive. In 1876, Sir Rutherford Alcock noted that 'it is to the development of the scientific features of geography that the attention of travellers and explorers, whether on land or water, require now to be directed, and in this there is an illimitable field' (*Proc. R.G.S.* **21**, 1876–7, p. 23).

Various speakers not only at the R.G.S. but also at Section E of the British Association, then run in close co-operation with the Society, were conscious of the same need for topographical discovery to merge into scientific investigations, and later in the 1876–7 session three lectures on physical geography were given with this aim in view. Lieutenant-General Richard Strachey (1817–1908) opened with an introductory lecture on scientific geography showing that a wide range of topics, culminating in 'the races of man and their dependence on geographical conditions', could be studied and Dr W. Carpenter followed later with a lecture on the temperature of the deep-sea bottom. The third lecture was by Alfred Russel Wallace (1823–1913) famed for his work on natural selection, on the 'comparative antiquity of continents, as indicated by the distribution of living and extinct animals'. In the next two sessions, six more lectures were given, of which two still provide fascinating reading: in 1878, the then assistant director of the Royal Gardens at Kew, W. T. Thiselton-Dyer, spoke on 'Plant-distribution as a field for geographical research' and gave an excellent summary of the work done on the world distribution of floras, with many comments on the specimens provided by various explorers including the Russian, Prejevalski. The influence of Sir Joseph D. Hooker was generously recognised. A year later John Ball spoke on the origins of the flora of the European Alps, and incidentally of various other mountain ranges. Associated partly with the study of glaciers and a pioneer in recognising the effects of past glaciation, Ball included a fascinating account of climatic influences on plants with spirited comment on the folly of merely using shade temperatures, and his lecture was enlivened by vivid descriptions of the actual habitat of some plants he had found (*Proc. R.G.S.* **21**, 1876–7, pp. 179–203, 289–323, 505–35; **22**, 1877–8, pp. 68–98, 188–216, 412–15; *Proc. R.G.S.* New Series 1, 1879, pp. 422–44, 453, 564–88). Interesting as the lectures were, and packed with strong meat, they attracted only small audiences. The Society decided that they did not in fact provide the kind of help that explorers needed, such as 'the use of instruments for survey and astronomical observations and route-mapping'. Certainly the strength of the lectures will impress anyone who reads them a century later.

Educational advance in geography teaching was slow in British schools, though the comments on page 35 show that it was desired by some who were practical workers in contact with the young. Year by year there were hopes that curricula might be broadened and that geography might be taught more intelligently. In 1878 Francis Galton† (1822–1911) referred to the recent publications of *Physiography*, by T. H. Huxley in the previous year, which 'starting from the simplest elements . . . led students steadily on to the higher conception of physical geography and the most recent discoveries in it' (*Proc. R. G. S.* **22**, 1877–8, pp. 300–1). Galton had a multitude of interests with a constant concern for education, perhaps in the hope that the young might have a better time at school than he did himself. He was a main advocate of the medals scheme established to reward good work by schoolboys (no girls entered). Each year, from 1869, two papers were set in physical and two in political geography, but only about one-quarter of the schools invited to compete sent candidates and many of the questions read oddly today, such as 'What is a bar?' 'Has the Nile or any river to the east of its basin, a bar?' or again, 'Give some account of the recognised forms of Government in the countries within the Nile Basin.' Another question asks for the area and population of Spain, Portugal, Algeria and Tunis and yet another the names of the states existing in the USA at the end of the War of Independence, with those added later. In 1884 this medal scheme was abandoned (p. 34).

Summarising the position about 1880, one is struck by the immense vitality of the age. The world was being opened up and many of its secrets, some of them dark but fascinating, revealed. The discoveries unfolded before large London audiences showed all the John Bullish tenacity of which Livingstone spoke and the vision of an empire on which the sun never set became more sure than ever. Intrepid sailors had penetrated the Artic and the *Challenger* had completed its long world voyage. Mapping at home and abroad was continued year by year and the map firms were producing the atlases without which no gentleman's library was complete. So much was known in a factual sense, so little in a comparative sense. Information was abundant but the need was to digest it, to relate one line of enquiry to another, and so to explore the growing belief in the scientific unity of the whole world that Darwin and others had studied. And one main educational need was to bring the thrill of geographical knowledge into the schools and universities for the rising generation. Clearly this could not be achieved by the type of teaching suggested by the examination papers noted above.

Chapter 3

The Eighteen-eighties

Effective beginnings made in geography teaching in the universities during the 1880s and growing support for geographical societies form part of a world movement of thought in an age when many new doors were opened to scientific enquiry, when the whole basis of traditional belief was questioned and when man's command of nature seemed to be greater than ever before. It was a new age, an age of spatial conquest, in which no people – however remote – seemed to be beyond the challenge of contact with others and no resources incapable of exploitation. Everywhere the explorer went, or could be expected to go in a near future. A limited number of great nations appeared to possess the resources and the determined resolve for indefinite expansion. Scientific civilisation was open – at least potentially – to all the world, to the infinite benefit of its people who would in varying degrees become richer in a general bonanza of progress. So much had been achieved that it was easy to believe that more could follow if one held the view that material progress was likely to be accompanied by the ability of nations, as of individuals, to live with one another in peace.

Nobody expressed the thrilling achievement of the time better than Sir Joseph Dalton Hooker, the botanist, in his presidential address to Section E (Geography) of the British Association in 1881. He noted that:

The veil has been withdrawn from the sources of the Nile, and the lake systems of Central Africa have been approximately localised and outlined. Australia, never previously traversed, has been crossed and recrossed in various directions. New Guinea has had its coasts surveyed, and its previously utterly unknown interior has been here and there visited. The topography of Western China and Central Asia, which have been sealed books from the days of Marco Polo, has been explored in many quarters. The elevations of the highest mountains of both hemispheres have been accurately determined, and themselves ascended to heights never before attained; and the upper regions of the air have been ballooned to the extreme limit beyond which the life-sustaining organs of the human frame can no longer perform their functions. In hydrography the depths of the great oceans have been sounded, their shores mapped, and their physical and natural history explored from the equator to beyond both polar circles. In the Arctic regions the highest hitherto attained latitudes have been reached; Greenland has been proved to be an island; and an archipelago has been discovered nearer to the pole than any other land. In the Antarctic regions a new continent has been added to our maps, crowned with one of the loftiest known volcanoes, and the Antarctic ocean has been traversed to the 79th parallel (*Proc. R.G.S.* New Series 3, 1881, p. 596).

Great as the achievement was, careful perusal of the above passage makes it clear that much more was to follow, not least through the development of aviation. Naturally Sir Joseph Hooker was deeply interested in the world distribution of fauna and flora, as the work of each day at Kew Gardens in systematic botany revealed unexpected relationships between plants from areas not only distant in space but also having varied climates. The theory of a former land connection between the three southern continents was already in being, but Hooker noted that 'the several south temperate floras are more related to those of the countries north of them than they are to one another'. As a proof of this he observed that 'the most interesting herbarium ever brought from Central Africa, that of Mr Joseph Thomson from the highlands of the lake district, contains many of the endemic genera, and even specimens of the Cape of Good Hope' (*Proc. R.G.S.* New Series 3, 1881, pp. 603–4, 606). Hooker praised the work of Alexander von Humboldt (1769–1859) on the distribution of plants and animals and commended a paper given by Edward Forbes to the British Association in 1846 which stressed the idea that geographical and especially climatic conditions controlled the migrations of plants and animals. Forbes, though 'the reformer of the science of geographical distribution', was pre-Darwinian in outlook, and to him 'the origin of representative species, genera and families remained an enigma'.

Hooker accepted the theory of Charles Darwin on the modification of species or their mutations in these words:

Now under the theory of modification of species after migration and isolation, their representation in distant localities is only a question of time and changed physical conditions. In fact, as Darwin well sums up, all the leading facts of distribution are clearly explicable under this theory: such as the multiplication of new forms; the importance of barriers in forming and separating zoological and botanical provinces; the concentration of related species in the same area; the linking together under different latitudes of the inhabitants of the plains and mountains, of the forests, marshes and deserts, and the linking of these with the extinct beings which formerly inhabited the same areas: and the fact of different forms of life occurring in areas having nearly the same physical conditions (*Proc. R.G.S.* New Series 1, 1879, p. 602).

The thrill given by the Darwinian views of evolution, of the relation of plants and animals to their environment, and to each other, to many natural scientists of the day, cannot be overestimated. And as Hooker with many more people looked to palaeontology, there too they saw the development of species from one climatic epoch to another, their failure or success in adaptation to changing conditions, their local modifications in certain circumstances. Environment became the consuming interest of the natural historian but also of many others who wanted to understand a world being rapidly opened to those fortunate people who could explore or even travel as well as those who could only do these things vicariously by reading.

The varied motives of explorers

The Royal Geographical Society, as the main inspiration of British geography, welcomed distinguished explorers from several countries, bestowed medals on those whose travels were of special note, and published a large amount of material annually, much of it on exploration but by no means all, for the editors were quick to recognise any developments of interest to geographers both in Britain and abroad. The Society's *Hints to Travellers* was first published in 1854, and reissued in successive editions to the eleventh, in two volumes of 1935 and 1938. From a modest work of 31 pages it grew to one of over 900 pages, edited and revised by secretaries of the Society and other experts. Explorers were able to borrow instruments, even to acquire practical instruction on techniques, to confer with experts and in other ways to find help (Mill, 1930, pp. 244–6). Every year in the 1880s the President gave an address on the general progress of geography, much of which dealt with exploration: in 1885, Lord Aberdare† (1815–95), then aged seventy, showed the dangers of international rivalry in exploration and in effect described the Scramble for Africa (and other tropical areas) as a threat to world peace:

To the politicians of all the great European nations the period has been one of intense interest and anxiety, connected more or less with questions of vast territorial acquisitions. To the geographer the interest, although less painful, has hardly been less keen. The French in Asia and Africa – the Russians in central Asia – the English on the Afghan frontier, on more than one border of India, on all sides of Africa, and in Oceania – and the Germans on the East and West coasts and among the islands of the Pacific and Australasian seas – have, while pursuing measures of national policy, made large additions to our knowledge of the globe, have stimulated enquiry into others. Never – and I need hardly even except that period of emigration which precipitated and followed the break-up of the Roman Empire – has the ferment among nations been so widespread or prophetic of such great consequences. The foundations of new empires, new civilisations, are being laid over vast portions of the earth (*Proc. R.G.S.* New Series 8, 1886, p. 192).

Lord Aberdare, who had held various cabinet offices in Liberal governments, was an enthusiast for the opening up of Africa and in 1882 became chairman of the National African Association created for the development of West Africa, and later incorporated as the Royal Niger Company working in the area which in 1900 became Northern Nigeria. In the 1880s new protectorates were founded: for example, Lord Aberdare notes that the Bechuanaland Protectorate had been established and that New Guinea had been partitioned between Britain and Germany. Other geographical societies abroad were showing comparable interests: for example, in 1885, the annual reports of the Paris Society had much to say on Africa and Morocco (*Proc. R.G.S.* New Series 7, 1885, p. 428) and in 1886 there was comment on the publication of the *Deutsche Kolonialzeitung* by the German Colonial Society of Berlin, which included some work on New Guinea (*Proc. R.G.S.* New Series 8, 1885, p. 192).

Obviously, it was not easy at this time to draw a sharp distinction between exploration and imperialism but, as noted above (p. 14), the Royal Geographical Society had every wish to avoid any governmental control of its activities. At Section E of the British Association, where the meetings were arranged by the Royal Geographical Society from 1851 to 1914 (Mill, 1930, p. 65), the contemporary interest in overseas territories was well shown. At Aberdeen in 1885, for example, one-third of the papers were on India. They included some of considerable value, notably on the rivers of Punjab and on the physiography of southern India (*Proc. R.G.S.* New Series 7, 1885, p. 674), and in 1886 at Birmingham, there were papers on the Canadian North-west, on the Canadian Pacific Railway ('the very essence of the agreement between the different parts of Canada to unite under one government') and on a possible railway to Port Nelson on Hudson's Bay. Several papers were given on exploration in Africa, New Guinea and elsewhere, and the question, debated so often later, of the possible acclimatisation of Europeans in tropical Africa was raised. A committee was formed on the limited possibilities of exploiting Arctic regions owing to the adverse climate and the permanently frozen soil. The *Challenger* voyages (p. 17) were the subject of a paper by John Murray (*Proc. R.G.S.* New Series 8, 1886, pp. 727–46). Public interest in these meetings was considerable and reflected the current satisfaction in the possession of a far-flung empire.

Hard-bitten scholars in other disciplines found it hard to accept and welcome a subject that appeared to furnish trivial information that might be a beginning of knowledge on some previously unknown area, but was quite clearly only a beginning. It was raw material, but very raw and the prospects of its systematisation into some kind of logical regional framework seemed to be remote. A second difficulty lay in the success of exploration itself. To become a geographer one must go somewhere extremely remote, such as Timbuktu or the Mountains of the Moon, or climb Mount Kenya as did H. J. Mackinder† (1861–1947) in 1899 because he thought that nobody would take him seriously as a geographer unless he had some exploit to his credit. Virtually all geographers have a natural wish to travel, but the operative question is not 'where' but 'how'. In 1880, Clements Markham (Markham, 1880) reviewed the progress made since 1830, when the Royal Geographical Society was founded. Atlases incorporated the discoveries of many explorers and were vastly improved in presentation. Little was known of the Arctic in 1830, but by 1880 the whole coast of Arctic America was delineated and the remarkable archipelago to the north was at least partly known, though the interior of Greenland was unvisited. In Antarctica nothing had been done since Sir James Ross penetrated to 78° 11′S in 1841. Africa was almost unknown in 1830 and maps of that date still included Ptolemy's 'Mountains of the Moon', but by 1880 the continent had become 'a glorious field of generous rivalry among civilised Europeans' and many famous explorers had contributed to knowledge of the interior.

Nevertheless, as Markham shows, much of the work to this date was of a reconnaissance character and systematic exploration and survey were needed. In Asia a great deal was known of India and the monsoon fringe, and generous tribute was paid to Russian explorers of the interior. South America was only partially known, but both in Australia and New Zealand the interior had been discovered and explored since 1830, when the maps showed only inaccurate coastlines. The next need was to learn more of the islands to the north of Australia. As one reads Markham's account the admiration for the achievement of the time mounts steadily. Looking forward he says that:'When, in the far distant future, the whole surface of the earth has been surveyed and mapped, the study of physical geography may be recommenced on a sound basis, and generalisations will become more accurate, and will be founded on more correct and reliable data.'

The new geographical societies

Several of the new continental geographical societies founded about 100 years ago were concerned largely with the development of commerce and on 27 October 1884 a meeting was held at the Mansion House in London to establish a British Commercial Geography Society (*Proc. R.G.S.* New Series 6, 1884, p. 666). This did not happen, nor was an earlier attempt in 1879 at Manchester successful. The Manchester effort was due largely to the enterprise of the Bishop of Salford (widely known and revered later as Cardinal Vaughan), who addressed a special meeting of the Chamber of Commerce called to discuss the promotion of trade with Africa. Five years later, however, the Manchester Geographical Society was founded and the first address was given by H. M. Stanley, on 'Central Africa and the Congo basin: the importance of the scientific study of geography' on 21 October 1884. On this occasion, Lord Aberdare brought greetings from the Royal Geographical Society and stressed the need to develop geographical education more adequately in Britain. The Manchester Society's constitution included a variety of aims such as education, exploration, research, publication and the acquisition of maps, books and specimens of raw materials and commercial products, but the appeal to the business community was clear in item 3 of 'Object and Work': 'To examine the possibility of opening new markets to commerce and collect information as to the number, character, needs, natural products and resources of such populations as have not yet been brought into relation with British commerce and industry.'

For many years the Society provided useful information to business men and a number of papers given at meetings and published in the journal were concerned with commercial matters, though this was only one part of its work. But interest in exploration was blended with interest in trade and warm approval was given by the *Manchester Guardian* to a lecture on 'Our commercial opportunities in Western Asia' in February 1885 by A. Arnold, a local Member of Parliament. Within the first year of the Manchester Geographical Society's life lectures were given on exploration between Lake Nyasa and the Indian Ocean, on Canada and the Great Northwest, on Siam and the Shan States, on northern India and Afghanistan and on British Honduras. The lecturers were of three main types: explorers, army officers and missionaries. Some of the lectures were little more than travel talks while others showed considerable powers of observation (Brown, 1971).

The Royal Scottish Geographical Society was founded at a meeting in the Edinburgh Chamber of Commerce on 28 October 1884, when the formal resolution was proposed by James Geikie† (1839–1915), the geologist, and seconded by the President of the Chamber of Commerce, James Currie. Support came from many quarters and branches were opened at Dundee and Glasgow in 1884 and in 1885 at Aberdeen. At the great opening meeting held in Edinburgh on 3 December, H. M. Stanley delivered much the same speech that he had given in Manchester a few weeks earlier and this was repeated at Dundee and Glasgow some days later. From the beginning the map-maker John George Bartholomew† (1860–1920) was associated with the Society. In 1884, he had recently returned from a world tour in search of health. In France he had found twenty geographical societies, in Germany many more, and even in Denmark a prosperous society with 1,000 members: surely Scotland could find 500 supporters for such a society? In fact, more than 800 joined in the first year and the membership doubled within a few years. Circumstances were favourable. The success of the map firms, Johnston and Bartholomew, the association with the *Challenger* expedition, the establishment of the Scottish Marine Station at Granton in 1884, the presence in Edinburgh of various publishing firms including A. and C. Black who were then producing the ninth edition of the *Encyclopaedia Britannica*, the interest of several lively and broadminded professors at the University, all helped to make a favourable climate for the growth of the new society (Newbigin, 1934; Mill, 1934; Freeman, 1976).

From the beginning the Scottish Society published a monthly journal. Although the title of 'Royal' was given in 1887, no governmental help with finance was available until 1908 when £200 a year was granted. The journals of the 1880s show a breadth of interest that is commendable. In the first number James Geikie gave an excellent account of the physical features of Scotland and commented that 'with a well-drawn and faithful orographical map before him the school-boy would not only have his labours lightened, but geography could become one of the most interesting of studies'. But perhaps the most interesting contribution was an article by H. A. Webster (1849–1926), a young scholar working for the *Encyclopaedia Britannica* on 'What has been done for the geography of Scotland, and what remains to be done'. Originally given as a paper at the Aberdeen meeting of the British Association, it included a suggestion that a series of handbooks should be prepared with such practical information as the area of Loch Lomond, the length of rivers and the extent of their basins, the tidal limits, or the area between chosen altitudes. With this there should be a bathymetric survey of all lakes (on which much useful work was done later, pp. 55–6), a hydrographic survey of all rivers, and the study of faunal and floral regions. Mr Webster also wished to see more mapping of statistical material, such as the density of population, of birth- and death-rates, the distribution of trade and commerce, even of education (*Scott. Geogr. Mag.* 1, 1885, pp. 487–96). Fine maps had been produced in the 1851 Census by August Heinrich Petermann during his long stay in Britain (1845–54) with the Johnston map firm in Edinburgh and later in London, but since his departure the standard had declined, notably in the *Statistical Atlas of England, Scotland and Ireland* published by Johnston in 1882. Other suggestions by Mr Webster included a close survey of administrative boundaries, especially those of Scottish counties and of the border between England and Scotland. He also welcomed the work of J. J. Egli (1825–96) on 'onomatology' or the science of place-names. Professor Egli of Zurich was the foremost European authority on this subject and a translation of one of his papers appeared in the September issue of the *Scottish Geographical Magazine*.

Many of the papers published were concerned with exploration, but there were others of more general interest. George Goudie Chisholm† (1850–1930), initially on the staff of a Glasgow publishing house, showed his capacity of crystallising wide reading in an article on 'Rapids and waterfalls' with examples drawn from Great Britain, Asia (especially China), North and South America and Africa. With F. W. Rudler, Chisholm had produced the two volumes on Europe which completed Stanford's *Compendium of geography and travel* in 1899–1900. He also edited Longman's *Gazetteer of the World*, published in 1895. But perhaps the most abiding contribution made in the first year of the *Scottish Geographical Magazine* was the short four-page article in which Rev. James Gall (1808–95) presented his stereographic, isographic and orthographic map projections, of which the first at least has been familiar to many generations of students ever since (Fig. 2). In short, the early numbers of the *Scottish Geographical Magazine* now provide fascinating if much neglected reading. It is hardly surprising to find that a note on British trade with Tibet says that 'at present there is practically none'. But the short modern history of western Canada is revealed in a study of the Canadian Pacific Railway:

The riches of the country which the main line will open up are not yet thoroughly explored . . . on the Pacific side there are vast and undeveloped fisheries, forests and mines; at the base of the Rocky Mountains there are immense cattle ranches; in the prairie country there are boundless possibilities of wheat-growing; and in the region bordering on the great lakes – bleak and almost desert as it is – there is much wealth both in minerals and timber. (*Scott. Geogr. Mag.* **1**, 1885, p. 264).

No time could have been more propitious for the organisers of geographical societies, for the opening up of new lands to trade and settlement was proceeding rapidly, especially in Africa. Joseph Thomson, who, as noted on p. 14, had been saddled with the vast responsibilities of an expedition through Africa at the age of twenty-one but met all difficulties with his humorous and even devastating charm, spoke in 1886 of the limitations of East Central Africa (*Scott. Geogr. Mag.* **2**, 1886, pp.65–78). (Asked once by J. M. Barrie what was his most dangerous journey, he replied, 'Crossing Piccadilly Circus'.) He suggested that the Niger area was economically of far greater wealth than other areas, for it had a good navigable river and was inhabited by a long-settled population renowned throughout Africa for their manufactures, their keen trading instincts and their industrious habits. Far less promising, the coasts of East Africa had a 'soil poor in the extreme', of brick-red clayey sand with little humus content due to the rapid decomposition under the prevailing climate. In the interior, around lakes Nyassa, Tanganyika and Victoria Nyanza, many products could be grown but in insignificant quantities; there were no known minerals and even the elephants were almost exterminated. But the real problem was the ferocity of the Masai: 'it is simply out of the question to talk about the civilisation within a generation of such a race as these terrible nomads'. South Africa offered far richer possibilities, as W. B. Tripp, a resident of Cape Colony from 1880 to 1883, noted (*Scott. Geogr. Mag.* **2**, 1886, pp. 257–62), for 'the plains and valleys . . . are frequently composed of the richest soil, only requiring water irrigation to change their too often arid and barren surface into most productive farms'. Some writers of the time were convinced that British influence was good everywhere: Rev. W. D. Cowan (*Scott. Geogr. Mag.* **2**, 1886, p. 336), writing on his travels in Madagascar, had no doubts at all when he wrote that: 'While the subjects of Britain are welcomed and trusted as friends, the name of "Frenchmen" stinks in the nostrils of the natives. . . . Great Britain is the type of all that is good and great as an Empire....' This must have been gratifying reading in the drawing-rooms of Edinburgh.

By 1888 the Scramble for Africa was an undeniable fact: its effects were summarised in an article by Arthur Silva White† (1859–1932) (*Scott. Geogr. Mag.* **4**, 1888, pp. 152–8, 298–311), illustrated by two coloured maps provided by the firm of Bartholomew. Mr White noted that the European powers had indulged in 'land-eating' to such an extent that protectorates, colonies and 'spheres of influence' covered virtually the whole of Africa. Not everywhere had the British, it was thought, been treated fairly, for in many parts of Africa British

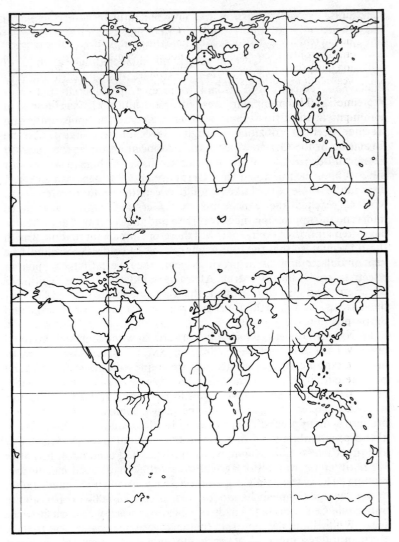

Fig. 2 Parson's pleasure: two of Rev. James Gall's map projections.
As Rev. James Gall's stereographic projection has been widely used in
atlases it is not shown here but these two others, long forgotten, appeared
in the same article in *Scott. Geogr. Mag.* **1**, 1885, pp. 121, 123. Reverend
James Gall, born in 1808, was a son of James Gall, an educational
publisher. Having spent some years in the firm he became an evangelist in
1848 and, from 1861 to 1871, a Presbyterian minister. Later he continued
his evangelistic work and also wrote several controversial works on the
Bible and on Christian missions. This he regarded as his main vocation, but
it is by one of his map projections, devised when he was in his late
seventies, that he is now remembered. He died in 1895. A note on his life
and his connection with the educational firm of Gall and Inglis appears in
Scott. Geogr. Mag. **79**, 1963, p. 177.

merchants, explorers, missionaries and philanthropists had explored and opened up the country only to find the fruit of their labours gathered by others. On the east coast the initial ventures were British, but French and later German merchants competed against those of Britain, and in 1884–5 Dr Karl Peters made treaties with various native chiefs and returned to Potsdam to receive an imperial 'Letter of Protection'. The remonstrances of the Sultan of Zanzibar and comments in the British Press were answered by the appearance of a German fleet off Zanzibar in August 1885. These events led to the formation of the German East Africa Association under the same Dr Peters and expeditions were financed to make fresh acquisitions. Mr Silva White, having noted that Germany and Portugal had in effect divided the whole of the Lake region between them without reference to Britain, reached the conclusion that Germany was powerless to intervene in suppressing the slave trade and that Portugal appeared to have no intention of doing so. It was therefore important that the British should remain so that the four primary aims of colonisation should be kept inviolate; now as in previous years they were first, to open an effective route into Central Africa; second, to create legitimate commerce and give employment; third, to ameliorate the condition of the natives; and fourth, to check the slave trade, tribal wars and barbarous practices.

Geographers were obviously concerned with practical matters, including national prestige. In 1886 and 1887, two articles by J. T. Wills, drew attention to the dangerous misrepresentations fostered by government handbooks on Australia (*Scott. Geogr. Mag.* **2**, 1886, pp. 733–9; **3**, 1887, pp. 161–9). It was, for example, stated that in South Australia apples and pears could be grown almost everywhere, and oranges in many places. The vine thrived and the mulberrry flourished in a climate resembling that of south Italy '. . . suitable for the vine, olive and other fruits'. Unfortunately, no statistics had been published after 1882, either for rainfall or agriculture as they made such melancholy reading. There were only 6½ million sheep in 500,000 square miles, though the government handbook suggested that 400–640 per square mile could be supported. Yields of wheat were as low as 3 bushels per acre. In New South Wales, said by the government handbook to have 'agricultural resources . . . of practically indefinite extension' with great plains of 'nearly level tracts, well watered, and clothed in good seasons with luxuriant verdure', only 150–180 sheep to the square mile could be maintained. In spite of an expenditure of millions of pounds on wells, dams and reservoirs, one-third of the sheep had perished in dry seasons within the previous few years.

Mr Wills, in calling attention to the climatic limitations of Australia, was a forerunner of (Thomas) Griffith Taylor (1880–1963) whose work on Australian meteorology was banned for many years though he had the satisfaction of being proved right in the end. In the 1880s little was known of rainfall variability and the number of climatic stations was far too small. It is still so. But one enterprise of note was the maintenance of the Ben Nevis Observatory from 1884 to 1903: in 1887 John Murray (of *Challenger* fame, p. 19) noted that observations had been made every hour on the summit and several times a day at Fort William. The initial cost was £7,000, acquired from subscriptions, and grants were given by various bodies such as the British Association and the Scottish Geographical Society. Records from this station gave the most complete sequence for any mountain area in Britain. Today the Ben Nevis Observatory is a ruin (Paton and Wilson, 1954).

Curiosity about the world was abundantly gratified by the publications of geographical societies during the 1880s. When Burma was annexed in 1886, articles were quickly written to describe the newest jewel in the British Crown. And wherever the railway went, the geographer followed. Many issues of geographical journals seemed to be exclusively concerned with remote and distant places, though Hugh Robert Mill† (1861–1950) sent reports on the waters of Scottish estuaries in 1886 based on observations at the Scottish Marine Station (*Scott. Geogr. Mag.* 2, 1886, pp. 347–54), and H. M. Cadell† (1860–1934), in 1888 (*Scott. Geogr. Mag.* 4, 1888, pp. 366–77), wrote on the 'utilisation of waste lands', forecasting the possible further reclamation of land in the Forth valley near Stirling. But probably such work seemed far less exciting than the traversing of pathless wildernesses by intrepid explorers. At least, H. A. Webster of the *Encyclopaedia Britannica* staff (cf. p. 29), was aware of the need for local study of the home environment when he expressed the hope that the Royal Geographical Society 'without intermitting its labours in the field of foreign exploration, will turn its attention homeward, and see that something worthy of England is done for English geography'. Never was a rebuke to the Royal Geographical Society more tactfully administered (*Scott. Geogr. Mag.* 1, 1885, p. 495).

The need for geographical education

Although geography had been taught at various times in English universities before the 1880s, the real need was to establish the subject on a permanent rather than an intermittent basis, and therefore the appointment of Halford John Mackinder to teach at Oxford in 1887 and of Francis Henry Hill Guillemard† (1852–1933) at Cambridge in 1888 was rightly regarded as a victory for geography. (In 1889 Guillemard was succeeded by John Young Buchanan, the oceanographer.) The propaganda for geography teaching in the universities by the Royal Geographical Society culminated in the publication of the Scott Keltie Report (*R. G.S. Supp. Pap.* 1, 1886), which showed that geography was better taught in continental European countries, largely because it was given full recognition in many universities. John Scott Keltie† (1840–1927) was particularly impressed by the teaching of geography in

Germany. He arranged an exhibition of aids to geography teaching, which was held in London and later in Manchester and Edinburgh. A Scottish observer (*Scott. Geogr. Mag.* **2**, 1886, pp. 27–31), noted that the exhibition included wall maps, globes, models and relief maps, geographical pictures, atlases and textbooks from many countries, though not, strangely enough, from the United States. Efforts to make a vivid impact included the attachment of a real cigar to Havana, of natural grains of wheat to south Russia, of gold nuggets (? presumably real) to Australia and California, and tea-leaves to India and China. Some maps, it was noted, tried to show so much that they merely created confusion. Particular praise was given to a number of German wall maps and school atlases.

Scott Keltie's report was well timed and the creation of the readerships of geography at Oxford and Cambridge, with considerable financial help from the Royal Geographical Society, opened an important new phase in geographical education. But the need had long been recognised. In 1855, Francis Galton had found geography to be 'a peculiarly liberalising pursuit. . . . It links the scattered sciences together, and gives to each of them a meaning and a significance of which they are barren when they stand alone'. (Galton, 1855, p. 81). He added that the acquisitions of various sciences meant little unless their relationship was considered, but that it was now possible 'to trace the harmonious way in which all the features of the earth are organised, and how every object has its own appointed post in the one mighty scheme'. This work of correlation owed much to the French (but Danish-born) geographer Conrad Maltebrun (1775–1826) and the two great figures of what is often called the 'classical period', Alexander von Humboldt (1769–1859) and Carl Ritter (1779–1859). The geographer, said Galton, should 'try to describe the world in its entirety, not superficially on the one hand, not with infinite minuteness on the other, but with the bold, graphic, accurate strokes of a well-educated and observant artist'. Galton was largely responsible for the medals scheme of the Royal Geographical Society which was in effect a failure, as only sixteen schools sent in candidates from 1869 to 1884, and about half the medals were given to pupils at Dulwich College and Liverpool College (crammed for the slaughter).

Initial efforts by the Royal Geographical Society to interest the two ancient universities in geography, in 1871 and 1874, were unsuccessful. The 1871 approach to the vice-chancellors of Oxford and Cambridge was contained in a letter written by Major-General Sir Henry Rawlinson, known chiefly as an eminent Assyriologist, which argued the case for improved teaching of geography in the schools as well as for its practical utility in a wide range of professions (Gilbert, 1971). Three years later, in 1874 (perhaps too soon), a second memorandum was sent, in which the Council of the Royal Geographical Society said that they wished:

the word Geography to be understood in its most liberal sense, and not as an equivalent to topography. They mean by it, a compendious treatment of all the predominant conditions of a country, such as its climate, configuration, minerals, plants and animals, as well as its human inhabitants; the latter in respect not only to their race, but also to their present and past history, so far as it is intimately connected with the peculiarities of the land they inhabit.

The geographer should not, in fairness, be regarded merely as a compiler of gazetteers but as a student of two main problems: the first was the reciprocal influence of man and his surroundings and the second the inferences that may be drawn from the present distribution of plants and animals 'in respect to the configuration of the surface of the earth in ancient times'. In short, scientific geography was the 'study of local correlations' and 'it is through Geography alone that physical, historical and political conditions are seen to be closely linked together'. They also noted the recognition of geography given in several French, German and Swiss universities and added that the objection that geography was a subject of such vast and undefined scope could equally well be made for history. Exploration was still in progress and 'although the number of young men who travel after leaving the Universities, for the sake of supplementing their education, is increasing every year, very few of them are qualified to make an intelligent use of the information they may or may not [*sic*] obtain and still fewer are qualified to make observations of the least scientific value'. How anyone was likely to make intelligent use of information he did not obtain was not explained. The memorandum concludes with a burst of the Victorian expansionist outlook: 'The colonies of England, her commerce, her emigrations, her wars, her missionaries, and her scientific explorers bring her into contact with all parts of the globe, and it is therefore a matter of imperial importance that no reasonable means should be neglected of training her youth in sound geographical knowledge' (*Proc. R. G. S.* New Series 1, 1879, pp. 261–4).

Educationalists of the day gave enthusiastic support to the claim of geography for recognition. In 1879 Rev. George Butler (1819–90), headmaster of Liverpool College, spoke of three advantages of geography teaching. Firstly, the systematic study of geography had greatly helped the intelligent appreciation of history; secondly, through geography the way had been opened to the thoroughgoing study of kindred branches of science; and thirdly, geography gave a comprehensive view of the greatness of the British Empire and of the undeveloped capabilities of the accessible world (*Proc. R.G.S.* New Series 1, 1879, pp. 469–70). But the wider educational question of the time was raised some years earlier by Rev. Edward Hale† (1828–94) at a meeting of the British Association held in 1872 at Brighton (*Brit. Ass., Rep.* 1873, pp. 209–10). Everyone, he said, is brought into contact with man and nature and the first aim of education should be to teach the duties we owe to man, our social duties, along with an appreciation of the advantages to be derived from a proper knowledge of nature. In theory this was the ideal of a classical education, but it was not honoured in practice, for classical education had degenerated into the mere teaching of Greek and Latin, or even of little more than Greek and Latin grammar. The study of nature had been practically ignored.

Far more breadth was needed in education, which on the human side should include literature and history, balanced by mathematics and scientific subjects. All schools beyond the primary stage should include in the curriculum an ancient and a modern language, arithmetic, geometry and geography, with history and science. Mr Hale, who was a master at Eton, noted that no textbook was used in the lectures he gave on geography, so pupils were tested by papers in which they reproduced the content of the lectures in their own words. This, naturally enough, would not now be regarded as the *ne plus ultra* of teaching methods, but it is not unknown even now. Mr Hale, however, said that his lectures were 'freely illustrated'.

As shown above, one problem of the time was the need to achieve more breadth in education, for geography was only one of a number of subjects aspiring for recognition in the schools and universities. Between 1887 and 1924, when its grants to the universities ceased, the Royal Geographical Society paid out £11,000 to Oxford and £7,500 to Cambridge, with smaller grants to the universities of Manchester, Edinburgh and Wales, and the Manchester Geographical Society made grants towards the salaries of teachers in the local university (Mill, 1930; Freeman, 1954; Brown, 1971). The Royal Scottish Geographical Society was active in propaganda for the teaching of geography in Scottish universities, but the first appointment came as late as 1908, when G. G. Chisholm became a lecturer in Edinburgh.

The academic contribution

Four remarkable books belong to this period, of which the *History of Ancient Geography* (1879) by E. H. Bunbury† (1811–95), and G. G. Chisholm's *Handbook of Commercial Geography* (1899) remain classics, though the latter has been revised by L. Dudley Stamp† (1898–1966) and others to meet changing circumstances. The standing of the third book, the *Historical Geography of Europe* (1881) by E. A. Freeman† (1823–92) is perhaps less secure than of those just mentioned, but it remains a fascinating work to read. The fourth work, *The Making of England* (1882), by John Richard Green† (1837–83) has had a far wider influence on the development of historical geography than most people realise.

Of the four books here mentioned, the *History of Ancient Geography*, in two volumes, by E. H. Bunbury has retained the respect of critics from the day of its publication. Bunbury was a classicist by training and a contributor of several articles to William Smith's *Dictionary of Greek and Roman Geography* (1870). He made a thorough study of ancient authorities and used the findings of modern travellers. Bunbury, however, dealt only with the period from Homeric times to Ptolemy and later Roman writers in his 1,400 pages, and C. Raymond Beazley† (1868–1959) continued this work to the period of Prince Henry the Navigator in his work, *The Dawn of Modern Geography*, published in three volumes, AD 300–900 (1897); 900–1260 (1901); and 1260–1420 (1906). Classical studies have led several authors to consider the geographical background of the Mediterranean and its borderlands and notable later contributions include the *Historical Geography of the Holy Land,* by George Adam Smith† (1856–1942) (p. 64). One may assume that in every age there will be some scholars who will be attracted to such studies, though possibly not in large numbers. In its long and notable history from 1846, the Hakluyt Society has published an extensive library of works of travel and exploration, deeply revealing of the state of geographical knowledge at various periods. That many such books should be written or edited by people who would not regard themselves as geographers is of no consequence: rather it shows that geographical study can be illuminating for any historical time and in any part of the world.

The Historical Geography of Europe by Edward Augustus Freeman, a Fellow of Trinity College, Oxford, and from 1884 Regius Professor of History, is a substantial two-volume work of some 600 pages of text and 65 maps ranging in time from the days of Homeric Greece to the nineteenth century. The maps include the major rivers but no other physical features, and in the preface the author explains that many of the maps are smaller than he would have wished owing to the expenses of production, and that therefore some details had to be omitted. Freeman states his purpose unequivocally in his first chapter: '. . . to trace out the extent of territory which the different states and nations of Europe and the neighbouring lands have held at different times in the world's history, to make the different boundaries which the same country has had, and the different meanings in which the same name has been used' (p. 1). He goes on to explain that 'great mistakes as to the facts of history' had been caused by the invalid assumption that 'for instance England, France, Burgundy, Austria have always meant exactly the same piece of territory'. Having stated that 'the physical nature of the country, and settlements of the different nations which have occupied it, have always been the causes of political divisions (p. 2)', the author says firmly that the first concern of historical geography is with political divisions, and that the nature of the land, and the people who occupy it, are only of interest in so far as they have influenced political divisions.

John Richard Green, in *The Making of England* showed a far broader outlook. According to the preface of 1881, Green had meant to produce a larger book concerning the whole of English history up to the Norman Conquest, but work on his other books and his precarious health (he died of tuberculosis) impelled him to limit his book to the period ending with the union of the three Saxon kingdoms into one England in 829. Nevertheless, the work, of some 500 pages, still provides fascinating

British names	**Iceni**
Roman names	LINDUM
English names	**Bedicanford**
Modern names	*Lincoln*

0   20
Miles

reading for Green was a born writer, or so it seems from his text. Like many authors before and after him, he was warned by candid friends that he was attempting the impossible but, also like many before and after him, he was not deterred. He used archaeological evidence and contemporary sources, including the work of the Venerable Bede. Most of all he tried to reconstruct the physical environment as it was in the times of which he wrote and included a series of maps showing the probable extent of forest, marsh, heath and mountainous country. He frankly admits that these maps would need later amendment as in fact so little was known of the physical geography of the time: eventually, though not until some fifty years later, evidence was accumulated on the climatic changes that made the vegetational history of prehistoric and later times more complicated than Green could possibly have anticipated.

But there is much that compels admiration. Having said that London stood at the 'one point by which either merchant or invader could penetrate from the estuary into the valley of the Thames', and at the first point at which rising ground existed for a town site on either side of the river, he shows that the site of London was steadily made by man from the time that the Romans built the first embankment. He continues (pp. 112–13):

Even as late as the time of Caesar the soil which a large part of it covers can have been little but a vast morass. Below Fulham the river stretched at high tide over the ground that lies on either side of its present channel from the rises of Kensington and Hyde Park to the opposite shores of Peckham and Camberwell. All Pimlico and Westminster to the north, to the south all Battersea and Lambeth, all Newington and Kensington, all Bermondsey and Rotherhithe,

---

Fig. 3 The Making of England: an historical map.
John Richard Green studied not only the penetration of England by various organised groups but also the environment they found in the lowlands, downlands and other units of a country as diverse in its physical geography as the English lowland. Several later workers followed the same idea and it became a major feature of archaeological work by the 1930s. But as more became known of climatic changes, efforts to reconstruct the landscape of various periods became a subject of increasing complexity, to which significant contributions were made by analysis of pollen found in peat deposits. Green had much of interest to say of the beneficent work of monasteries from the seventh century. Monasticism 'brought with it a transfer and readjustment of population which changed the whole face of the country. Here and there it revived the civilisation of the past by bringing fresh life to the ruins of a Roman town. . . . It broke the dreary line of the northern waste with settlements which proved forerunners of some of our busiest ports. . . . It set agricultural colonies in the depths of vast woodlands, as at Evesham or Malmesbury, while by a chain of religious houses it made its way step by step into the heart of the fens.' Green, J. R., *The Making of England*, vol. 2, 4th edn, 1897 (1st edn, 1882), map p. 55.

formed a vast lagoon, broken only by little rises which became the 'eyes' and 'hithes', the 'islands' and 'landing-rises' of later settlements (Vol. 1, p. 112).

He vividly describes the outpouring of the sea into the Thames in a wide estuary which at its mouth spread over the mud-flats that were eventually embanked to form the Isle of Dogs.

After his death in 1883 his wife, Alice Stopford Green† (1847–1929), herself to become known as an author as well as the editor and reviser of some of her husband's books, published *A Short Geography of the British Islands*, in 1884, as their joint work. This book had been planned by both authors, but the sections on Wales, Scotland and Ireland were the work of Mrs Green. The opening sentence in their preface says that: 'No drearier task can be set for the worst of criminals than that of studying a set of geographical textbooks such as the children in our schools are doomed to use.' Though this book naturally seems old-fashioned now, it is well written and read with a suitable atlas would give quite an effective general picture of the countries described. Character-istically for its time, the counties are treated as separate entities with some mention of agriculture and industry as well as the main physical features.

To many modern readers the work of E. A. Freeman and J. R. Green will seem speculative: hard and practical common sense is the main characteristic of the *Handbook of Commercial Geography* by George Goudie Chisholm. First published in 1889, it went through ten new editions and twelve other reprintings to 1925, after which the eleventh edition was prepared in 1928 by L. D. Stamp. Chisholm is reported to have said that this work was a millstone (perhaps a profitable one) round his neck as such frequent revision was required. Broadly the work falls into three parts, giving a world view, a study of a vast range of commodities that enter international commerce and an analysis of the commerce of various countries. In the original preface, Chisholm said that he had tried to impart an 'intellectual interest' to the study of geographical facts relating to commerce. The book was written for three groups of people: teachers dealing with commerce, pupils in schools and colleges where commercial geography was taught, and those entering commercial life. Much statistical information was included, and Chisholm was careful to point out their limitations (and, one cannot help commenting, he was far more careful than many modern quantitative geographers). As far as possible, all import and export statistics were given on a five-year basis to mask accidental fluctuations from year to year. The *Handbook* changed its character from one edition to another and, as an attempt was always made to be contemporary in approach, it has become recognised as an important contribution to economic history.

Chisholm had an assured place among all geographers using works written in English. Asked why he had written the *Handbook*, he wrote an account of his views on the flyleaf of the copy in the library of the American Geographical Society. In it he said that:

The subject had a strong appeal for me, chiefly, I believe, in consequence of an obscure but growing sense of uneasiness as to the economic position of my own country. That arose from the conviction that the increasing dependence of Great Britain on imports of food paid for by exp͡rts of manufacturers and coal, and by shipping and financial services of various kinds to other countries put the country in a dangerous position ever tending to become more dangerous so long as the dependence on external sources of food continued to increase.

Clearly this comment is controversial but interesting, and so too was his later comment here reproduced:

I believe that the working classes all over the world are showing a sound instinct in striving after as close an approximation to equal conditions of labour as can be attained with advantage to themselves. I am, however, disposed to believe that they are on a false scent in their suspicions of capitalism, and that they would raise their status more rapidly if they trusted capitalism but determined to turn to account their growing political power by making use of it, and in particular by seeing that the backward peoples and classes of the earth are provided with capital which will gradually enable them to give a bigger and bigger return per head for what we give them in exchange. (Information from the late John McFarlane† (1873–1953), Reader in Geography, University of Aberdeen.)

The educational challenge

All the books discussed so far are of interest as works of sound scholarship of a somewhat specialised character. To some it would seem that they provided any justification that might be needed for geography as a subject, but H. J. Mackinder's paper given in 1887 to the Royal Geographical Society (Mackinder, 1887) was designed to justify its recognition as a specialisation in universities. He states the problem in a rhetorical question, 'Can it become a discipline instead of a mere body of information?' Much of the appeal of geography lay in the explorations that thrilled audiences at geographical societies, for by 1887 the polar regions were the only substantial blanks on world maps, though much further exploration was needed, for example, in New Guinea, in Africa, in central Asia and in subpolar areas. Inevitably the tales of adventure would diminish, but the makers of Ordnance Survey maps would prove to be no less dramatic figures than H. M. Stanley revealing the savage vastness of the Congo basin to a delighted world. Geography, so often divided into physical and political in Mackinder's day, should be more than an appendage of geology on the one hand and history on the other. In his view, political geography must be based on physical geography, and the whole could be defined as 'the science whose main function is to trace the interaction of man in society, and so much of his environment as varies locally'. He also said that: 'Physiography asks of a given feature "Why is it?" Topography asks "Where is it?" Physical geography asks "Why is it there?" Political geography asks "How does it act on man in society, and how does he react on it?".' These four points were the concern of geography, while geology was concerned with another problem, 'What riddle of the past does it help to solve?'

Mackinder was obviously interested in the work of J. R. Green as an example of the influence of geographical conditions on the course of hsitory. He also mentions the relationship between county boundaries and physical features, a subject on which he wrote later in *Britain and the British Seas* (Mackinder, 1902). Realistically, Mackinder noted that knowledge is indivisible and that its separation into subjects was a concession to human weakness. The teaching of geography and history might begin as one whole, later to be divided as the historian went to his original documents and the geographer to the influence of scientific aspects of the environment on historical development.

As a guide to teaching, Mackinder thought that a general view of the world should be given. This would naturally include the irregularities of mountain chains, of thermal causes of monsoon winds and rainfall, and other influences that determine climatic and other distributions. With this, there should be local work. 'An environment,' he said, 'is a natural region' (not a view that would be widely held today). The smaller the area included, the greater tends to be the number of conditions that are uniform or nearly uniform throughout the area. Similarly (and here perhaps an argument by analogy seems all too easy) a 'community' is a group of men having certain characteristics in common, and the smaller the community, the greater tends to be the number of common characteristics. But there is constant change through human discovery and scientific advance. When the Cape route to India and the Atlantic route to America developed, Venice could no longer be the great trading city of the world, for the main commercial routes lay elsewhere. Equally notable was the invention of the steam engine and the electric telegraph, which made possible the great size of modern states. The paper finished with a peroration on the possibilities of geography: 'To the practical man, whether he aim at distinction in the State or at the amassing of wealth, it is a store of invaluable information; to the student it is a stimulating basis from which to set out along a hundred special lines; to the teacher . . . an implement for the calling out of the powers of the intellect.'

Mackinder was by nature an advocate and at the age of twenty-five stated his case with consummate skill. He had learnt his craft of speaking not only in the Oxford Union but also in the hard school of university extension work to a varied range of audiences. His later work has, in the present author's view, been overpraised, but nobody could doubt that he was, as J. F. Unstead† (1876–1956) said, 'the right man in the right place at the right time' (Unstead, 1949, p. 57; Gilbert, 1951). He was not by nature the quiet scholar like J. R. Green but a man of affairs, able to seize an idea and present it forcefully, to attract the attention of those who walk the corridors of power not only in universities but in the

State. For geography he had a good case and he knew exactly how to present it.

During the 1880s two vigorous new geographical societies had been established, several books of abiding interest had been written, and the subject had at last achieved a permanent position in the two oldest universities. J. Y. Buchanan at Cambridge was an oceanographer, but H. J. Mackinder at Oxford was a powerful advocate of a 'new geography', at once physical and political and deeply concerned with human life in relation to the environment. In time Mackinder became an advocate of regional geography, so long associated with the Oxford school, while at Cambridge the trend from the beginning was towards a systematic approach: each was to prove productive in time. As the tide of discovery swept forward, and as commerce increasingly penetrated the remoter recesses of the world, the possibilities of geography seemed vast. At last the hidden mysteries of the world were being solved, not only by discovery but by the marked advance of the natural sciences. So much of the world seemed new, and as its vast potentialities were revealed the zeal of geographers to analyse the whole earth seemed natural enough, even if somewhat naïve to later generations. But geographers were few while their subject-matter was limitless and therefore the need to find more students in universities and to ensure that better teaching was given in the schools. Naturally enough, therefore, education was a major concern of geographers and pioneers like Mackinder, and many more after him, went out into the small as well as the large towns up and down the country talking to audiences of teachers and others in the hope that they would generate further enthusiasm for the subject. The geographer of the day could not live in an ivory tower, but had to go out into the highways and hedges and compel them to come in. And as academic salaries were very low, he was probably only too glad to do so.

Chapter 4

The last Victorian years

Queen Victoria had been, said Sir Clements Markham in 1901, one part of the life of all her subjects from the time of their earliest memories. He added that very few people could remember any other sovereign in Britain, but that he was 'one of the few' for he first saw her, as Princess Victoria, in 1836, escorted in to dinner at Windsor by King William IV. Three years earlier, in 1833, she had given a case of mathematical instruments and a pocket compass to Captain Beck, who was leading a relief expedition to find the Rosses, then lost in the Antarctic. In the original loyal address on the accession of Queen Victoria in 1837 the hope was expressed that the reign 'would be famed for its glory and prosperity, and for the promotion of geographical knowledge; that it might be rendered illustrious as the era of important discoveries which may diffuse the blessings of civilisation throughout the globe . . .'. To Sir Clements Markham and the various speakers who followed him, it seemed that all this had happened. Anyone now reading the twenty-eight pages of the *Geographical Journal* which contain the speeches given at a special memorial evening meeting on 11 February 1901 may be fascinated by the confident imperialism that shines through them, for never was more pride expressed in an empire on which the sun not only never set but should in no circumstances ever be allowed to set (*Geogr. J.*, **17**, 1901, pp. 225–52). They are a magnificent period piece.

Beyond question, the Victorian period was an age of expansion in which the world was opened and its vast resources revealed. Explorers had penetrated every continent except one, for Antarctica was still almost unknown; and the explorers had been followed by the builders of roads, railways and ports eager to provide beneficent trade. With them, even in some areas before them, there had come Christian missionaries, and with them too came the military forces and administrators to civilise and organise the newly acquired territories. Knowledge of freshly explored lands poured into the editorial files of geographical societies and a vast stream of books of travel filled the shelves of libraries. The academic advance was less certain.

Education appeared to offer a solution to many problems, or perhaps more accurately frustrations, of which geographers were conscious in the 1890s. The brightest hope of the time was the recognition of geography in the universities of Oxford and Cambridge, combined with the expectation that other universities would follow their lead. So many efforts had been made with such little effect that the Royal Geographical Society gave a warm welcome to the Geographical Association, founded in 1893 with the avowed purpose of encouraging geography teaching in the public schools and, in time, in colleges and other schools (p. 66). The Scottish and Manchester societies (pp. 27–33), and those founded on Tyneside in 1887, at Liverpool in 1891 and Southampton in 1897 all maintained an interest in education. The need of the age was not only the inclusion of geography in the school curriculum but also the modernisation of education to include such studies as history, the natural sciences and modern languages.

Dramatic explorations, especially those in polar regions or previously unknown continental interiors, naturally attract far more attention than such advances as the provision of Ordnance Survey maps, Admiralty charts or new atlases, though the cartographic progress made was faithfully recorded year by year in the *Journal of the Royal Geographical Society*, which thoughtfully arranged that Ordnance maps could be bought by schools at a special discount price. Far more significant was the gentle penetration of geographical journals by articles of an academic character among accounts of exploration. In some cases, for example, these were printed in smaller type than the main contributions on exploration, but a number of them have abiding significance. And with this there was a slow but steady trickle of scholarly books of which some, such as George Adam Smith's *Historical Geography of the Holy Land* are still eagerly read in recent editions. That some such books were written by a biblical scholar or, as in the case of A. Haviland† (1825–1903), who wrote on *The Geographical Distribution of Disease in Great Britain* (1864 and 1892), a medical man shows the appeal of a geographical approach to a variety of circumstances. The few people who were in a more restricted sense professional geographers showed commendable enterprise, not least in travelling up and down the country to lecture on various aspects of geography.

One of the most arresting figures of the time was Patrick Geddes† (1854–1932), the Scot who held a post at the University College of Dundee as a botanist but was only required to lecture in one term. His fertile mind led many to think of planning a new Britain, even a new world, but his address to the Royal Geographical Society on his hopes for the future in 1898 appears to have puzzled an audience accustomed to a more restricted diet (p. 53). Politely talking of 'food for thought' they went away and probably thought no more of what had been said (Geddes, 1898).

Much that was written at this time was severely practical in tone, and concerned more with the scientific analysis of an existing world than the creation of a new and better one. So much of the impetus to geographical study had come from the natural sciences that much of the writing was based on observed physical features, such as the vivid

demonstration by John Walter Gregory† (1864–1932) of the existence
of the Great Rift Valley extending through East Africa into the Jordan
valley, hailed by George Adam Smith as an illuminating contribution to
the geography of the Holy Land (Smith, 1966 edn, p. 301). This was not
the end of Gregory's work, for later he was to put forward the
tetrahedron theory of the earth's cooling, which has amused and
fascinated, though not convinced, many students of a later time.
Vaughan Cornish† (1862–1948) began his work on sand dunes and
especially on the influence of wind on these and other sand- and later
water-covered areas. The idea of relationship was developing strongly,
with climate and weather as one of two or more crucial influences not
only on landforms but also of vegetation, on which some remarkable
pioneer work was done by a young Scotsman, Robert Smith†
(1873–1900), who mapped the vegetation of two areas, one around
Edinburgh and the other in the Scottish Highlands (p. 61).

  H. R. Mill, drawn into geography from oceanography, was equally
sure of the idea of the unity of nature, and in 1896 put forward a plea for
the publication by the Government of a short memoir on each Ordnance
Survey sheet, comparable with those issued for the 1:63,360 sheets of the
Geological Survey. G. G. Chisholm, already well known for his
Handbook of Commercial Geography, issued a number of papers
showing the vast range of his interests over the world. A quiet,
meticulous scholar, he never showed the panache of H. J. Mackinder.
Also of a quieter nature than Mackinder was A. J. Herbertson†
(1865–1915), in time to be his successor at Oxford, but in the 1890s
concerned with the compilation of the great Bartholomew *Meteorology*
volume of the *Physical Atlas*, published in 1899 and widely acclaimed for
its excellence at the time, as indeed since. And yet, with all this progress
the two main sources of disappointment were the slow advance of
geographical education and the perpetual frustration that beset all
efforts to promote Antarctic exploration. In spite of the academic
promise revealed by the writers of the day, attention was still given
primarily to exploration by the geographical societies and especially by
the Royal Geographical Society. It is therefore proposed here to deal
first with exploration and mapping and then to turn to the academic
contribution and finally to education.

Exploration and mapping

By the 1890s there was general agreement with Sir Clements Markham's
view that the time for desultory exploration was past and the need was
for scientific mapping (*Geogr. J.* **2**, 1893, pp. 481–505). Most of the
world was still unmapped except for countries in Europe, British India,
the coasts of the United States and a limited part of its interior and small
parts of other countries. Even in Canada much of the interior was still
unknown or only partially explored despite the expectation of great

mineral resources. Little accurate mapping had been done in Australia and New Zealand, even in their more fertile areas. In some less promising areas, such as the western deserts of Australia, explorers from Edward John Eyre (1815–1901) in 1840 to David Carnegie in 1896 found conditions repellent, with little water, salt marshes and lakes, barren hills and overabundant spinifex: as it happened little was done until the 1950s when four-wheel-drive vehicles became available.

Explorers of the time included some notable people, of whom George Nathaniel Curzon (1859–1925) (later Marquess) made various journeys in Russia, French Indo-China, the Pamir mountains and in Persia, and ultimately became Viceroy of India. Markham said that his explorations were all the more valuable because he went with a thorough knowledge of both the history and the geography of the regions he visited and added that this was 'quite as essential a qualification as the ability to map a country and fix positions' (*Geogr. J.* **6**, 1895, p. 9). Another interesting explorer was Sir William Martin Conway (1856–1937), who in 1897 returned from Spitsbergen, crossed for the first time by a party that included Dr John Walter Gregory, then most famed for his work in Africa (*Geogr. J.* **9**, 1897, pp. 353–68). Later Sir Martin Conway went to the Bolivian Andes and Edward Whymper's book on the Andes in Ecuador appeared in 1892. Many other travellers achieved fame including several women of whom Dorothy Middleton has written in *Victorian Lady Travellers* (1965). Rightly the Royal Geographical Society was concerned about the quality of the explorers, as indeed they had been for a long time. New editions of *Hints to Travellers* (R.G.S. 1854) were issued and in 1897 Sir Clements Markham (*Geogr. J.* **9**, 1897, p. 602) announced that a diploma was to be awarded to people who had taken a course of instruction under John Coles, a retired naval officer who was the map curator at the Royal Geographical Society. In 1899 it was reported that sixty-two intending travellers had followed these courses in the previous year of whom eleven had been given diplomas. During the previous years, five other diplomas had been awarded, but of the sixteen successful candidates ten were army officers and two were naval officers.

Queen Victoria's Diamond Jubilee gave an opportunity of reviewing the progress made since 1837, which was eagerly seized by Sir Clements Markham (*Geogr. J.* **9**, 1897, pp. 589–604), who loved anniversaries. In 1837, only 75 of the 120 Ordnance Survey sheets of England and Wales had been published and in Scotland the primary triangulation was not completed. India was only partially surveyed, with 36 of the 150 sheets needed to provide the general atlas: the great achievement had been the completion of the trigonometrical survey of India, 'the grandest monument of the Queen's reign on the Asiatic continent'. Elsewhere in Asia, the interiors of China and Japan, of central Asia, Tibet and Afghanistan, were almost unknown. Africa was known only in parts such as Morocco and the Atlas lands, the Barbary states and Egypt to the second cataract, with part of Abyssinia. The travels of Mungo Park on the Niger had given some knowledge of the river and the neighbouring coast, but South Africa was known only to the mouth of the river Orange and most of the continent had three black caterpillars on it, one marked the 'Mountains of the Moon' another the 'Kong Mountains' and the third the 'Lapunta Mountains' meaning the 'spine of the world'.

Africa had been opened through the enterprise of Richard Francis Burton (1821–90), John Hanning Speke (1827–64) in 1857, of David Livingstone from 1852 to 1872, of H. M. Stanley and the much loved Joseph Thomson who was revered for 'his human treatment of the natives, his inexhaustible patience with them, and cool enduring courage'. And there were many other explorers, including Sir Francis Galton who went to Damaraland from 1850 to 1852. Vast areas of North America were unknown and so too were many islands in the Pacific and Indian oceans, though marine survey was stimulated by the work of Francis Beaufort (1774–1858), hydrographer for twenty-six years from 1825 who sailed the coasts of Australia, New Zealand, South America, the West Indies and China and brought the technique of maritime sounding to great efficiency. He is best known for the Beaufort Scale of wind force. In Australia the mouth of the Murray river had been explored and the city of Melbourne founded, but much of the map was blank in 1837 and extensive areas of the interior were still little known in 1897. Of Canada there had been advances in knowledge during the reign of Queen Victoria, but progress was less marked in South America.

In the Arctic and even more notably in the Antarctic, progress had been slow. Englishmen had discovered the whole of the American side of the Arctic regions from Behring strait to the north coast of Greenland and explored the intricate system of channels and straits that separated the numerous islands, but there was still much of the frozen north to conquer and in Antarctica scarcely any progress had been made since Sir James Ross crossed the Circle on 1 January 1840 and discovered the continent. Knowledge of the polar areas was sought not only for the satisfaction of conquering the world but also as a contribution to climatology and especially to oceanography. The interdependence of these studies had become increasingly apparent, and in 1894 the Royal Geographical Society appointed a committee to encourage Antarctic exploration. Its members included Sir Joseph Hooker, Sir John Murray and Sir George Nares, the only living naval captain who had been to the Antarctic (cf. pp. 70–76). From the days of the *Challenger* expedition, many geographers had been drawn to studies of the temperature of sea-waters at various depths, as well as of marine fauna: the actual form of the sea-floor raised fascinating problems of the possible former relation of the continents, and there was also a practical use for knowledge of the ocean floor for laying telegraphic cables. Possibly the nineteenth century saw more scientific advance than all previous time, but all the discoveries served only to show how much more knowledge of the world was needed.

Writings of the 1890s

Geographers of the 1890s were as prone to soul-searching as many of a later time and occasionally caused exasperation to colleagues who wanted to see the work advance in a practical manner. But it would be a fallacy to divide geographers into two classes of researchers and practical men, for many were more effective workers because they studied the purpose underlying their activity. Early in the 1890s, for example, H. R. Mill having been drawn into the geographical fold after an education in chemistry and physics, wrote two fascinating articles on the possibilities of geography. Of these, a paper of 1892 is well worth reading again (Mill, 1892a). For him geography was 'the focus at which all the physical and historical sciences converge to throw light on the world as an organic whole'. Later he explains concisely the development of the globe (as it was then understood) in the solar system and points out that the development of the known world may be thought of in terms of the origin of the physical universe, the origin of life and the origin of 'that which distinguishes man from other animals – call it mind, or soul or spirit': 'each requires' he continues, 'as far as modern sciences can ascertain, an act of creation by some power external to the physical universe'. The impact of Darwin on thinking people of the time not only led to the appreciation that the world had evolved during millions of years but also to a deeper appreciation of the interdependence of all life, spendidly stated by Mill: 'Man belongs to the Earth as the Earth belongs to him . . . in order to attack the problems of adjustment which beset our time . . . more knowledge of an accurate kind is desirable . . . this knowledge can be supplied when the scope and power of the science of geography are understood, and advanced study is adequately recognised' (Mill, 1892a, p. 93).

In short, the purpose was to study man in relation to the animal and vegetable kingdom, for it was patently clear that marked differences existed between the lives of people of varied races. Mill found in the temperate climatic regions of the world a natural stimulus to activity for the regular recurrence of winter and summer, of seasons of abundance and dearth, necessitated a certain degree of forethought: by contrast in the climatic regions having extremes of heat and cold it was hard to pass beyond 'the satisfaction of immediate needs'. Heat debilitates and little enterprise is needed to collect food or even to grow it, but cold made the Eskimos and others slaves to survival, engaged in a perpetual struggle to exist at all. Though conscious of racial differences, Mill says little of them and he is on shaky ground when he says that 'a community under a recognised form of government forms a nation and a nation in possession of a region constitutes it a country'. Elsewhere (Mill, 1895b, pp. 49–56) in a paper published three years later, he recognises that 'the hold of nations on regions is subject to continual change' and that 'political geography is stability itself compared with . . . commercial geography'.

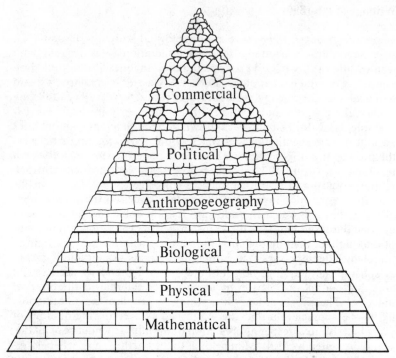

Fig. 4 H. R. Mill's conception of geography.
Essentially a geographer with a strong scientific basis, Mill saw the subject as concerned with the interrelation of mathematical, physical and human distributions, best treated in an orderly sequence. Redrawn from the original diagram in *Scott. Geogr. Mag.* **11**, 1895, p. 53.

For geography Mill provided what has become fashionable eighty years later, a model, reproduced here as Fig. 4. He speaks of it as several courses of masonry differing in material and finish, but each supported by those below and supporting those above. At the base is mathematical geography, 'of great blocks hewn from the quarries of the only absolute science, accurately squared and fitted'. The second tier of the pyramid is physical geography, quarried from chemistry, physics, geology, meteorology and oceanography. Here is the concern with the suface forms of the earth, moulded by many forces including climate. And on this rests the third tier, biogeography, in which the life forms are considered, with anthropogeography as the fourth tier, concerned with the action of mankind on the globe. This raises many problems, as Mill makes clear when he says that 'the unit of consideration is mankind as a whole' with its variety of races, life conditions and density of population. These have not remained stable through historical time and historical geography, has been expressed, in Mill's view, largely through political geography, always changing and ephemeral. This fourth tier is capped by the last, commercial geography, in which the individual comes to the fore. The commercial motive is strong and may 'consolidate national life, accentuate racial differences, redistribute animals and plants, modify physical conditions, start investigations into the nature of the Earth and even invade the solid groundwork of mathematics with the practical counsels of common sense'. Mill's model may seem simplistic now, but it emphasises the concern of the time with the unity of geography (*Scott. Geogr. Mag.* **13**, 1897, pp. 532–3).

Presidential addresses to Section E of the British Association have often been an expression of academic faith in geography and that of H. J. Mackinder at Ipswich in 1895 was no exception. Its title, 'Modern geography, German and English', perhaps reveals the veneration that many British geographers then had for the geographers and especially the cartographers of Germany, though in his address Mackinder also shows an awareness of the work of French and other geographers (*Geogr. J.* **6**, 1895, pp. 369–79). In his view the British had no need for dissatisfaction with their contribution to precise survey, to hydrography, to climatology and to biogeography, but on the 'synthetic and philosophical and therefore on the educational side of the subject the British contribution was far inferior to that made by geographers of other countries and especially of Germany'. Raising an issue to be frequently debated later, he said that 'treatment by regions is a more thorough test of the logic of the geographical argument than is the treatment by types of phenomena'. This was shown first in the work of Alexander von Humboldt whose *Essais politiques sur la Nouvelle Espagne*, published in 1809, revealed 'for the first time . . . an exhaustive attempt to relate (causally) . . . relief, climate, vegetation, fauna and the various human activities'.

Here was the problem of the geographical environment, but regional surveys could be made on a basis of systematic geography. Scientific analysis of the environment depended on geomorphology, 'geophysiology' and biogeography, but anyone considering human geography which (following German workers) he terms 'anthropogeography', needed a knowledge of all the rest. Geomorphology was 'the half-artistic, half genetic consideration of the forms of the lithosphere' (not a definition that would satisfy modern geomorphologists), 'geophysiology' covered oceanography and climatology, and biogeography organic communities and their environments. Characteristically, Mackinder thought in terms of communities, biological and human: human communities could move from one environment to another, could adjust – with varying success – to an environment that altered through time, and could themselves be due to the fusion of two or more communities coming from differing environments.

In these views Mackinder showed an awareness of migration as an instrument of geographical change, though he could not know that French geographers were in time to pour out torrents of eloquence on this theme. A human community was influenced by the geographical environment but gathered traditions and practices through experience. The Normans, for example, were affected by their Norwegian origins, and Americans with a European background had developed a civilisation that could not have arisen in the Mississippi plains. In some ways human genius appeared to be limitless in meeting adverse circumstances yet it never could be completely so for nature could assert its final supremacy: put differently, this means that a phrase popular at the time, 'man and his conquest of nature', was of questionable value for there never could be any final conquest as, for example, later experience of semi-arid lands cleared for agriculture and turned into dustbowls was to show. Nevertheless, human communities by the exercise of ingenuity could maintain themselves in apparently unfavourable environments or in those which had become unfavourable after some initial advantage, such as the possession of mineral resources, had been removed. Mackinder was deeply aware of the economic necessities of life and regarded the study of them as crucial. Somewhat tentatively in 1895 he looked forward to studying political geography on which he was to make a dramatic contribution a few years later (p. 82). Basically, political geography rested on economic and strategic factors, but there was also a historical urge in a people derived from their inherent qualities: here Mackinder was unconsciously forecasting some of the views of the geopoliticians of a later time (p. 158).

Ideas flowed from Mackinder, some of them worked out and some not. He came to geography with a background of rigid historical study and he also saw the relevance to the subject of a solid scientific (especially biological) foundation on which the human geographer could build. He had a natural appreciation of the economic aspects of life and, perhaps even more, a love of politics conceived as an expression of a corporate spirit. As a regional geographer he was completely outclassed by many people working at his time, particularly by Vidal de la Blache (1845–1918), yet he did a great deal to encourage regional study in Britain. His peroration in the address of 1895 might be described as inspirational for it shows that he, as others before and since, found it good to be a geographer. 'The ideal geographer', Mackinder writes,

... is a man of trained imagination, more especially with the power of visualizing forms and movements in space of three dimensions ... he has an artistic appreciation of land forms obtained, most probably, by pencil study in the field; he is able to depict such forms on the map, and to read them when depicted by others, as a musician can hear music when his eyes read a silent score; he can visualize the play and the conflicts of the fluids over and around the solid forms; he can analyze an environment, the local resultant of world-wide systems; he can picture the movements of communities ... acting and reacting on the communities around.

No doubt a modern geomorphologist with a well-equipped laboratory will be contemptuous of a phrase like 'an artistic appreciation of land forms' but Mackinder wrote in 1895, not 1980.

Patrick Geddes in an essay of 1898 expressed several ideas comparable with those of H. J. Mackinder, though from a biological rather than a historical background (Geddes, 1898). Like many people of his time, he was thrilled by the demonstration as a scientific fact of the ordered evolutionary unity revealed in the world, and the possible correlation of relief, climate, natural resources with the distribution of races, their economic possibilities and aptitudes, their commercial and military history. But there was a need to go further, to relate everything already mentioned to social organisation in tribal types or castes, or in religious groups. Such ideas were not new, as Geddes points out with references to earlier workers and notably to Frédéric le Play (1806–82). Inevitably the problem arose of the relation between man and his environment: how had nature determined man and how had man reacted or his environment? Geddes focused attention on human activity and emphasised that detail mattered, for the salmon-fishers of Norway, the whalers of Dundee, the cod-fishers of Newfoundland, the sponge-fishers of the Aegean were all distinct communities . . . 'each a definite type'. Stability of social development was not assured, for in many parts of the world there was conflict between the people of the plains and those of the steppe. In times of peace, irrigation and intensive agriculture penetrated new lands, while at other times hunters and shepherds, so gentle in peace and so ferocious in war, descended to the plain, sometimes as a ruling race or caste, sometimes as settlers seizing land from those there before them.

Geddes was by no means averse to a generalisation, as for example in his pen picture of the Scottish population which was composed of 'the thrifty agricultural Saxon of the Lothians, the adventurous Scandinavians of the Northern and East Coast, the pastoral and imaginative Celts, and the social as well as the racial hybrids of all three'. In his view the essential study was of place, work, family (or folk) which could be reversed as society (meaning the ideals and institutions developed from the family units), work and place. But above all education must include a regional study and only with this basic was it possible to plan a better society: later the famous Geddes slogan became 'survey before action'. Many of the geographers of the time found in Geddes a source of inspiration, firmly expressed by H. R. Mill (Mill, 1951, p. 24) who speaks of him as

the most inspiring influence in Edinburgh in the early eighties when inspiration blew from many quarters. He soon showed himself more of a humanist than a biologist, and he came in to his own in later years as a sociologist, the promoter of all sorts of schemes for social reform and human happiness. He attracted a swarm of disciples, not all of whom were able to profit from his scientific zeal without being dazzled by his amazing versatility and the kaleidoscopic plans he was continually launching, leaving the navigation to his followers.

Geddes has remained a source of fascination to many people, and his ideas on town planning long survived his death in 1934.

Mill, Mackinder and Geddes have been mentioned here as men who wrote on the possibilities of geography in the last years of Queen Victoria's reign when many people were eager and ready to demonstrate the strength of the 'new geography' (there is always a 'new geography') by practical activity, not least H. R. Mill. To the older generation of geographers this meant exploring new lands, but to some of the new academic workers it meant field study in the broadest possible sense. They may have been eager to disprove Mackinder's acidulated comment (made in the 1895 address discussed above) that the English were 'good observers, poor cartographers and teachers perhaps a shade worse than cartographers', but perhaps they cared little for this remark. Work of a detailed character included significant contributions in cartography (apart from the fine work of the Ordnance Survey), in oceanography and lake survey, in climatology with some interesting essays on geomorphology, as well as on botanical distributions. What failed to achieve acceptance, regrettably, was the plan of H. R. Mill to make a regional survey of Britain on an official basis (pp. 59–60) though his suggestions bore rich fruit in the training of generations of students in universities. Also in this period a few remarkable works appeared, of which some discussion appears on pp. 62–5.

Mapping and field work

By the end of the nineteenth century it was clearly understood that any adequate survey of the world and understanding of its geography could only be achieved by local study. The much-read text, T. H. Huxley's *Physiography*, first published in 1877, worked – as D. R. Stoddart explains – 'from the familiar to the unfamiliar' (Stoddart, 1975a, pp. 17–40). In it Huxley 'dealt with springs, rainfall and climate, water chemistry, denudation, glacial erosion, marine erosion, earth movements and volcanicity, deposition in the ocean and the formation of rocks, the geology of the Thames basin, and finally the earth as a planet, its movements and its seasons, and its place in the solar system'. Huxley said that science was 'nothing but *trained and organized common sense* beginning with observation, facts collected, proceeding to classification, facts arranged and ending with induction, facts reasoned upon and laws deduced'. The aim was to show young people the fascination of the brook which ran through the village, or the gravel pit from which road metals were quarried, of the Ordnance map which revealed their own neighbourhood. From this basis one could work forward to an understanding of the world: without it the world would be an abstraction. Teachers and parents welcomed the book. Stoddart notes that the redoubtable Rev. E. Hale of Eton (p. 35) commended it to his class and 'never found that they had any difficulty in understanding it', while Joseph Hooker, the botanist, found that each of his six sons was unwilling to pass on his copy to a younger brother.

Essentially geographers looked to the world and to their own environment, their parish. World maps in atlases had been built up by observations recorded by travellers, whether explorers, scientists, traders, armed forces, surveyors, administrators, missionaries or others, many people fell into more than one category. The world expedition of the *Challenger* of 1872–6 provided so much material for investigation that the publications were not complete under 1895, when the last of the fifty volumes appeared. The whole set included 29,500 pages, with 3,000 plates and maps, and was twice the size of the then current edition of the *Encyclopaedia Britannica*. Forty of the volumes were on zoology and the remaining ten dealt with the narrative of the cruise, the physics and chemistry of sea-water, the deep-sea deposits and botanical findings, finishing with a two-volume summary. The basic feature was the study of the submarine relief of most of the ocean floor, but the contribution to climatology was considerable and the observations on the salinity of the sea, on currents, tides and other marine phenomena were of vast significance (Mill, 1895a). But like all such successful enterprises (including the voyage of the *Beagle* in Charles Darwin's day) the end proved to be only a beginning. Oceanography could be studied at home, as Sir John Murray appreciated. At the Scottish Marine Station, investigation of coastal and marine waters continued, as H. R. Mill shows in his *Autobiography* (Mill, 1957). It included weather and climate as shown for example in the Annual Report for 1893 of the Fishery Board, in which H. R. Mill and A. J. Herbertson dealt with observations of water temperature at 9 a.m. and 3 p.m. at four stations on the west coast and four on the east coast for the years 1890, 1891 and 1892. They noted that the water was warmest in August to September and coldest in February to March, and that the normal monthly range was 15.5 °F, but 20–24 °F between the warmest and coldest days.

Survey of inland lakes had been advocated for several years by a committee of the British Association, but without success. Eventually John Young Buchanan, the chemist on the *Challenger*, worked with H. R. Mill on Loch Katrine and Loch Lomond. Mill had worked for several years on the physical geography of the river Clyde and the Royal Society of Edinburgh gave him a prize and a medal; they also published his work. Finally the Royal Geographical Society provided a small grant for work on English lakes. H. R. Mill with his wife, Edward Heawood† (1864–1949) the librarian of the Royal Geographical Society and, for part of the time A. J. Herbertson, began to work on English lakes, first on Derwentwater, then on Bassenthwaite, Ullswater, Coniston and Windermere. Heawood continued with Buttermere, Crummock and Ennerdale Water and in 1894 Mill and Heawood surveyed Haweswater. The results were published in the *Geographical Journal* with splendid maps by the Bartholomew firm (*Geogr. J.* **4**, 1894, pp. 237–46; **6**, 1895, pp. 46–73, 135–66). The effect of deltaic deposition was noted and the volume of water in each lake calculated, but the most unexpected feature was that Wastwater, Windermere and Coniston all had considerable areas below sea-level, which raised problems for glaciologists and geomorphologists. Later, Sir John Murray with a young business man from Perth, Frederick Pattison Pullar (1875–1901), surveyed Scottish lochs and published their findings with layer coloured maps by Bartholomew (*Geogr. J.* **15**, 1900, pp. 309–53; **17**, 1901, pp. 273–95; **22**, 1903, pp. 237–69, 521–41). Mr Pullar had a passionate interest in meteorology and oceanography, notably in the Marine Biological Station at Millport; he died in a skating tragedy.

The inspiration given by the *Challenger* expedition was also seen in the work of Henry Newton Dickson† (1866–1922), originally a physicist, who worked under John Murray at the *Challenger* office, under Alexander Buchan† (1829–1907) at the Ben Nevis Observatory and also at the Marine Biological Station on marine biology and salinity. Dickson wrote papers on marine biology and salinity in 1896–7. In 1899 he became Lecturer in Physical Geography at Oxford and in 1906 he moved to University College, Reading.

Effective demonstration of the growth of climatology came in 1899 with the publication of volume 3, *Meteorology*, of Bartholomew's *Physical Atlas*. There were to have been five volumes, but only this and the zoology volume appeared. H. R. Mill, who welcomed it with enthusiasm, pays tribute to the *Physical Atlas* published by the Johnston firm in 1854 as a fine achievement for its time, but adds that this new atlas 'far outstripped' 'the admirable meteorological atlas' compiled by Professor Hann, as part of the last edition of Berghaus's *Physikalischer Atlas* in 1887. In fact the right to use any maps in this atlas had been acquired but the number adapted from the German source was comparatively small. Several maps had been prepared by A. Buchan but many were by A. J. Herbertson, and of these a number, notably those of rainfall, were from new data. Monthly climatic maps were included and such features as isanomalous temperatures were treated. Notable also was the attention given to the 'chief stormtracks' of the world, including western Europe and areas subject to tropical cyclones. A special note of praise was given for the 'scrupulous acknowledgement of sources . . . not universal in cartographic work' or one may add, much other work. Mill seized the opportunity of noting the absence of material on Antarctica, no doubt as part of the campaign for exploration there to be

---

Fig. 5 The zoological regions of W. L. Sclater.
Atlases of the nineteenth century (and fortunately later) generally included maps of the world distribution of climate, vegetation and animals. In the introductory chapter to *Principles of Human Geography*, English edition of 1926, but based on articles published in 1917 and 1918, Vidal de la Blache refers to the publication of Heinrich Berghaus's *Physikalischer Atlas* (1837) as a great advance for it showed 'the close relationship between climate and vegetation'. This was extended to faunal and other distributions and became the basis of much geographical research and teaching.
Redrawn from *Geogr. J.* **3**, 1894, opp. p. 169.

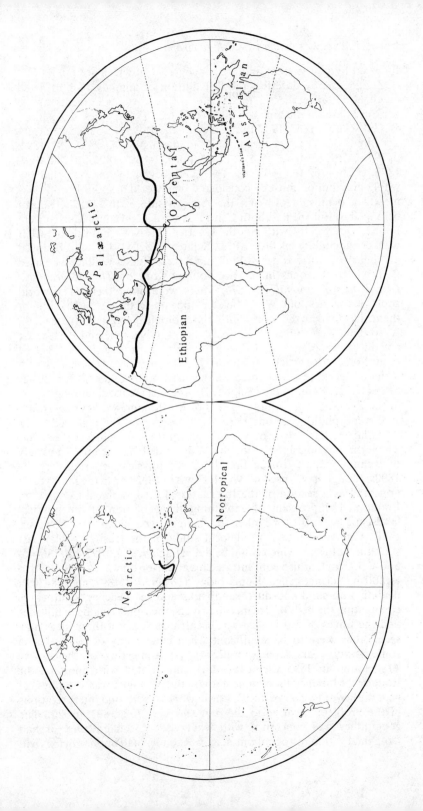

financed by government and other agencies (on which see pp. 70–6).

Zoogeography, in effect the distribution of animals, had attracted much attention earlier in the nineteenth century, as students of the various atlases of the time will discover. From 1893 a series of papers by W. L. Sclater (1863–1943), secretary of the Royal Zoological Society appeared on 'The geography of mammals' (*Geogr. J.* **3**, 1894, pp. 95–105; **4**, 1894, pp. 35–52; **5**, 1895, pp. 471–83; **7**, 1896, pp. 282–96; **9**, 1897, pp. 67–76; **10**, 1897, pp. 84–9). He began by showing that the whole distribution must be considered on a world basis, as Europe was merely a peninsula of Asia, the African side of the Mediterranean belonged to Europe and both Central America and south Mexico were linked zoologically with South America. He was faithful to earlier workers, including his father P. L. Sclater† (1829–1913) who advanced his theory of world zones in 1857 and Arthur Russel Wallace who used P. L. Sclater's zones in his two-volume work on *The Geographical Distribution of Animals* in 1876. There were other theories of world zoological zones, but W. L. Sclater appears to have thought little of them: he divided the world into six zoological 'regions' (so called), Australian, Neotropical, Ethiopian, Oriental, Nearctic and Palaearctic and in his six papers goes through each in turn (Fig. 5). In 1899 he republished these articles in a book, *The Geography of Mammals*, which included several other chapters on the distribution of particular species by his father, Philip Lutley Sclater. His regions are used, among others, in the *Zoogeography* volume (1911) of Bartholomew's *Physical Atlas*.

Geomorphology as one part of physiography was regarded as an essential and basic element in geographical study long before the 1890s. The term 'physiography', though not discarded, had acquired a variety of meanings apart from a broadly based physical geography by the 1890s, though it was used by W. M. Davis in 1895 and in the same year it appeared as a section of the International Geographical Congress in London. The problem of explaining the evolution of the physical landscape lay in the time taken for changes to occur. In 1897, however, F. P. Gulliver wrote a vivid local study of the (easily visible) past shorelines of Kent, which could be dated (*Geogr. J.* **9**, 1897, pp. 536–46) and Vaughan Cornish concentrated his attention on waves. He hoped to establish a science called 'Kumatology' (*Geogr. J.* **9**, 1897, pp. 278–309), dealing with sand and dust, sandbanks and sea beaches, sand waves corrugating the beds of streams and rivers, the ripple ridging of hillsides and the waves of drifting snow. Eccentric as some of these ideas may seem, they were to be significant when close study of coasts began some thirty years later (pp. 122–4). At a meeting of the British Association in 1893 Clements Markham quoted with approval Sir Roderick Murchison's comment that 'the geologist was the physical geographer of former periods', whose work was 'to find interpretations of the problems relating to the past'. (*Geogr. J.* **2**, 1893, p. 520). The geographer was concerned with what was now happening, or had happened within historical times, as J. R. Green had implied in his vivid description of the river Thames (pp. 39–40). Similarly, there was firm historical evidence that at Sluys, 12 miles north of Bruges, Edward III had defeated the French fleet on a spot now surrounded by rich cornfields and meadows.

Geographers using material provided by geologists for world regionalisation or for more local work naturally needed to understand the perils of generalisation. At the 1893 British Association meeting W. Topley, a fieldworker of the Geological Survey, gave a meaning that might have been better heeded by geographers and archaeologists (pp. 114–16) who wrote glibly of 'old hard rocks' and 'young soft rocks'. He said that the question of the age of rocks with hardness or softness and with resistance to erosion was fallacious. The soft clays, thin limestones and sandstones of the Jurassic rocks of England were represented in the south and east of Europe by thick masses of limestone forming prominent mountain ranges and the soft Triassic rocks of England were contemporaneous with huge masses of resistant limestone and dolomite in the Alps, though with intermediate softer beds and layers of volcanic rock. (*Geogr. J.* **2**, 1897, p. 527).

In the search for explanation of the physical landscape, the work of W. M. Davis (1850–1934), Professor of Physical Geography at Harvard, on the cycle of erosion was warmly welcomed. In 1895 Davis published a paper on 'The development of certain English rivers' (Davis, 1895) in which he suggested that those in the east had evolved initially on a gently inclined plain composed of sedimentary strata of varying resistance: during this development the land had been worn down at least once to a lowland of faint relief, and a second cycle of denudation opened in which the adjustment to structure had been carried to a higher degree of perfection than it would have reached in the first cycle. In this paper he uses the terms 'consequent' and 'obsequent', and mentions that 'consequent' was first mentioned by the American geologist, John Wesley Powell (1834–1902) and 'subsequent' by Joseph Beete Jukes (1811–69) in his classic paper on rivers of southern Ireland (Jukes, 1862; Chorley *et al.*, 1964). Davis discusses the questions of marine and subaerial erosion and the work of other writers on the history of rivers. He uses the term 'peneplain' to indicate an 'almost-denuded surface'. That such matters as the evolution of river systems attracted attention at the turn of the century is shown, for example, by H. J. Mackinder, who in *Britain and the British Seas* of 1902 gives it almost forty pages.

Emphasis on local geography was the theme of a paper in 1894 by H. R. Mill advocating the publication of memoirs for each Ordnance Survey 1:63,360 sheet on the same lines as those planned sixty years earlier for the Irish Survey for each parish. Of these only one, for the Templemore Parish, Co. Derry (1837), was published, largely on the grounds of expense, but the idea put forward by Dr H. R. Mill was for a simpler and less expensive series of memoirs. The paper, prepared at the request of the Royal Geographical Society, suggested that for each sheet there should be a memoir of 8–32 pages, but 48 in a few cases, where it was warranted by special interest (Mill, 1896). There would ultimately be regional memoirs, covering areas such as the Weald, the Devon – Cornwall peninsula, Wales, the Lake District, east Yorkshire, the Southern Uplands, the Central Plain (*sic*) of Scotland, the Highlands, and finally these would be generalised into one great memoir of the whole of Great Britain and Ireland. Mill noted, perhaps without complete fairness to others that 'the attention of geographers has hitherto been directed mainly towards the collection of facts; we now require to discuss and arrange them'. Abundant material was available, including geological maps, charts and publications of the Hydrographical Department, records possessed by the meteorological societies based in London and Edinburgh, rainfall statistics kept by J. G. Symons (1838–1900), census reports (inferior, it was true, in many ways to those of the USA), reports of births, deaths and marriages (which could be used to make maps similar to those of Dr A. Haviland on which see p. 63), material available from government departments including the Board of Trade, information possessed by various societies including the Royal Agricultural, Archaeological and Statistical with the Institution of Civil Engineers and even photographic material such as that available in the Birmingham 'free library'.

Each memoir was to include an index of names with the length of streams, notes on place-names, a calculation of the mean elevation (then a popular item) with the area between contours, a physiographic section to comprise landforms and geological structure, the stage reached in the cycle of geographical development (W. M. Davis's ideas were spreading fast), soils, minerals, local magnetic conditions and climate in relation to physical features. A section on vegetation and agriculture was to include flora and fauna, woodland, moorland, pasture, arable land and crops and there was also to be a political and historical section concerned mainly with boundaries and historical sites. All this was to be correlated on a human basis, which could include a variety of subjects such as the sites of towns and villages, the distribution of population, the use of natural resources and the historical development of industries. Even local vocabularies could be included. Mill produced a specimen study, published as 'A fragment of the geography of England: south-west Sussex' (Mill, 1900). Nothing more happened and later on Mill spoke of it as 'one of the worst disappointments of a life rich in such fiascoes' (Mill, 1951). He lived long enough, however, to see some of his ideas carried out in the work of the Ministry of Town and Country Planning after the Second World War and in the reports of the Land Utilisation Survey of L. D. Stamp (pp. 135–7).

H. R. Mill was a forward-looking man of abundant common sense, clearly seen in his essay on 'The development of habitable lands: an essay in anthropogeography' (Mill, 1900b). He was eager to look at world problems as well as local landscapes. The aim for the future must be to secure 'a permanent adjustment of people to the land on which they live' and he made the normal distinction between non-renewable resources such as mineral ores and stones, and vegetable or animal products. A civilised people needed materials for food and clothing, houses, implements, machinery and transport with power resources, which might change: Mill noted that 'the industrial monopoly held by the coalfields is being threatened'. How right he was! Foresight demanded that any area should have a range of developed resources rather than one that might be exhausted or no longer required through changes in demand. In the end no country in the modern world could be self-sufficient and Mill was obviously feeling his way to the view that the scientific unity of the globe must involve its economic unity. He also turned a somewhat critical eye on the development of new lands and, like others before and after him, viewed with distaste the widespread use of a rectangular plan in town building, in many cases unsuited to the site. The fear of degradation of aborigines and earlier settlers by the new immigrants is also mentioned and he notes that some Jesuit missions had been remarkably successful in maintaining the life and self-respect of isolated tribes in South America. In planning any country there must be a thorough survey, trigonometrical, cadastral, topographical, geological, hydrographic, climatological and biological.

Plant geography became a recognised specialism by the turn of the century. Pioneer studies came from a young man, Robert Smith of University College Dundee, who had been influenced by Patrick Geddes and – more scientifically – by Charles Flahault (1852–1935) of the University of Montpellier; he produced two papers of a botanical survey of Scotland, the first on the Edinburgh district and the second on north Perthshire (*Scott. Geogr. Mag.* **16**, 1900, pp. 385–416, 441–67). The surveys of Flahault were based on dominant trees, but as this method would be inappropriate for Scotland, Smith devised a new classification. Working from sea-level, this included a littoral zone, cultivation with and without wheat, woods of deciduous and coniferous species, hill pastures and moorlands. Unfortunately Smith died at the age of twenty-six in 1900, but his work was continued by others later (pp. 85–7). Each of his zones could be subdivided: for example the littoral zone of the Firth of Forth included halophytic and sand-dune vegetation. Of special interest in the cultivated belt was the upper limits of crops, for example wheat, found to 500 ft with a north exposure, but 700 ft and even in the case of one field 900 ft, with a south exposure. Oats showed a similar divergence, reaching 900 ft with a north exposure, but 1,000 ft and in a few cases 1,250 ft on south-facing slopes. Deciduous trees were mainly on the lower grounds, but to 800–900 ft on the north-facing slopes and 200 ft higher on those facing south in the Pentlands. Coniferous trees occurred mainly below 1,250 ft but a few persisted, though in a stunted form, to 1,500 ft. The hill pasture and moorland vegetation was varied, though heather occurred on the driest and sphagnum on the wettest soils with many transitions between them. Grasslands appeared to vary according to the parent materials of the soils with much gorse and bracken on those derived from basalt and considerable heather mixed with pasture species on Silurian soils. There was also a Pentland type in which the vegetation was influenced by drainage and partial cultivation. Smith also noted that gorse and bracken were better developed on slopes with a dry south-aspect than those on the north: for example gorse was seen only to 600–800 ft on the north-facing but over 1,000 ft on the south-facing slopes, and bracken occurred to 1,250 ft on the north but as much as 1,500 ft on south-facing slopes. Little of the vegetation could be regarded as 'natural'; for example grass growth was made possible by sheep manuring and heather burning. Throughout the work Smith emphasised that there were many transitions. In north Perthshire many of the upper limits of cultivation were much the same as those in the Pentlands, but the Scots pine was found to a height of 1,500 to 1,800 ft and the larch woods, developed after this tree was introduced to Scotland in 1738, ascended to 1,300 to 1,800 ft: the limit of birch trees was 1,500 to 2,000 ft with isolated trees to 2,300 ft. An extensive range of alpine vegetation occurred in the area between 2,000 and 4,000 ft. This pioneer work was followed by Pennine surveys later, on which see pp. 85–7.

Much of the research discussed in the last few pages received little attention at the time when it was written, for the main supporters of the geographical societies were still primarily interested in exploration, as indeed many still are eighty years later. Ideas were flowing in a plentiful stream that was to fertilise new fields of enquiry later on. And geography was proving its value by works rather than by faith, for its status was enhanced by a few books of considerable interest and, at least in the case of George Adam Smith, abiding value.

Books of the eighteen-nineties

Three books are discussed here, but others published in English at this time include H. R. Mill's *Realm of Nature* (1891) which gives an effective training in basic physical geography and is a practical expression of the views Mill expressed in the paper of 1892 discussed on p. 49. Of the three books now to be discussed Dr A. Haviland's *The Geographical Distribution of Disease in Great Britain* (1892), is almost forgotten but worthy of rereading as an example of the application of geography to medical observations, though few are likely to agree with his conclusions. George Adam Smith's work the *Historical Geography of the Holy Land*, has won veneration from countless students of the Bible for it combines scholarship with felicity of writing, eloquence and – in the right place – imagination: to a geographer not the least interesting feature is the faculty for observation that is shown. The *Historical Geography* is the kind of book one 'ought to read' but when one does so duty becomes pleasure and time slips away as one continues to read. The last of the three, the *International Geography* is useful and informative but pedestrian. It belongs to the encyclopaedic category and was the work of some seventy authors (Mill, 1899).

Haviland's book was mentioned by H. R. Mill as 'applied geography' in a review in the *Geographical Journal* (*Geogr. J.* **2**, 1893, p. 87) but it would now be termed 'medical geography'. (In the same journal the term 'applied geography' also appears in a letter from Mr A. Silva White (pp. 178–9), in which he spoke of it as the study of man related to environment in social units, as man in the state and man in his world relations. The first of these could lead on to the study of demography, the second of sociology and the third of philosophy.) Dr Haviland, described as 'Late Lecturer in the Geographical Distribution of Disease' in St Thomas's Hospital, London, was obviously a man of experience for he mentions that he had worked in a town (unnamed, but he was in practice with his father at Bridgwater, Somerset) during the cholera epidemic of 1849 and observed that the disease was worse during periods of calm weather. He published numerous papers from 1855 and the 1892 work, of over 400 pages, was in effect a rewritten and fully revised version of a book that originally appeared in 1875 (Haviland, 1892). The aim is threefold: first, to ascertain the geographical distribution of certain diseases; second, to discover where diseases prevail and where they do not; third, to search for the causes of prevalence, absence or scarcity of diseases, which involved a study of 'local airs or waters . . . general or local climates, geological structure, physical configuration or social surroundings'. Dr Haviland read widely on climatology, glaciology and geology and shows in his book that he was an acute observer of the landscape. Much of his detailed work deals with the Lake District and its surroundings, which he divides into a northern section sheltered from dangerous winds and a more exposed southern section. In general, the more dangerous winds were those from the north, northeast, east and southeast 'of bad repute in the estimation of the public and the medical profession; as a rule they are drier, colder and contain less ozone' (Haviland, 1892, 237). But this was only a generalisation and Dr Haviland was fully aware of the local character of climate, or in modern terms of the microclimates. He paints a gloomy picture of health conditions near the actual lakes.

The imprisoned waters . . . are seen to have brought with them, not health and vigour, but death and destruction in all their varied forms, the foul washings from cultivated land, manured with every kind of filth, the excrement of man and the lower animals that surround him, dead and dying vegetable matters; the sewage from towns and villages, and the out-casts of factories; and lastly the newly dead trees and herbs that have been overwhelmed by the extravasated flood. (Haviland, 1892, p. 68).

Inadequate medical research made it difficult to draw firm conclusions: for example, Haviland comments that 'the hidden cause of cancer still baffles the most expert microscopist' (as to this day), that little was really known of rheumatism though much more of phthisis. From his long-continued work it appeared that the highest mortality in female cancer was in southeast England, with a decrease to the west and northwest, where the mortality was lowest. Even there, however, local differences were found, for in Cumberland cases were more frequent in the Eden and Derwent valleys than elsewhere. The best location for a cancer patient appeared to be high-lying dry districts, with a limestone (including chalk) soil. For phthisis, however, the favourable conditions were almost the reverse of those for cancer, as in warm, protected, fertile tracts, such as those around the Lake District floored by red sandstones, or the low-lying damp but sheltered valleys of southeast England, the death-rate was low. High-lying areas and those near the coast with strong winds beside the coast were unfavourable to phthisis sufferers who should therefore seek a sheltered situation. It would appear that Dr Haviland's views were not those of many later specialists who placed sanatoria in extremely airy situations. He says that although the disease was not caused by 'strong sea-breezes' the 'strong atmospheric currents, more or less ozoniferous, produce the pulmonary catarrh that may precede phthisis'. Patients with heart disease and rheumatism appeared to do best in well-ventilated areas of open aspect, such as those exposed to the prevailing westerly winds on the coastal side of the Lake District and, further south, in those areas where wheat was grown. Much of this will probably seem naïve to modern readers, only too conscious of the association of disease with urban conditions, but Dr Haviland noted (1892, p. 364) that 'bad streets and other insanitary arrangements antagonised the natural advantages derivable from local configurations and local climates'. And he was also aware of the limitations on comparative studies in medical geography imposed by administrative divisions, but for that very reason he used all possible detailed sources. Inadequate statistics both for diseases and for weather and climate make Haviland's book seem speculative rather than definitive, especially as some of his theories would not now command acceptance from medical experts.

Vastly more convincing, for its almost inestimable depth of scholarship, is the *Historical Geography of the Holy Land*, first published in 1894, and now known mainly in the twenty-fifth edition 'revised throughout' of 1931 (and reissued by Fontana in 1966). Its author, Rev. Sir George Adam Smith, was an Old Testament scholar who made several visits to Palestine and its borders, and all through the text there are vivid descriptive sketches that show an intimate acquaintance with a country the author had traversed on foot. But this is not by any means all, for there is a rich knowledge of the biblical sources and of the commentaries and other studies of them in various languages. There is also a profound appreciation of post-biblical history, notably of the Crusades and even, in the later editions, of the campaigns fought over this territory in the First World War. And as if this were not enough, it is eminently readable: in a modern introduction the biblical scholar H. H. Rowley speaks of it as 'a classic which has fascinated and instructed generations of students', and adds that it gave him fresh illumination on many biblical passages with a realisation of 'the close interrelation between geography and history'. In passing one may note that many geographers have thought deeply on this relationship, so richly seen by G. A. Smith. One is tempted to quote many passages, some of which are reminiscent of oratory poured forth in austere Presbyterian churches discreetly providing the substance the hearers expected: here is such a passage (pp. 272-3):

To her dependence on the Lebanons Galilee owes her water and her superiority in fruitfulness to both Judaea and Samaria. This is not because Galilee has a greater rainfall; her excess in that respect is slight, and during the dry season showers are almost as unknown as in the rest of Palestine. But the moisture, seen and unseen, which the west winds lavish on the Lebanons is stored by them for Galilee's sake, and dispensed to her with unfailing regularity round the year. It breaks out in the full-born rivers of the upper Jordan Valley, and in the wealth of wells among her hills. When Judaea is dry it feeds the streams of Genesserat and Esdraelon. In winter the springs of Kishon burst so richly that the Great Plain around Tabor is a quagmire; even in summer there are fountains on Esdraelon, round which the thickets keep green. . . .

A severely practical, but useful, work published in 1899 was the *International Geography* edited by H. R. Mill. There were seventy authors from a variety of countries, and contributions were written in the contributors' own languages and translated, primarily by the editor. It was a work of more than 1,000 pages, of which the first 100 deal with the general background under such familiar titles titles as principles, mathematical, landforms, climate and, characteristic of the time, the oceans (by Sir John Murray and H. R. Mill). Rather quaintly the flags of all the various countries are shown. The main part of the book deals with the continents and is naturally mixed in quality though it was the kind of book which many people found valuable. In some ways it is of the encyclopaedia type, and so too were many of the comparable books of the time, including the *Universal Geography*, a translation of Elisée Reclus's *Nouvelle Géographie Universelle* published in 1878-94.

Geography in education

For many years the Royal Geographical Society's campaign for improved geographical education in England covered not only the education of travellers, of whose deficiencies as geographers the Society was fully aware, but all schools and colleges. After years of frustration, the universities of Oxford and Cambridge appointed specialist teachers in geography (p. 33) and in 1899 the Oxford School of Geography, the first in any British university, was established, and given its own quarters in the Old Ashmolean building. At Cambridge the department was founded in 1903. But in other universities progress was much slower where indeed there was any at all. The status of geography was at the most contributory to other subjects so that in effect it was a kind of academic maid in waiting, to be summoned when needed. Here and there the idea developed that it would be good to teach commercial geography, so some economist was asked to do it. In some cases the need to teach physical geography was recognised and the work was handed to some geologist who, like the economist, was probably only too glad to have a little extra paid employment at a time when academic salaries were low.

The provision of geography courses in the day training colleges for teachers was met by engaging a variety of people of whom some, such as A. J. Herbertson, found with regret that they received only the weaker students, as those who had reached an adequate standard in the preliminary examination were given an 'exemption' from the course, a practice of which many university teachers were critical, not to say condemnatory. Few geographers could expect to find a university post, and those who did were obliged to supplement their earnings by writing textbooks, encyclopaedia articles and other remunerative effusions, by examining or, just as usefully, by lecturing to audiences in towns and villages up and down the country. H. R. Mill has given an entertaining account of his experiences as a university extension lecturer from 1887, at first in Scotland and then also in the north of England from 1891 to 1892, when he moved to London and did similar work organised from the universities of Oxford and London (Mill, 1951, pp. 63–4). He describes the time-honoured ritual of such courses, with a lecture in the evening followed by a discussion. This was repeated on the following afternoon for 'the leisured classes' and overnight hospitality was provided by 'members of the peerage, rich manufacturers, earnest ministers, opinionated schoolmasters, self-satisfied shopkeepers, poor widows, consequential town councillors, showing every variety of individuality, aptitude, convictions and eccentricity'. This was certainly carrying the gospel of geography out into the streets and lanes of the city.

Campaigns for the educational advance of geography were pursued actively by the Geographical Association, which developed from a meeting held in Christ Church, Oxford on 20 May 1893 attended by H. J. Mackinder and ten public school masters among whom Mr B. B. Dickinson of Rugby was a dynamic influence. In 1901 the Association began to publish a journal called the *Geographical Teacher* to 1926 and then *Geography*, but in the early years only an annual report was issued (Fleure, 1953). By 1899 it was noted that their efforts to improve school examinations, through a Memorial to Boards of Public Examiners, had received a favourable response from the Central Welsh Board for Intermediate (meaning secondary) Education, that there had been some improvement in the work of English boards, but that the various examining boards in Scotland had merely expressed sympathy with the aims of the Association. Generally favourable comments had been made on the use in teaching of lantern slides, of which the Association had a large collection. The initial emphasis was on work in the public schools, but as the day grammar schools developed the Association seized the opportunity of bringing geography into the new, and in many cases experimental, syllabuses that they provided. They also watched with care the teaching of geography in other schools and colleges, and from the beginning were quick to study any new visual aids that became available.

Taking a broad view, therefore, encouraging signs in geographical education could be found, even if they took some finding. It was in the universities that progress was slow, but ironically enough the two great modern periods of university expansion came after the First and Second World Wars. During the 1890s little was done outside Oxford and Cambridge. At Owens College, Manchester, before John McFarlane arrived as 'Lecturer in Economic and Political Geography and Lecturer in Economics' in 1903, the teaching of geography was done by historians, geologists and economists as a sideline. But at least an effort had been made in Manchester to find practising geographers to teach the subject from 1892 to 1896 (Freeman, 1954) and these included H. Yule Oldham from 1892 to 1894 and A. J. Herbertson from 1894 to 1896. Even in Oxford and Cambridge progress was slow. True, Mackinder was working at Oxford, where by 1899 he had the help of A. J. Herbertson as assistant, of H. N. Dickson (later of Reading) as Lecturer in Physical Geography and of George Beardoe Grundy† (1861–1948) as Lecturer in Ancient Geography. In 1899–1900 the teaching consisted of two lectures a week from Mackinder on the historical geography of the British Isles, two by Dickson on the climate of the British Isles, one by Herbertson on the geomorphology of Europe and one by Grundy on the 'general historical topography of Greece'. Herbertson also gave instruction in cartography and practical geography (including map work and map projections) and led field tours (Scargill, 1976).

Although Oxford has traditionally been a stronghold of regional geography, it was not a marked feature of the courses noted above. Cambridge had from the first been notable for systematic geography (Stoddart, 1975b). It was most unfortunate that Guillemard (p. 33) resigned after only one year at Cambridge from 1888 owing to ill health (he lived to be over eighty), for his notebooks and publications show that he was an excellent fieldworker. James Young Buchanan, his successor, and Henry Yule Oldham† (1862–1951) who followed him in 1893 both attracted systematists to the staff such as Philip Lake† (1865–1949), whose book on physical geography was known to many generations of students, and Arthur Robert Hinks† (1873–1945), best known for his publications on surveying and cartography, and for his work as secretary and editor at the Royal Geographical Society. By 1900, there were distinct signs of educational advance in these two universities, and also in the London School of Economics, where H. J. Mackinder was combining work as Reader in Geography with his post at Oxford and also with that of Principal at University College, Reading. Students always need an objective, provided by the establishment of a diploma in geography at Oxford in 1901 and in Cambridge two years later. Happily people still attended courses with no thought of an eventual reward in a qualification: indeed it is still possible, though in many universities few do so. But the diploma was a recognisable qualification which in time was awarded by several universities and to some extent provided a framework for the honours degrees that were never intended to give a complete geographical education but at least to show students how to educate themselves through the years.

Chapter 5

Exploration research and education (1901—1916)

Although the world had been opened to explorers on a vast scale during the nineteenth century it still had its mysteries, and of these the greatest was Antarctica. But exploration of previously unknown, or little-known, areas of Africa, Asia and South America continued steadily as perusal of the pages of the *Geographical Journal* and of other contemporary material will reveal. Even large parts of North America were little known, but as the maps on p. 90 show, the trend of the times was to settle and develop the new lands of the Canadian prairie provinces with rail communications and new roads. It was, in fact, part of the last great expansion into the world's grain-producing lands that was seen also in the Ukraine, in Manchuria and in Siberia. Sooner or later, however, the pioneer must come up against a frontier of settlement, though nobody has ever convincingly shown how much of the world is available for profitable agricultural use. Probably this is one of the questions people must go on asking without ever finding a satisfactory answer. Much as one admires the courage of explorers braving devastating and debilitating polar cold, one also salutes the courage of those who went through steaming Amazonian forests or similarly difficult environments in which the social attitudes of the natives could be described as repellent. Penguins in the Antarctic might be stupid enough to sit on blocks of ice expecting them to hatch, but at least they did not use poisoned arrows.

Beside the solid hunks of British manhood who came home and thrilled audiences with accounts of perilous journeys over Arctic or Antarctic ice-caps the struggling academics of the time could hardly expect to become glamorous public heroes, even if they desired to do so. But they were laying effective foundations in British geography for the later extension of research and teaching. The signs in the early years of this century were encouraging. The Geographical Association was advancing in strength and the universities were appointing specialist lecturers in geography, some of whom were vigorous exponents of their subject both within and outside the academic enclosure. A stream of articles in journals and of new books, including many suited to the needs of school pupils, appeared at the very time when secondary education was expanding under far-seeing national legislation. Some of those devoting their time to geography may have noted the vast range of its enquiries, from geomorphology to climatology and biogeography through regional study to specialist lines such as economic and political aspects. And as if this was not enough, historical geography appealed to many experts of the time, partly because they had been trained as historians themselves. And there was always a contemporary challenge, such as that discussed on pp. 93–6, when the First World War obviously presaged some rearrangement of Europe's political frontiers. More than once in the modern history of British geography knowledge pursued for its own interest has suddenly acquired significance in the regard of a public wider than those who first heard it presented in some paper or read it in some published form. Heroic exploration was not everybody's line even though everyone admires heroism, but on reading the story of some expeditions one wonders if it was really necessary for men to endure so much. Here it is proposed to deal first with exploration and then with research and education.

Antarctic adventure

When Sir Henry Rawlinson advocated African exploration in 1872 (p. 13) he said that the English had 'no reason to shrink from the honourable competition of other European nations, either by sea or land'. He might have been more tactful to say the British, to include the numerous Scotsmen, and even some Welshmen, who were prominent members of Antarctic expeditions. Although there were disclaimers of the view that the British wanted to reach the South Pole first, there was acute disappointment when Amundsen did so before Scott. In 1909, H. R. Mill said that 'there must always be for the geographer a feeling that it is . . . a very great thing to press towards the mark of 90° . . . to wipe out the *terra incognita*' (Mill, 1909). He adds that in 1774, Cook reached 71° 10′S, Weddell 74° 15′ in 1823, Ross 78° 9′ in 1842, Borchgrevink 78° 50′ in 1900, Scott 82° 17′ in 1902 and Shackleton 88° 23′ in 1909.

In such matters 'C'est le dernier pas qui coute' as the first step had been made by Cook in the eighteenth century. The story of the various Antarctic expeditions has been frequently told and full accounts, now of great historical interest, were published by the Royal Geographical Society. In Antarctic exploration the whole interest was scientific and in 1900 Sir Clements Markham noted that there was an agreement made through negotiation with Baron F. von Richthofen (1833–1905) that the Germans should explore the Weddell (90° W to 0°) and the Enderby (0°–90° E) quadrants and the British the Victoria (90° E to 180°) and the Ross quadrants (180°–90° W) (Markham, 1900). A main task was to raise money for expeditions from private subscribers as well as from governments, and it was noted that German explorers were more favourably received by their Treasury officials than the British, who nevertheless were likely to subscribe once private sources had been tapped and were ready to allow members of expeditions to be drawn from the Navy. Aspirants for such experience were numerous and the scientific staffs included many men of high calibre.

The International Geographical Congress held in London in 1895, under the presidency of Sir Clements Markham, was deeply concerned with Antarctic exploration. To many this appealed mainly as an enterprise in completing the world map and few can have realised the immense scientific significance of some of the observations made (Mill, 1905, pp. 384–431). Two Norwegian-built ships were used for the first two of a series of expeditions. Adrien de Gerlache, a Belgian Navy lieutenant, left Antwerp in one of these, renamed the *Belgica*, on 16 August 1897 and crossed the Antarctic circle on 15 February 1898 to reach 71° 30′ S on 3 March. Frozen into the pack-ice for ten months the ship finally left on 14 January 1899, and arrived in Tierra del Fuego at the end of March and Belgium in the following November. Meanwhile Castens Egeberg Borchgrevink, a Norwegian so eager to see the Antarctic that he spent a preparatory year as a seaman on a whaler, persuaded Sir George Newnes to fit out an expedition on an old Norwegian whaler refitted as the *Southern Cross*, in which he left the Thames on 22 August 1898 and Hobart on 19 December. At Cape Adare, 71° 15′ a storehouse was built in which ten men stayed while the ship returned to New Zealand. Little land exploration was possible, and the main contribution of this enterprise was made by the voyage in February 1900 along the Ross barrier, which was shown to be some 30 miles further south than expected. Unfortunately, much of the zoological material was lost or damaged and one misfortune was the death of the expedition's zoologist (Fig. 6).

In 1898 the Royal Geographical Society launched a vigorous campaign to send a British expedition to the Antarctic, but appeals to the Government for funds were unavailing until July 1899, when £45,000 was granted. Private benefactions included £25,000 from Mr L. W. Longstaffe and £5,000 from Sir Alfred Harmsworth. The *Discovery* was built of oak at Dundee, and the party under Commander Robert Falcon Scott (1868–1912), who was described as 'formerly a torpedo lieutenant, and a man born to command, but sympathetic with every branch of scientific work', included four warrant officers, seven petty officers and twenty-seven crew. There were also two surgeons, a physicist, a zoologist and a geologist. The *Discovery* left Cowes on 6 August 1901, penetrated the pack-ice at 62° S, 140° E, on 16 November, and then sailed to New Zealand. The southward journey began on 24 December, the pack-ice was re-entered on 1 January 1902, and Cape Adare reached on 9 January: a month later the ship anchored a few miles south of Mount Erebus where huts were built. In the following spring sledge journeys began and the most southerly point, 82° 17′ S, was reached on 30 December. These were extremely arduous, for the sledging parties were away from the ships for as long as three months. The Royal Geographical Society, straining its resources to supplement

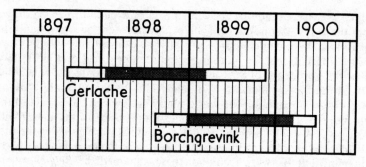

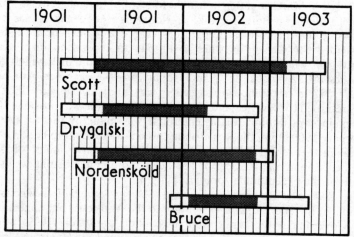

Fig. 6 The revival of Antarctic exploration.

More than fifty years separated the 1842 Ross expedition from its successors and many comments were made on the lack of Antarctic exploration. But before the end of the century exploration began again and H. R. Mill constructed these diagrams to show the time spent in transit and that actually spent in the Antarctic. There was no possibility that Mill might visit the far south or even the Arctic, but this did not preclude him from becoming an expert on polar areas.

Redrawn from Mill, H. R., *The Siege of the South Pole* (London) 1905, pp. 397, 430.

an appeal for funds, sent out the *Morning* on 9 July 1902 under Lieutenant Colbeck, R.N., who had served on the *Southern Cross*. On 25 January 1903, the *Morning* came within 10 miles of the *Discovery* and stores were carried by sledge across the pack-ice. In the following summer Scott conducted further sledging expeditions, with no dogs, as all had perished in the earlier traverses. Finally, in January 1904 the

Morning and the *Terra Nova* (to be used later) came as relief ships and all three sailed northwards on 18 February 1904. The *Discovery* was rapturously received in England in September after an absence of three years.

Clearly Scott was looking forward to conquering the Pole. He had gone further than anyone else and had shown a degree of fortitude that few could emulate. The drama was unfolding towards the final tragedy of his death less than ten years later and there were no misapprehensions about the hardships of the Antarctic. A German expedition under Professor von Drygalski of Berlin in the *Gauss* left Kiel on 11 August 1901 but never crossed the Antarctic circle, though important scientific observations were made before the arrival home on 24 November 1903. Otto Nordensköld, a member of a famous Swedish family, left Göteborg in October 1901 with a fine staff, but suffered terrible privations before the expedition was rescued by a naval ship from the Argentine. More fortunate experiences, and important scientific results, marked the *Scotia* expedition financed by the Coats family of Paisley under W. S. Bruce. The *Scotia* sailed from the Clyde on 2 November 1902, arrived at the Falkland Islands on 26 January 1903, crossed the Antarctic Circle on 18 February and wintered in Scotia bay from 26 March. A solid stone house with walls 4 ft thick was built and a meteorological station and magnetic observatory set up. The meteorologist, R. S. Mossman, with various companions, including a group of Argentinian meteorologists, remained there until February 1905 when he was taken away on an Argentinian ship: the main party, which included R. N. Rudmose Brown† (1879–1957) as a 'naturalist', had returned to Scotland by January 1905. A French expedition, in the *Français*, spent the winter of 1904 locked in Antarctic ice and made various observations in the summers of 1903–4 and 1904–5. Other enterprises included the *Pourquoi Pas?* of 1909–10, a German and a Japanese expedition in 1912 and Sir Douglas Mawson's 1911–14 expedition from Australia. Earlier, in 1909, Sir Ernest Shackleton (1874–1922) had penetrated to 88° 23′ S, within 100 miles of the Pole. All these expeditions made some contribution to the knowledge of Antarctica, and if an element of international rivalry and national prestige existed that was not to be deprecated unless it resulted in a cult of heroism at the expense of prudence and – especially important – scientific advance.

Scott's expedition of 1910–13 drew on the vast experience acquired during the previous twenty years of experimental onslaught on the Antarctic. The *Terra Nova* left London on 1 June 1910 and New Zealand on 29 November as the British Antarctic Expedition. With Scott there were fifty-nine officers, scientists and seamen (Evans, 1913). The equipment included provisions for three years, two huts, forty sledges, fur sleeping bags, bales of clothing, all kinds of instruments and much else that might be needed. There were 19 Siberian ponies, 34 dogs and 3 motor sledges with petrol and paraffin. After various vicissitudes

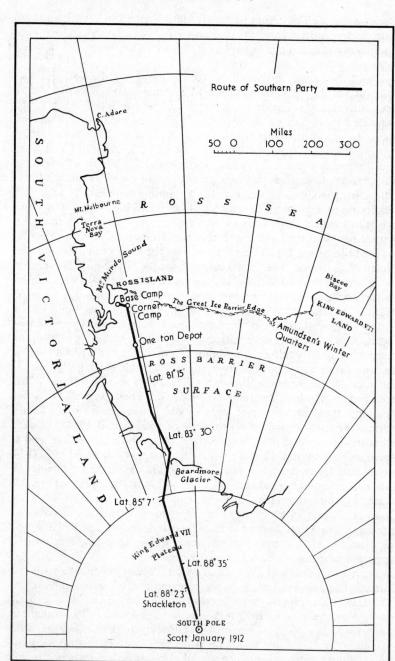

Route of Southern Party ———

Miles

50 0   100   200   300

C. Adare

SOUTH

ROSS   SEA

Mt. Melbourne

Terra
Nova
Bay

VICTORIA

Mt Murdo Sound

ROSS ISLAND

Base Camp

Corner
Camp

The Great Ice Barrier Edge

Biscoe
Bay

KING EDWARD VII
LAND

Amundsen's Winter
Quarters

One ton Depot

ROSS   BARRIER
Lat. 81° 15'

SURFACE

LAND

Lat. 83° 30'

Beardmore
Glacier

Lat. 85° 7'

King Edward VII
Plateau

Lat. 88° 35'

Lat. 88° 23'
Shackleton

SOUTH POLE
Scott January 1912

including a gale that nearly wrecked the enterprise, winter quarters were set up at McMurdo Sound (Fig. 7). For some the next summer was spent in conveying stores to various depots, while others, including (Thomas) Griffith Taylor (1880–1963) made a geological reconnaissance around McMurdo Sound. In the second part of the winter of 1911 final preparations were made for the journey to the Pole, which began on 24 October: one by one the ponies were killed and eaten, but in spite of blizzards and natural hazards such as crevasses or deposits of soft snow, the advance continued until 4 January 1912, when Scott went forward with his four companions and reached the Pole on 17 January. The return journey began on 19 January, but all the five members of the polar party died before the end of March. Various sledging parties carried out local topographical, geological and vegetational surveys under conditions of great hardship and danger to life, and the expedition finally reached England early in 1913. Among the survivors was Frank Debenham† (1883–1965), later Professor of Geography at Cambridge.

Nine thousand people were present in the Albert Hall, London, at a meeting on 21 May 1913 arranged by the Royal Geographical Society to hear a lecture by Commander Evans who had become the leader on Scott's death. His lecture is fascinating reading still, even though it is naturally concerned with the technique of exploration rather than with its scientific purpose. With Evans on the platform were several other members of the expedition, including H. G. Ponting the photographer and the perpetually unquenchable Griffith Taylor. The chairman was Lord Curzon (*Geogr. J.* **42**, 1913, pp. 8–10), who gave a brief initial speech in which he said that the 'scientific results . . . will provide a contribution of the first rank to our knowledge of the Antarctic continent and seas, and this will be the real monument to Scott and his men'. After Evans's lecture he wisely said little, for the audience had come to see and hear the explorers.

Possibly explorers elsewhere thought that too much was made of the Antarctic and little concern felt for work that might eventually be of far greater national and human importance. Sir Clements Markham in 1905 pointed out that it was fallacious to assume that the work of exploration was complete, for nothing was known of vast areas in Asia, Arabia and even the Americas (Markham, 1905). Nevertheless, much good work had been done in Asia, where Lord Curzon (then Viceroy of India) had solved the problem of the source of the Oxus, and Sir Francis Younghusband† (1863–1942) had opened Tibet. He 'first beat down the opposition of the lamas and then won their hearts'. In the following year

---

Fig. 7 The Scott expedition to the South Pole (1910–13).
This expedition became part of the national story in Britain for its heroism, its tragic ending after reaching the Pole and the final irony that Amundsen had been there first.
Map redrawn from *Geogr. J.* **42**, 1913, p. 18.

Sir George T. Goldie, speaking at the British Association meeting in York on 'Twenty-five years' geographical progress', mentioned the stimulus of the *Challenger* voyages and of later useful but less noticed enterprises and even of material from the cable companies, and spoke also of the encouraging work in polar latitudes: nevertheless, some 2–3 million square miles of South America were still unknown and there were great gaps in the knowledge of Asia. In Africa, however, 'all that remains to be done is to fill in ... with local details and to give precision to our maps by careful triangulation' (Goldie, 1906). Possibly he was a shade optimistic, for in 1911 F. R. Cana commented that in Africa more than 1 million square miles, one-eleventh of the continent, was still unexplored, and that though three-quarters of this was in the Sahara, 'there are considerable areas of fertile country never visited by a European' (*Geogr. J.* **38**, 1911, p. 457). The President of the Society, Sir Leonard Darwin (1850–1943), in the same year, looked forward to the extension of mapping on the 1:1,000,000 scale and took a broader view of the next stage of the next stage of geographical enterprise, which was to aim at

systematic and detailed examinations of comparatively small areas, and not merely to cover long distances with the result of doing little more than confirm the impressions of previous explorers. These surveys should be as good as is possible in the circumstances, and the information they collect should be extensive, varied, systematic, and recorded with reference to the needs of science and history, as well as the man of commerce (Darwin, 1911).

It is not possible to distinguish any series of phases in exploration, ranging from pioneering to comprehensive analytical survey, for at any one time each phase was apparent somewhere on the earth's surface. Naturally the exciting pioneer exploration hit the headlines and much was owed to the Press which, Sir George Goldie noted, had become interested in outlying lands during the 1880s.

The research frontier

Sir Clements Markham was not addicted to sensational headlines, but had he been his comments on the need for a research committee of the Royal Geographical Society in 1903 might have been headed, 'How little we know'. Fortunately, this committee was set up with an annual grant (not always completely used) of £200 (*Geogr. J.* **22**, 1903, pp. 5–6) and readers of some now historic papers, including A. J. Herbertson on 'natural regions', in the *Geographical Journal* will note that they were published with the help of this committee. The aim was in part to give an opportunity for young geographers to present their work to an interested, if comparatively small, audience while the great meetings addressed by explorers pulled in the crowds and sustained the finances. The subjects suggested for consideration by Markham covered every branch of geography as then understood, surveying and mapping, geomorphology, hydrogeography, meteorology, regional ('a county, or the Fens as a natural unit') distributions (for example of 'some crop in relation to natural facilities and access to markets, or of villages and town sites'), plant associations, history of cartography, physical changes in historic times (as of British coasts, or continental desiccation), military geography, landforms and life (human and animal), colonisation, and detailed regional survey of any area, especially one of small size in an unexplored or partially explored territory. Many of these ideas were used later, or perhaps conceived independently by others, as in the case of J. F. Unstead's close study of wheat production (pp. 91–2). Obviously the possibilities were wide and exploration was still needed though it must, Markham noted, become more exact and scientific in character.

Evidence of the need for geographical knowledge was adduced with ease. A short, unsigned, hard-hitting article on 'Geography and education' in 1905 quotes an incisive article by the military correspondent of *The Times* thundering away on the failure of the War Office to learn from the mistakes of the South African War (*Geogr. J.* **25**, 1905, pp. 17–22). Commercial firms made numerous errors, especially dangerous in an era of growing international competition, in dealing with overseas markets, and the ignorance of other countries led to reckless writing in the Press with increasing isolation of England in a hostile world. Scott Keltie had pointed out that a country with a far-flung empire ought to be a pioneer in geographical science and teaching, though in fact it was far behind foreign rivals, especially the Germans. How far this was due to ignorance and how far to British arrogance is perhaps a psychological problem, but in the early years of the twentieth century the method of systematising the abundant raw material was always in question.

A. J. Herbertson found, as others have done before and after him, the idea of distribution crucial and summarised this view in the first part of his paper on natural regions (Herbertson, 1905, p. 300):

In this country we are less tied to tradition than in some others, for there is practically no systematic geography to bind us. In Germany the Ritter and Humboldt traditions give rise to two schools. To America the Ritter tradition was carried over by Guyot, but a new one developed by geologists has superseded it. For long in our country geographical progress meant exploration, mainly with a commercial or political bias, and descriptive and statistical geography was taught. It was only with the rise of an academic geography that the wider conception of geography as the science of distributions developed.

Herbertson wanted to give cohesion to geography and his theory of natural regions appeared to offer a fruitful scheme of world division (Fig. 8). Though they are strongly reminiscent of climatic regions, he stated categorically that geography 'is not concerned with the distribution of one element on the Earth's surface, but with all'. He begins with a map of structural divisions based mainly on the work of

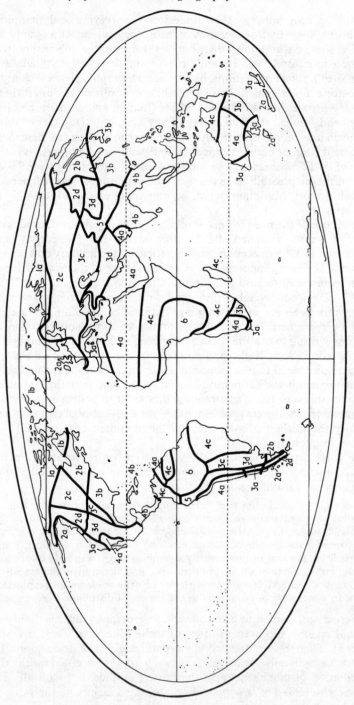

Suess with six categories, areas mainly of archaean rocks, areas of old unfolded sedimentary rocks which were either tablelands or tabular lowlands, areas mainly of folded Palaeozoic rocks, of Tertiary folds and finally unfolded Tertiary and Recent rocks. As a basis for world division he uses the 'critical temperatures' of 0°, 10° and 20°C and distinguishes his 'natural regions' mainly on climatic conditions, including seasonal rainfall, in relation to physical features so that, for example, the vast mountain and upland belts of the interior of Asia emerge as distinct regional entities, of far more significance than political units, which on a historical view may be ephemeral. And even the distribution of population gives no basis for delineating natural regions, though it is significant as 'the most direct expression of the actual economic utilization of the natural region'.

Cold water was poured on Herbertson's blazing enthusiasm by various speakers. H. R. Mill found it impossible 'to get a classification of the world that will satisfy the workers in several branches of science' except for 'coast-lines and the degree net', and decided that any attempt to make such a classification should not 'go beyond the merely orographical'. Douglas Freshfield† (1845–1934) agreed. Yule Oldham made the obvious point (well known to Herbertson) that mountain climates had special qualities, and E. G. Ravenstein† (1834–1913) said that: 'There can be no question that the great plain of India, extending from the Ganges to the Indus, constitutes one of these natural regions,

---

Fig. 8 Herbertson's natural regions.
As explained in the text Herbertson was fully aware of the major landform units of the world, but he regarded climatic distribution as the main feature to be considered in dividing the continents into regions. Climate was itself closely related to the natural vegetation and crops grown: extensive upland areas have their own climatic features. Distribution of temperature within the year, related to depressions and anticyclones, was also relevant. In the hands of many earlier university and school-teachers Herbertson's regions were used to give a fascinating picture of the varied climates of the world. The divisions are as follows:
1. Polar: (a) lowlands (tundra); (b) highlands (ice-caps).
2. Cool temperate: (a) western margin; (b) eastern margin; (c) interior lowlands (Siberian); (d) interior mountain.
3. Warm temperate: (a) western margin with winter rains (Mediterranean); (b) eastern margin with summer rains (China); (c) interior lowlands; (d) interior plateau.
4. Tropical: (a) west tropical deserts (Sahara); (b) east tropical (monsoon); (c) inter-tropical tablelands (Sudan).
5. Mountain areas in tropical or subtropical latitudes.
6. Equatorial lowlands (Amazon type).
This scheme was modified for the textbook of Herbertson, A. J. and Frances, D., *Senior Geography* (Oxford) 1907, but remained the basis of regional teaching for many years. It was first published in *Geogr. J.* **25**, 1905, p. 307, from which this illustration has been redrawn.

and has its analogue in the great plain of Scotland.' Herbertson, however, said relief was 'not a complete guide' as in South Africa, where there was no marked difference in the southeast and the southwest but the rainfall conditions were 'as far apart as Spain and China'. He held his conviction that a regional classification was useful to the early end of his life as a speech of 1913 clearly shows (Herbertson, 1913–14). In this he says that a natural region is

a vital unit as well as a physical one, a symbiosis on a vast scale. It is more than an association of plants, or of animals, or of men. It is a symbiotic association of all these, indissolubly bound up with certain structures and forms of the land, possessing a definite water circulation, and subjected to a seasonal climatic rhythm. As each element in a region has its own history, and as each varies in its rate of change, so the evolution of the region is highly complex.

The paper continues with a questioning approach to the biological analogy and Herbertson seems undecided about the value of an analogy between regional units and 'orders', that is with organisms, organs, tissues, cells. Taking the example of the Cotswolds, he notes that 'each incised river-valley' is 'a sub-division of the natural region and the relatively flat land between them . . . another sub-division'. In a mountainous area the valleys seem to be the natural units, divided by crests: in the plains the land between the rivers forms natural units with the rivers themselves as the dividing lines. One can work forward from the smaller to the greater units, from individual valleys and interfluves to the English scarplands or the Western Highlands. Botanical division into plant societies was regarded by Herbertson as significant, not least because of its relation to climatic distribution which, he states categorically, is the basis of the larger divisions. Finally he comes to the human aspect and says of man that 'regions exist whether he is part of them or not', for 'the entity higher than the individual is not the family nor the race' but 'the more complex association of the natural region'. Nevertheless he taught human geography at Oxford, though the only published evidence of this is a fragmentary outline of his views published posthumously (Herbertson, 1915–16). These notes are in accord with his earlier statement, in the British Association speech of 1913 (*v.s.*) that human activity had 'profoundly changed the surface as in the Fens or the Lancashire Coalfield or in China'. Then, too, there are the recollections of his students and his deep interest in sociology, shared by his wife, who wrote 'The life of Frédéric Le Play', ultimately published in its entirety as section 2, volume 38, of the *Sociological Review* (1946). Like Mackinder, Herbertson was a firm believer in the value of writing local studies, such as those prepared by students for the diploma in geography at Oxford.

While Herbertson and others were concerned with major world problems, some useful detailed work was carried out by the Royal Geographical Society. In 1904 a research committee consisting of G. G. Chisholm, H. J. Mackinder and H. R. Mill was appointed to name the larger physical features of the English landscape, especially those to which no single name was commonly applied (Mill, 1904). From this committee's work, using a Bartholomew relief map as a base, came such names as the Hampshire Downs, the East Anglian Ridge, Norfolk Edge, the Northampton Uplands, the Forest of Arden, the Humberhead Levels, the Midland Gap, the Morecambe Plain, the Plain of Gwent (often wrongly applied to include lowland Glamorgan) or the Vale of Taunton. Most students will have encountered these names and some may be surprised to find that they were invented, or at least allocated to various areas, comparatively recently. It is perhaps unfortunate that more attention was not given to some names of historic origin, such as the Fylde or the Forest of Rossendale in Lancashire.

H. J. Mackinder's *Britain and the British Seas* appeared in 1902 and long remained a venerated work among geographers, some of whom spoke of it as a great contribution to regional geography, 'a classic, a work of art' (Mackinder, 1902). It is, like all Mackinder's work, admirably easy to read: unfortunately it is indifferently illustrated. It is also inadequately provided with bibliographical references. On re-reading it yet again, one wonders if it is in fact a regional geography at all. Like many geographical works of its time, it is deeply imbued with a sense of history and the constant emphasis on the English county as a unit shows a divergence of view from A. J. Herbertson's almost contemptuous dismissal of political boundaries. The plan of the book is interesting. A short initial chapter of a dozen pages places Britain, 'of Europe, yet not *in* Europe', in its world situation throughout history, and then follow three chapters on the seas around Britain with the continental shelf, five chapters primarily on physical features and two on climate and weather. These eleven chapters cover almost half the book, and are followed by ten more, headed racial, historical, metropolitan England, industrial England, Scotland, Ireland, strategic, economic, imperial Britain, with a final summary. Some of these chapters, such as that on racial geography, are period pieces. Other parts of the book, such as the chapters on the surrounding seas, evoke the keen interest in oceanography characteristic of the years around the turn of the century through the *Challenger* voyages, while the effort in the physical chapters to explain the evolution of river systems would now appear to be more appropriately a subject for special study than a necessary inclusion in a regional text.

Even so the book should still be read, for it opens many enquiries taken up later. On pp. 63–8 the division of Great Britain and Ireland into 'lowland' and 'highland' zones is discussed: it was foreshadowed, and cautiously expressed in the first sentences of the chapter on 'The structure of Britain' (Mackinder, 1902 (1907 edn) p. 63): 'The contrast between the south-east and the north-west of Britain, between the plains and the low coasts towards the continent, with all the resultant differences – agricultural, industrial, racial and historical – depends on a fundamental distinction in rock structure.' This theme is developed on the familiar line that the old rocks of the north are harder and more resistant to erosion, though with the proviso that not everywhere in the world are older rocks necessarily resistant to weathering as in Britain (cf. comment of Topley on p. 59). Another theme that emerges is the distinction between metropolitan England and industrial England, broadly divided by a line from the Wash to the Severn, and Mackinder has much of interest to say of the diversity of scene and life in the four separate sections of metropolitan England he describes. Possibly the secret of the immensely ambitious character of *Britain and the British Seas* is to be found in the comment Mackinder made in 1905, in the discussion following Herbertson's paper on natural regions (p. 79), to the effect that while *regional* geography was a term generally understood, he hoped that the term *systematic* geography would never take root. In short, regional geography was the core and substance of the subject, but he included much that would now be regarded as 'systematic' in his regional work.

Few papers have more fascination than H. J. Mackinder's 'Geographical pivot of history' (Mackinder, 1904) later developed into his book *Democratic Ideas and Reality* first published in 1919 (pp. 106–08). Apart from its obvious political significance, it was characteristic of its time in possessing a world outlook. If it was desirable to give students a world view of landforms, climate, vegetation or fauna, it was at least as desirable, if not indeed more so, to give a world view of past history extending to the present and possible future. Mackinder opens by saying that future historians might refer to a Columban epoch in world history, lasting for rather more than four centuries and terminating early in the twentieth century, marked by the effective discovery of the entire world and its appropriation by various powers, in effect 'the expansion of Europe against almost negligible resistance', leading to a closed political system in which, however, modifications of the balance of power were to be expected. Future developments could never be prophesied with certainty: what for example was likely to be the eventual world political significance of South America, which conceivably could become commercially rich and possibly a naval power of significance? Or if, for example, China were to

---

Fig. 9 Mackinder's world strategy.
Mackinder defended his somewhat dramatic views by historical examples and his division of the world into a few major units made stimulating generalisations possible. Later in his long and purposeful life Mackinder, like some of his critics, recognised that world strategy had been considerably changed by air power, as well as by the industrialisation of North America and of the USSR. In time he became a venerated figure, but in his earlier years he was regarded as a whizz-kid by some members of the elderly establishment of the Royal Geographical Society, only they would not have expressed it that way.
Redrawn from a map originally published in *Geogr. J.* **23**, 1904, p. 435.

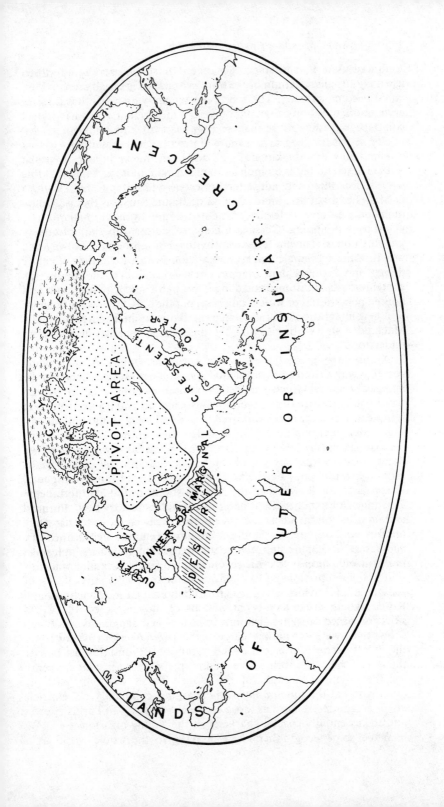

conquer Russia at some stage, then indeed the so-called 'yellow peril', to use the journalistic jargon of the time as Mackinder unashamedly does, could become a reality. The article has the undying merit that it raises even more questions than it answers and for that reason it is still compulsive reading more than seventy years after its publication.

Figure 9 is the geographical core of the argument. Essentially Russia is a land power in Mackinder's view and he mentions the sale of Alaska to the United States as an indication of Russian understanding that this was so, for outer dependent territories were unsuited to her strategic needs. The 'pivot area' had been made by the Russians themselves by their conquest and settlement of the steppes and by the gradual move by vigorous conquering Cossack horsemen across Siberia, effectively united to the European territories by the Trans-Siberian Railway line which, although single track, was obviously to be the first of many driven into forests and steppes. Horses had carried conquerors contemptuous of distance and danger through a land with few roads and limited possibilities of water transport, but the railway gave the promise of a new integration of power from the Baltic to the Pacific. Naturally Mackinder was writing before the possibilities of air transport were understood.

Around the pivotal area, which resembles but does not exactly coincide with the area of continental and Arctic drainage, there was the marginal crescent which included two outer groups of islands, Britain and Japan, of which the former obviously had a naval tradition of great significance and the latter appeared to be developing along similar lines. The inner marginal crescent included China and India with the peninsular area between them, the Near(er) East as it was then known (later to be confusingly called the Middle East) in the settled lands around Arabia (the 'Fertile Crescent') with Egypt, and continental Europe west of Russia with the African shores of the Mediterranean. This inner marginal crescent had throughout its history been menaced and on occasion invaded from the interior steppelands, but historically the Russians, originally a people of the forest belt, had incorporated the peoples of these same steppelands within their own territory, at least in part. It would be easy to criticise much of the article in detail, for little is said of the fluctuations of Russian and Chinese power in the interior of Asia or of the rivalry of China, Russia and Japan in Manchuria and Korea. There are many broad sweeps of judgement on the world situation based on generalizations in history and geography. As Fig. 9 shows there were two natural barriers, the frozen Arctic in the north and the desert barrier south of the Mediterranean. Beyond this last barrier the rest of the world formed the lands of the 'outer or insular crescent', for the potential strength of the United States was only partially understood at the time. Many of the marginal comments in the article are of great interest, such as those on the ebb and flow of Turkish power and the essentially coastal character of the Viking invasions.

While some geographers were looking to the whole world as a

theatre in which the great human drama of all time was played, others were happily engaged in detailed investigation of areas close to their homes. On pp. 61–2 some of the pioneer work in Scotland is described: happily this was continued in England during the early years of this century, at first by William Gardner Smith† (1866–1928) and others (Smith, 1903a, b), whose work on the geographical distribution of vegetation in Yorkshire was published in 1903 in two papers, of which the first dealt with the Leeds and Halifax district and the second with the Harrogate and Skipton district. These authors first describe the geology and climate, especially rainfall, and observe that wheat cultivation is restricted to areas with an annual average fall of 30 in. or less. They then proceed to discuss the plant associations and suggest that despite long-continued human occupation some of the pine-woods on the heather moors are 'natural', which in fact would not now be accepted. Pine-woods were found to 1,400 ft and the general upper limit of birch-woods was 1,250 ft in the cloughs and gills (sheltered valleys) with isolated trees to 1,550 ft. Four types of moorland are distinguished, natural limestone pasture, heaths of two kinds (grass to 1,000–1,500 ft and heather to 1,250–1,660 ft), cotton grass moors at 1,250 to 1,500–2,000 ft, and summits with *Vaccinium* at 1,500–1,900 ft with Alpine vegetation from 2,000 to 2,300 ft. Much depended on local conditions of drainage and exposure. For the cultivated farmlands they make a simple division between those areas with wheat, generally to 500–700 ft and those without wheat, to 1,000–1,100 ft.

In 1904 F. J. Lewis (1875–1955) published the results of a similar study in the northern Pennines (Lewis, 1904) with broadly similar findings (Fig. 10). Lewis (who was a botanist in Liverpool University and from 1905 to 1912 had the title of 'Lecturer in Geographical Botany' – did anyone else have this title?) opens his paper by distinguishing four 'chief factors governing the distribution of plant associations'; of these the first was the chemical composition of the soil, the second the soil's physical characteristics such as texture, the proportion of air and water retained, the third climatic, depending on land slope, aspect, drainage and altitude, and the fourth artificial agencies such as human and animal influence. Lewis divides the area into two 'regions', temperate and subalpine. The temperate area had oats as the main crop (with no wheat) to 800–1,000 ft, and a permanent pasture belt to 1,200 ft. There were oak-woods to 800 ft and mixed deciduous woods in sheltered valleys with ash, alder, rowan, hazel and hawthorn. In the subalpine belt birch trees occurred to an upper limit of 1,000 ft and coniferous trees to 1,300 ft. Above the tree limit there were grass heaths, natural pastures (in well-drained positions free from peat), heather moors to 2,000 ft, restricted but definite areas of sphagnum bog, and cotton grass bogs to 2,000 ft, especially on sloping ground at 1,200–1,600 ft. On the summit areas there was an 'alpine region' of varied vegetation. Comparison with the vegetation of north Perthshire (p. 62) showed, no doubt unexpectedly, that the average limits of cultivation, notably of oats, in the Pennines was some 300 ft lower and so too was the upper limit of deciduous trees. The Pennines also had a much greater development of the wetter types of heather and sphagnum vegetation.

As it happened, the various studies of vegetation fostered by geographers through their journals laid the foundations of plant ecology, which owes much to the work of A. G. Tansley's long editorship of the *Journal of Ecology* (from 1916 to 1937) and of his books on British vegetation (Tansley, 1911, 1939). But as the preface to Tansley's 1939 volume shows so clearly, the splendid work done by the authors mentioned here and by many more (for example in C. E. Moss, *The Vegetation of the Peak District* (Cambridge, 1913)) revealed a mass of problems still to be solved for although 'the knowledge of our natural and semi-natural plant communities is much wider and especially much deeper than it was in 1911 . . . various problems that we then envisaged as relatively simple have shown themselves upon further study to be very complex indeed and not yet susceptible of satisfactory solution' (Tansley, 1939, p. v.). Though this was written forty years ago it is still true. And Tansley also points out 'the available meteorological records are quite inadequate for any precise correlation between climatic factors and vegetation'. Biogeography has never been completely neglected, but its devotees have been few. It matters little whether the type of vegetation enquiry noted here, deriving much of its initial inspiration from Flahault (p. 61), was done by people trained in geography or botany or – desirably and perhaps essentially – both.

In 1907 E. J. Russell (later a familiar and much revered figure as Sir John Russell† 1872–1965) of Rothamsted wrote a paper on climate and crops, based largely on records made at the Wye Agricultural College, Kent (Russell, 1907). He noted that successful crops needed a sufficient but not excessive supply of water, suitable temperatures and shelter from strong winds. Many of his observations were drawn from Kent and Sussex, where hilltops were rarely cultivated as the water was drawn downwards to the hill slopes, which had the best land for farm crops, fruit and hops. Shelter from north winds gave favourable conditions for market gardening crops as for others, and a series of observations made in August 1906 showed that a south-facing slope was on the average 4 °F

Fig. 10 Vegetation survey of a Pennine area.
F. J. Lewis's survey owes much to earlier work done in Scotland (pp. 61–2) as well as in other areas of the Pennines. In the valleys there is improved land to an altitude of more than 1,000 ft, above which there was some grass heath and also heather moor, sphagnum bog and – much associated with Pennine moorlands for its distinctive flecking of a grey-brown landscape – cotton grass moor. Whether the limit of *Vaccinium* moor on Mickle Fell exactly corresponds to the area above 2,000 ft, as Lewis shows it to do, may perhaps raise doubt. The surveys of Lewis and a number of others were significant in the development of plant ecology. Redrawn from a map in *Geogr. J.* **23**, 1904, opp. p. 420.

Miles

CULTIVATION

Cultivation, with Oats
Upland Cultivation, no Oats

WOODLAND

Deciduous
Coniferous

SUB-ALPINE MOORLAND

Natural Pasture: Grasses dominant
Grass Heath: Grasses with general heath flora
Heather: with Cotton Grass
Heather Moor: *Calluna* dominant
Sphagnum Bog: *Sphagnum* dominant
Cotton Grass Bog: *Eriophorum* dominant

ALPINE MOORLAND

Vaccinium Moors
Pasture, with Alpine Plants
Grass Heath, with Alpine Plants
Alpine Plateau

warmer than the north-facing slope. On a south slope a market garden crop might be ready days or even a week earlier than on the opposite slope, and fetch higher prices. On the other hand the slower growth on the north-facing slopes might give a higher yield, and the greater evaporation on the south-facing slope might cause drying-out of the soil in August or September. It was also observed that valley floors had greater extremes of temperature, with an acute danger of late frosts harmful to fruit trees. Even a river induced warmer conditions: strips of gardens in Worcestershire within 50 yards of the river Avon suffered less from frost than gardens at a greater distance. In fact there was a microclimatological basis for the Kent saying: 'Grow hops in the valley – fruit on the hill.'

In the early years of this century the need for research of a geographical character was widely recognised in principle but on occasions, indeed quite frequent occasions, there were questioning speeches and papers on the place of the subject in the general academic scene. Of these, one by Colonel C. F. Close (later Arden-Close† 1865–1952) begins with the naïve comment that 'the geographical world is not unanimous about the meaning and object of geography' (Close, 1911). Why should it be? Close's somewhat restricted view was that the purpose of geography was to be a popularising medium bringing together the workers in geodesy, geology, climatology and anthropology. He recognised that government surveys had been of immense service to geographers and that without the steady advance of cartography the modern development of the subject would not have been possible. Nevertheless much put out as geography, especially on the human side, appeared to be vague: he even made a comment that would make modern 'quantifiers' whoop for joy: 'Before this human aspect of geography – or, for that matter, any other aspect of the subject – is recognized by the world of science as an independent, indispensable and definite branch of knowledge, it must prove its independence and value by original, definite, and, if possible, quantitative research' (Close, 1911, p. 409).

Close noted that of all the papers published by the Royal Geographical Society from 1906 to 1910, 57 per cent were on exploration, 3 per cent on mathematical and cartographic topics, 26 per cent on physical geography (general, vulcanicity, hydrography and oceanography), 3 per cent on meteorology and climatology, 1 per cent on biological geography, 3 per cent on anthropology and ethnography and 7 per cent on economic and social geography. This analysis could mean that the Royal Geographical Society gave priority to exploration, possibly without distinguishing the quality of the material, but other British geographical journals of the time showed broadly similar qualities. In short, Close showed the need for careful thought on the position of geography, especially when he observed that 'the papers on vulcanology and seismology could have been read with perfect appropriateness before the Geological Society; those on meteorology and climatology before the Meteorological Society; and those on anthropology and ethnography before the Anthropological Society' (Close, 1911, p. 406). Here then was an essential problem, even an indictment of geography as an academic subject. Reservations such as those felt by Close may well have influenced many geologists and others who were willing to give considerable service to geographical societies, but were lukewarm in their support of full academic recognition.

Claims for such recognition could be made in two ways: by argument and by demonstration of what had been or might be done. Inevitably both of these interpenetrated, as was clearly shown in 1912 by J. L. Myres' analysis of the work of the Research Department of the Royal Geographical Society from 1903 onwards (*Geogr. J.* **40**, 1912, pp. 356–77). Fifty papers had been presented of which 12 dealt with cartography, 12 with geomorphology (including hydrography), 8 with exploration, 7 with historical evidence of changes in physical geography of which 3 were also concerned with human distributions, 4 with regional study and 3 each with climatology and crop or plant distribution. Naturally these papers given under the research scheme were of mixed quality, though they indicated vigorous activity by some pioneer workers. Myres notes that there had been no contributions on historical cartography, on military geography and on the special problems of the development and colonization of Central and South America.

Victor Branford (1864–1930), known and respected as a business man with a deep interest in geography and sociology, expressed his views on the neglect of geography quite forcibly in 1909 during a discussion (*Geogr. J.* **33**, 1909, p. 39) following a paper on the economic geography of the Parana river. Great Britain, he said,

had fallen a little behind in . . . attention to the economic importance of this region. For many years it has been customary to appoint to the Ministry in Buenos Aires a German representative of first-rate ability and experience. . . . Germany has discovered that there is such a thing as applied geography. The German government provides its diplomatic representative with an expert in economic geography . . . the German government, German traders and German settlers are equipped, not only with fuller information about the present, but are more adequately guided in their policy for the future than other peoples interested in the region.

In short, there was an unexploited, or at least a partially unexploited field of enquiry in Britain relevant to its advance in trade and industry. And expansion of settlement, still continuing, meant great changes in the landscape as in Canada, where the significance of the data shown in Fig. 11 was vast: the maps are drawn from an informative paper of somewhat stodgy tendencies by A. Silva White, (White, 1913). Within the ten-year census period from 1901 to 1911, the population of Manitoba had increased from 255,000 to 456,000, and of Saskatchewan and Alberta from 164,000 to 867,000, while British Columbia's population had more than doubled, from 179,000 to 392,000, so that at

Edmonton

Calgary

Vancouver

Winnipeg

Quebec

Montreal

Toronto

200 0 200 400
Miles

Principal Minerals

Gold   □
Silver   +
Coal   ●
Iron   ○

Industrial District
Present Agricultural Land
Land likely to be opened up for Agriculture in the near future
Present Grazing Land
Present Forest Land
Fisheries

last Canada was effectively occupying its prairie provinces and its Pacific coast. Nothing could illustrate more clearly that the geographer was dealing with a dynamic situation meriting intense local study, but the geographers were not there at the time.

But was this ever fully appreciated? Some local studies were little noticed though of considerable merit, for example a paper by A. J. Sargent on the Tyne (Sargent, 1912), which J. F. Unstead welcomed as 'a real contribution to geography' in which the geological, topographical and economic facts were 'related in the way that neither the geologist, the topographer, nor the economist could do'. Study of the river Tyne as done by Sargent is undoubtedly fieldwork even if this term would seem even more appropriate to another distinguished local analysis of the time by Marion I. Newbigin† (1869-1934) on the Swiss Valais (Newbigin, 1907). This paper, longer than most, begins with an account of the physical features which is mainly topographical without any detailed geological treatment. Climate is then studied and there is an excellent section on the forests and isolated trees which owes much to the author's biological training: the vegetation, crops and alpine grasslands are considered in relation to the period needed for growth. There is in the final section a word of tacit admiration for the people which many visitors to the Alps have shared, though one wonders if the comment on the Scottish Highlands is quite fair. Some readers may be uneasy at the use of the phrase suggesting man as a 'conqueror' of nature, or 'conquered' in certain areas.

Almost every feature of the canton is determined by the mountains. It is the mountain ring which produces the warm, dry climate, while the glaciers supply the water necessary to make up for the deficient rainfall . . . [but] . . . the Alpine regions benefit a proportionately much larger number of persons than . . . the Highlands. In the Alps one sees man as, at least to some extent, the conqueror of nature, rather than as the conquered, as in the Highlands (Newbigin, 1907, pp. 238-39).

Though not strictly fieldwork in the same sense as the contrasting yet in some ways comparable studies of Sargent and Newbigin, J. F. Unstead's work on 'The climatic limits of wheat cultivation, with special reference to North America' commands admiration for its thorough analysis of the crop and its world markets (Unstead, 1912-13). He reaches the conclusion, after using such data as accumulated temperatures and the development of new strains, that the output from the

---

Fig. 11 Canada in its pre-1914 expansion.
Mr A. Silva White's study of Canada may have been somewhat optimistic though its resources in oil (which he did not map) have proved to be considerable and are still only partially exploited. With irrigation some of the areas he maps as grazing land support more intensive farming, and under modern conditions timber is a much valued resource, still only partially exploited.
Redrawn from a map in *Scott. Geogr. Mag.* **19**, 1913, opp. p. 547.

United States and Canada could in time be more than doubled. This work, published with the assistance of the Research Committee of the Royal Geographical Society, was partly in the tradition of G. G. Chisholm who through these years was writing a number of interesting papers and perpetually revising his famous book originally published in 1889.

Ideas flowed plentifully on human influence on the landscape: the first of two notable papers in 1914 was an address by Sir Charles P. Lucas to the Geography Section of the British Association and the second, by R. N. Rudmose Brown, was given to students of Sheffield University. Lucas quotes John Scott Keltie's dictum that 'man is the ultimate term in the geographical problem' with Sir Clements Markham's statement that 'geography is a description of the earth as it is, in relation to man' (Lucas, 1914). But he goes back further to the classic work of George Perkins Marsh (1801–82), called the 'first conservationist', who said that: 'Every plant, every animal, is a geographical agency, man a destructive, vegetables, and in some cases even wild beasts, restorative powers.' Marsh had been impressed by the dangers of clearing forests and natural sheep pastures (as in Palestine) but Lucas noted that there were signs of reconstruction, such as the afforestation in the Savoy Alps and, nearer home, the efforts of Birmingham University's Midlands Reafforestation Group to plant the pit mounds and ash quarries of the Black Country. He also quotes the vivid sentence in J. L. Motley's *Rise of the Dutch Republic* that in Holland 'A region, outcast of ocean and earth, wrested from both domains their richest treasure.' But there was no need to go beyond London to see areas reclaimed from marshes, and in England the wealthy land of Romney marsh and the Fens had been drawn from the sea. While it was hardly credible that all the schemes would be carried out, such as flooding the Sahara to make it blossom as the rose or cutting a canal from the Mediterranean to the Jordan, there were ship canals to Manchester and, in effect, to Glasgow and Newcastle upon Tyne and hope existed of a Channel tunnel. And who would estimate the effects of rapid aviation? Year after year, it seemed to Sir Charles Lucas 'under an all-wise Providence the earth was being replenished, recast and contracted by men'. Truly it was a changing world.

Rudmose Brown began his talk by quoting Chisholm's statement that there were two schools of geographers, one of which 'insisted on taking men as determining the supreme aim of geographical studies' while the other was concerned with 'the forms and physical conditions of the earth's surface' (Brown, 1914). In his view the essential study was centred, as Patrick Geddes ('one whom I must always recognise as my greatest teacher') said (following Frédéric le Play) on

PLACE————WORK————FOLK

which he correlated with Environment, Function and Organism (biosocial terms). In itself the study of distributions was not adequate, as the real concern was with people, with man and environment. This was a study of wide scope and the geographer would need to know something of many sciences, desirably to have some training in geology, meteorology, oceanography and anthropology and if possible economics and biology, as well as with the essentially distributional studies of climatology and demography. In short, geography was not in itself a fundamental science but derivative, based on a synthesis of other sciences, themselves derivative, geology, meteorology, biology, anthropology and economics. Geography, therefore, was on the same plane as sociology or history, both of which were deeply rooted in the physical sciences. Rudmose Brown quotes with approval the view of J. L. Myres that geography essays 'to discover what happens, where, and to explain why anything which happens just *where* it does, and under what combination of circumstances it *does* happen *just there*'. Generously for one who had endured the rigours of polar exploration, he also quotes Jean Brunhes's (1869–1930) 'view that the construction of the Suez and Panama canals was of far greater human significance than the discovery of the north and south poles'. And he underlines the need for travel (not exploration, which was an activity for certain special people). A rich variety of landscape could be seen within Britain and Ireland, and many people could extend their travels to the Arctic and the Mediterranean. The paper ends with words that could be echoed by many teachers of geography:

... while my aim ... must be to bring you to an understanding of how the surface features of our globe came to be a fit dwelling-place for man and how the multiple phenomena of nature act and interact on one another and influence man and his activities, who in turn reacts upon them, my success would be one-sided and incomplete if I failed to deepen your feeling of the beauty of it all, or was unsuccessful in awakening in you some sense of its wonder.

By the time these words appeared the First World War had begun, though few people anticipated that it would last for more than four years and there was a distinct atmosphere of 'business as usual' in the issues of the *Geographical Journal* for 1915. Some peacetime enterprises now became of strategic significance, such as the 1:1,000,000 map advocated initially by Albrecht Penck (1858–1945) at the 1891 International Geographical Congress held in Berne, as John Scott Keltie pointed out in a review of fifty years of geographical progress (Keltie, 1915). In his view the discoveries of the previous fifty years had been so great that the historian would 'have to go back to the half-century which followed 1492' to find any comparable time. In the 1860s the coast of Siberia was imperfectly mapped, the depth of the Arctic was unknown and the area between Spitsbergen and Novaya Zemlya unexplored, but by 1910 Greenland had been explored to 83°N, almost its whole coast charted, the Arctic archipelagos penetrated, the Arctic Ocean at least partially sounded and even the Pole located. The map of Asia had been to a large extent reconstructed and much of Europe had been resurveyed. In North America there had been remarkable development, for in 1860 'much of the region west of Lake Ontario in the north and of the Mississippi in the south was the home of the Indian, the trapper and the buffalo'. Vancouver did not exist and Vancouver Island was, like Fort Garry the site of Winnipeg, only a Hudson Bay Company's post. The population of Canada had increased from 3 million to 8 million and in Scott Keltie's opinion would eventually become 80 million. Australia had been explored systematically and in New Zealand the population had increased from a few thousands to more than a million while its export trade, mainly in wool and other agricultural produce, was valued at £23 million. Africa had been explored and partitioned, and by 1914 Britain controlled two-thirds of its export and import trade. Scott Keltie also notes the great developments in oceanography to which attention has been drawn repeatedly here, and comments on the excellent work done by various international commissions such as the production of a bathymetric map of the oceans under the care of the Prince of Monaco. Some of these international commissions, then as now, are sponsored by the International Geographical Union, in some cases in co-operation with other worldwide scientific organisations. Scott Keltie's view, fortunately widely shared at the time, was that pioneers of the future would have more than 'a daring spirit and a geographical instinct' and go forward with a sound academic training, 'content to devote themselves to a limited region, and work it out in all its details of feature, and geological character and meteorology, and animals and plants; ever keeping in mind that man is the centre of it all'.

Of the geographical literature generated by the war, the contributions of Marion I. Newbigin on the Balkans are of particular merit (Newbigin, 1915a, b). In two articles and the book, published in 1915, she gave a close analysis of the intricate mixture of actual or – more commonly – supposed racial groups in the Balkans, with all the complications added by differences of religion as well as those provided by the awkward physical geography of the peninsula. National aspirations, cultural divergencies and ruinous recent wars had all combined to present apparently intractable problems for a future peace settlement which Dr Newbigin feared might bear little relation to 'the principles of modern geography' and much more to the balance of power in Europe once hostilities were over. This work was overshadowed by the vital and timely publication in 1918 of *La Péninsule Balkanique* by J Cvijić (1865–1927) of Belgrade, who won great respect at the deliberations preceding the Treaty of Versailles in 1919: nevertheless it shows that at least one British geographer was informed on the problems of the time.

By 1915 the Royal Geographical Society was already interested in the possible recasting of European frontiers after the war, on which a paper was given by L. W. Lyde† (1863–1947), and other papers read in the same year dealt with European influence around the Pacific Ocean and with the 'Near East', broadly equivalent to what was more recently called the Middle East. Lyde's paper is of special interest as it shows the growing awareness of racial characteristics found from this time and (regrettably) unscientifically treated by several authors (Lyde, 1915). He argued that these were three desirable features of any new state. Firstly, it should be at once a racial and a geographical unit, especially so if the race had proved 'incapable of assimilation'. Of this the clearest example was Albania, which was populated by 'the most ancient, existing race in Europe, speaking a language older than classical Greek.' (Incidentally Lyde was annoyed with Marion Newbigin for speaking of the Albanians as 'a comic opera people'.) Secondly, in choosing a new political owner of any inhabited area, prime consideration should be given to the capacity of the new owner to assimilate others. Lyde says unequivocally that the Prussians could not assimilate others but that the French could do so, for in spite of all the misrule in the eighteenth century and at other times they had made the people of Alsace and Lorraine into 'worshippers of France . . . French to the core in sentiment'. And this led to his third point, that a frontier should be some natural feature where people naturally meet, rather than a desert or a mountain range. An obvious example of this was the Rhine which, though not a good military frontier and still less a political barrier, was a splendid political frontier as a zone of fusion between two nations, 'the best geographical means of drawing the dwellers on its banks together'. This argument was supported by the supposed racial unity of the people of the Rhinelands. 'The whole population from Bavaria through Alsace and Luxemburg to Walloon Belgium is of a single general type – blessed with a rounded skull inside which the brain seems to have a perfect freedom of development in all directions. Wherever that is found, you have a people who are naturally idealistic, artists and dreamers, willing to fight and to die – for an idea such as honour or freedom' (Lyde, 1915, pp. 135–6). Those with Nordic long-headed skulls may not care for Lyde's views.

Lyde did not advocate a new Rhineland state, and this idea gained only slight support during the war. The discussion that followed the paper was marked by a fierce argument with H. J. Mackinder, who spoke at some length and said that while some people imagined that at the end of the war a new Europe would be set up in accordance with scientific ideals, it was far more likely that the old idea of the balance of power would assert itself. He thought that Germany, with 60–70 million people, must remain a territorial state in Europe, but that in the southeast the best hope of stability lay in a federation led by Hungary, which would come to terms with Italy on the Adriatic, surrender the Romanians of Transylvania to Romania, and induce both Serbia and Romania to deal generously with Bulgaria. Another problem was that a reconstituted Poland would need access to the sea through German territory. Mackinder finished by saying that:

When our geographers . . . apply scientific generalizations to human geography where human initiative comes in, the result is to make Colonel Close and others blaspheme and say that there is no such thing as geography in the large sense, but only map-making. . . . If we try to obtain laws from our human geography, and especially laws which will govern our action politically, we are attempting that which I believe is doomed to failure (*ibid*. p. 143)

In a spirited reply Lyde stuck to his principles, especially on the 'capacity for assimilation' and said that he wanted Germany divided into four parts and that the Poles had no interest in the sea as 'their objective is Cracow'. He finishes by saying that he had no political bias but a leaning to the Labour Party, because it was 'not run by lawyers'. The President's final summing-up has a somewhat dazed air and contains the statement that he had 'thought of running along the Alps' (very good training no doubt) to show how a supposedly ideal frontier had failed to remain a political frontier. It must have been an interesting evening, though some of those present apparently thought that it would be best to win the war first and arrange the new Europe later.

Geography and education

Much has been said of the deplorable character of many geographical textbooks written during the nineteenth century, and indeed later. But a few books of promise appeared, among which was *The Relation of Geography and History* by H. B. George† (1838–1910), published in 1901 and followed three years later by *The Historical Geography of the British Empire*. George's book on geography and history went into two new editions by 1907. The argument advanced is that 'history is not intelligible without geography' and that 'the destinies of man are very largely determined by their environment'. But no simple relationship is discerned for H. B. George, having earlier written works on military history, had a considerable regard for chance circumstances. Even the site of Paris was not the only one possible for the capital of France as other towns had equal advantages: the growth of Paris was due more to the centralisation on the capital so characteristic of French life. Many interesting ideas appear in George's book, such as the concept of a Rhineland state, which came up again after the First World War and the threat to India from possible Russian control of Afghanistan. The book is now an interesting period piece: its successor, on the British Empire, is a careful but mainly historical study with some comments on geographical influences.

Undoubtedly such books were useful, but much more was needed as this quotation shows. The Geographical Association reported that: 'By almost every post come letters to University and Training College lecturers, professing the anxiety of the writers to investigate a mysterious phenomenon which they term 'the new Geography', and pleading for information about books and maps.' This cry from the heart, made by the kindly and generous P. M. Roxby, which appeared in 1910 (*Geogr. Teach.* 5, 1909–10, p. 292), shows the difficulties experienced by teachers in various schools, especially the new secondary grammar schools. Many of them had no training in the subject at all, or very little, but much was done to help them. From 1901 the Geographical Association published a journal in which most of the space was given to education and at various times it has issued special publications for teachers, such as *Hints to Teachers and Students on the Choice of Geographical Books and Maps* (1897), reissued as *Guide to Geographical Books and Appliances* in 1910. The number of suitable textbooks was increasing steadily and their authors included A. J. Herbertson (with his wife), H. J. Mackinder and M. I. Newbigin: these and other academic geographers were eager to see an advance in school teaching of the subject which could, however, only be part of a general development at all educational levels to the university. A useful review of the growth of university teaching in geography is given in the *Geographical Teacher*, 5, 1909–10, pp. 228–40.

In 1901, Oxford University awarded diplomas in geography to four successful candidates and in later years many of the country's professional geographers, including O. J. R. Howarth† (1877–1954) (1902), Eva G. R. Taylor† (1879–1966) (1908), C. B. Fawcett† (1883–1952) (1912) and E. W. Gilbert† (1900–73) (1924) took this examination. Others, including J. McFarlane, A. G. Ogilvie† (1887–1954) and P. M. Roxby† (1880–1947) studied geography at Oxford without taking the examination. It was also possible to take a B.Sc. degree by thesis as A. G. Ogilvie did. In 1911 the diploma examination was enlarged and divided into two parts, with a field survey or 'geographical description': some twenty years later the diploma course was abandoned when an honours degree was established, though from 1905 the diploma or the 'Certificate in Regional Geography' courses could rank as one of the final B.A. groups. In Cambridge, from 1905, geography could be offered as a subject for the ordinary B.A. and a more advanced examination for a diploma was instituted.

In other universities progress was less sure but apparent. In London there were developments at the then new School of Economics where H. J. Mackinder arrived in 1900 and at University College, where L. W. Lyde joined the staff in 1903. Mackinder's helpers included A. J. Sargent, then Reader in Foreign Trade, whose work on the Tyne has already been noted (p. 91). Lectures were also given in 1902 at Birkbeck College by G. G. Chisholm to 1908 and afterwards by J. F. Unstead. In other universities some progress was made, notably in Manchester where in 1903 John McFarlane became a teacher of geography (full time from 1910) having previously worked in history and economics, on condition that he spent one term studying geography at Oxford! Other university developments included new lectureships at Liverpool (P. M. Roxby, 1903), at Reading (H. N. Dickson, 1904, but some earlier help from Oxford), Aberystwyth (H. J. Fleure† (1877–1969) 1908 but earlier work was done for teachers), Edinburgh (G. G. Chisholm, 1908) Glasgow (Capt. H. S. Lyons, 1909), Sheffield (R. N. Rudmose Brown, 1908) and Southampton (C. B. Fawcett, 1913).

Promising as this might seem, there was much to impede the development of geography in the universities. In some cases physical geography was taught by geologists, botanists and others with little reference to the needs of geographers, so that any kind of regional synthesis was hard to appreciate. Clearly it was useful for any geographer to have a knowledge of stratigraphical geology or systematic botany, but he also needed a knowledge of geomorphology, later well developed by numerous geographers deriving much of their inspiration from American and continental workers. Another difficulty, perhaps inherent in the nature of geography was that its affiliation to other subjects within universities was so varied. In some cases historical geography, as at Oxford, was an optional subject for the history honours degree and in London, geography was a compulsory intermediate subject for everyone taking the B.Sc. (Econ.) degree with optional courses in the second and third years as well as in the arts degree courses. At Manchester one year's geography was compulsory for the Bachelor of Commerce degree and it could also be taken in the arts degree courses and in the B.A. honours degree in political and economic science. By 1914 it was also a subject for the degree of Master of Arts by examination. Similar conditions prevailed in Liverpool, where the M.A. course consisted of two obligatory papers on general principles and either a dissertation or an examination on some special region or on some selected aspect of geography. There were courses in the School of Commerce, for students in the 'Day Training College' (on the British Empire) and for students in the Honours School of History on modern historical geography or on classical geography. In Edinburgh there were the normal 'ordinary' optional courses given to students for the pass Master of Arts degree, and Chisholm's distinguished experience is reflected in the inclusion of a special 'Honours half-course' (taken with economics) on the 'economic and commercial development of the leading commercial countries of the world during the last forty or fifty years with special reference to geographical conditions', together with practical work.

It was hardly surprising that courses should be varied, as such a wide variety of people had been chosen to lecture in the universities, ranging from the historically minded P. M. Roxby in Liverpool to Rudmose Brown in Sheffield (initially a naturalist but inspired by Patrick Geddes to take a wider view of humanity) or even Captain Lyons in Glasgow who had become Secretary of the Royal Scottish Geographical Society after a long overseas career in which he became director of the Survey of Egypt. In 1911 he was succeeded by Dr J. D. Falconer, whose main work had been in geology, as assistant to James Geikie in Edinburgh and in the Northern Nigerian Mineral Survey. Economists were represented by John McFarlane and G. G. Chisholm, while L. W. Lyde studied classics, taught English and spent four years as a (tough) headmaster in Bolton, Lancashire, before entering on a career in geography.

Of all the people who came to geography, Eva G. R. Taylor and H. J.

Fleure had perhaps the firmest scientific training. Eva Taylor had a first-class honours degree in chemistry and Fleure had a first-class honours degree in zoology at Aberystwyth in 1901 and subsequently became Assistant Lecturer in Zoology, Botany and Geology, and later Professor of Zoology. Eva Taylor, strongly influenced by Herbertson and from 1908 to 1910 his assistant in Oxford, made many distinguished contributions to geography, notably on navigation and on the geographical views held in the Tudor and Stuart periods. Fleure was a geographer of unusual range of mind and spread his researches over archaeology and anthropology. Archaeology has developed as a separate subject, but the study of physical anthropology is now little followed though social anthropology remains popular. Fleure had much to say on the distribution of races in time. He was a tireless worker for the advance of geography in education, notably through the Geographical Association. With people having all these varied talents, university geography teaching was obviously entering an experimental stage in which the teaching varied widely from one university to another and even in the various colleges which used the London syllabus. Teachers developed specialisms according to their inclinations and abilities, but many had to provide courses in aspects of the subject of which they knew little, though this could be a stimulating and even a fruitful experience as their interest developed.

A main need was to help school-teachers who found themselves charged with the responsibility for a subject in which they had had virtually no training at all. This was splendidly met by summer schools or vacation courses, already familiar as part of the programme of the extramural teaching provided by universities: there was for example a 'summer meeting' at Exeter in 1904 lasting for almost four weeks arranged by the Cambridge Local Examinations and Lectures Syndicate, dealing with the geology, fauna and flora of the southwest, with Elizabethan geography (including six lectures by Yule Oldham on discoveries of the time), and on the history of the British Navy (*Geogr. Teach.* 2, 1902–4, p. 229). Such courses were less specialised than those arranged specially for geography teachers, notably at Oxford: of these the first in 1902 was attended by thirty teachers including thirteen women. A. J. Herbertson lectured on landforms and economic geography, H. N. Dickson on major world physical features and C. R. Beazley on exploration and trade routes, and the course included many hours of practical work and various excursions. Judging by the accounts published by members of the Oxford course and at the Cambridge summer meeting (which included daily lectures on history, literature, physical and natural science, as well as geography and other subjects) these enterprises were successful though a practical Scotswoman in Oxford found the ability to use 'as teachers' several lectures on the history of exploration and of trade routes 'doubtful'. Two on each topic, she thought, would have been enough (*Geogr. Teach.* 1, 1901–2, pp. 124, 172–83).

Meanwhile in Scotland Patrick Geddes, with his base in the Outlook Tower in Edinburgh, had begun his influential 'summer meetings' which lasted for almost the whole of August. The 1903 course, warmly commended by the Geographical Association, was on 'Edinburgh and its region considered as a type' and in 1904 the subject was 'Central Scotland: its natural and historic interest' (*Geogr. Teach.* **2**, 1902–4, pp. 77–8, 229–30). A large number of lecturers appeared and the course included field study of geology, botany and zoology with historical and social surveys. There were lectures on the health of school-children, on the history of religion in Edinburgh, on 'literary landmarks and associations (with excursions)', on Scottish art and on old Scots music by the folk-tune collector, Mrs Kennedy-Fraser. And, to quote the note on the 1903 meeting, 'No part of the British Isles is better suited for such a study; for in no part are so complex physical conditions crowded within so narrow an area, and none has a more varied history.' Suffused with the overflowing interests of Patrick Geddes, these courses gave inspiration to hundreds of people who were prepared to be, as his son Arthur† (1895–1968) noted, 'interested in ideas'. Patrick Geddes was a frequent lecturer at other summer schools. He appeared, for example, at the fifth Oxford course held from 19 to 26 August 1910 and spoke on the geography, history and life of cities. This 1910 course was attended by 250 people and over 20 lecturers gave single talks or short courses, and the usual indoor practical work and fieldwork was arranged. A full account of this course has been given (*Geogr. Teach.* **5**, 1909–10, pp. 337–53).

Undoubtedly the summer meetings met a great need. In 1914, for example, these included meetings at Aberystwyth, Oxford, Whitby and Dublin, all held in August (*Scott. Geogr. Mag.* **30**, 1914, pp. 207, 328, 378, 437–8, 549–52, 604–06). At Aberystwyth courses given by H. J. Fleure included a series of lectures, 'correlating the geography of Europe with the history of its civilisation', and on 'England – and more particularly Wales' while W. E. Whitehouse taught climatology, cartography and teaching methods. In Oxford the seventh biennial course had a wide range of lecturers including A. J. Herbertson, H. O. Beckit (1875–1931), C. B. Fawcett and H. J. E. Peake† (1867–1946), on 'home geography' with a course on the British Empire by Herbertson who, with O. J. R. Howarth, had edited the *Oxford Survey of the British Empire* (Oxford 1914). A large number of visiting lecturers included Patrick Geddes on cities, F. J. Haverfield on Roman Britain, and P. M. Roxby on modern China. The Yorkshire summer school was inaugurated in 1913 with the aim of 'providing instruction on geography and furnishing opportunities for discussion connected with the teaching of the subject', and repeated in 1914 under the direction of the geologist P. F. Kendall of Leeds University, where one lectureship in geography was held from 1913 in the Geology Department by Ll. Rodwell Jones† (1881–1947). In 1914, 100 people attended and the main topic was the British Isles, on which a general course was given, followed by alternative courses on agriculture, rocks and soils, or on oceanography, rivers and the evolution of transport and communications. Rodwell Jones spoke on economic geography and five lectures were given by W. G. Smith, then of Edinburgh,whose work on the botanical survey of Yorkshire was noted on page 85.

All of these courses (and there were others, for example at Reading in 1913 under H. N. Dickson) show the varied preoccupations of geographers at the time, but the course in Dublin, named a 'Summer School of Civics' was partly sociological in character. Patrick Geddes spoke on geography and nature study, which he regarded as a basis for human investigation and, with H. J. Fleure as a collaborator, on regional surveys. C. B. Fawcett gave an account of his survey work in his native area of northeast England in and around Teesdale, and various local experts, including Grenville Cole of Dublin, also lectured. At this time, Geddes was increasingly concerned with town planning and his ideas were eagerly discussed by many geographers, not least Fleure and Fawcett. Fieldwork, seriously organised, was included in all the courses.

Inevitably the war disrupted development but, as shown in Chapter 6, there was a considerable advance in geography from 1919 onwards. This would not have been possible without the work done by 1914. Steadily, through the devoted work of a comparatively small number of people, instruction had been given to teachers not only within the walls of universities but outside them, conferences and summer schools had been organised, textbooks had been written and geographical societies had brought together a wide range of interested people. The view was expressed at times that the work of geographical societies was almost finished as to some extent at least geography had achieved recognition but in fact, as their subsequent history shows, it was only just beginning, for the war and the hard-won peace posed new problems which some geographers were quick to recognise and eager to study.

Chapter 6

The inter-war period: some broad views

Only twenty years separated the signing of the Treaty of Versailles in July 1919 from the outbreak of war in September 1939 and approximately half-way between these two cathartic events the world economic crisis began in a panic on Wall Street that initiated a period of mass unemployment, a sharp decline of international trade and growing tension among minority groups in numerous countries, notably those defined at Versailles in 1919 and immediately afterwards. So many bright hopes of the younger generation, not to mention older people who refused to lose their faith in the possibility of world peace, were shattered as the League of Nations sank into oblivion through its failure to prevent aggression, especially the movement of the Japanese into Manchuria in 1931. To historians of a later day this twenty years may seem to be a short interval between two phases of the world conflict, originating in Europe but spreading to the ends of the earth. But that would hardly be an adequate assessment of a period of marked scientific advance, not least in aviation, and also of general cultural and educational activity. In Britain the inter-war years saw the rapid development of the grammar schools and of the universities, varied in origin but in many cases assisted in their progress towards full status by the paternal care of the University of London whose degrees could be taken externally. Many university teachers during the inter-war years gave substantial service to the various school examining boards which awarded certificates normally taken at the ages of sixteen and eighteen, of which the latter provided a suitable basis for university work.

At last, it seemed, there was some tangible realisation of an educational advance for which the Royal Geographical Society and the Geographical Association had fought for so long. Recognition was now given to several other subjects whose friends had fought similar battles, including modern languages, history and even the natural sciences. Some of these subjects achieved full recognition long before the first full honours course in geography was established at Liverpool University in 1917, but several other subjects have achieved it since then, notably in social studies. After the First World War the interest of students and the general public lay primarily in large issues, especially those of international affairs, of the world economic order, of colonial territories. It was regarded as an essential part of a geographical education to have some knowledge of the entire world and this was made possible by the patient accumulation of material through the work of earlier generations, especially since the last quarter of the nineteenth century. Such feelings were natural for, as H. J. Mackinder noted, what happened in one area, however apparently remote, could have international implications. Courses with titles like 'The New Europe' or 'The British Commonwealth', even on broad issues of political geography, had a natural appeal and so had lectures on China, India or Africa, especially if given by such charismatic figures as P. M. Roxby of Liverpool. It was a time of broad views, some of which are discussed in this chapter. But this was not all, for there was also an increasing devotion to detailed research, discussed in Chapter 7.

The immediate post-war years

Local surveys had been a main concern of geographers for decades before the war and were regarded as a normal activity of a university staff, but at the same time many geographers shared the view but not the aims of John Wesley when he said that 'the World is my parish'. Knowledge of many foreign countries made it possible to produce the *Handbooks* of the Geographical Section of the Naval Intelligence Division of the Admiralty, with H. N. Dickson initially at the Royal Geographical Society and then in other premises, and by July 1919 fifty handbooks and manuals had been printed. In 1921 they were released for general sale. Each handbook followed the same general pattern with these sections: physical features and boundaries; climate; history; administration; inhabitants; religions; trade and finance; hygiene and social conditions; economics; flora and fauna; communications with a gazetteer, a section on vocabularies, an index and maps. These handbooks were clearly intended to provide practical information for military and civil purposes and were naturally somewhat encyclopaedic in character. Considerable as their merits were, the great advance in British geography during the inter-war period can be seen by comparing these volumes with those written during the Second World War (p. 143).

Europe's new map was a source of widespread interest and some essays by geographers on various countries appeared in journals. In 1920, for example, G. G. Chisholm wrote a short article on the new free city of Danzig, in which he said that the Poles were inclined to overestimate the significance of the river Vistula, for under modern conditions rail transport was far more important (Chisholm, 1920). There was the distinct possibility that for some merchandise, especially that of high value, Bremen and Hamburg would remain the major ports, even though the rail journey from Polish industrial centres was longer. As it happened both Danzig and the new port of Gdynia were very successful in later years; Chisholm's published work was always thoughtful and interesting. In the same number of the *Geographical Journal* there was a short unsigned paper on geography at the Paris Peace Conference, in which it was stated that while there had been much study 'of a geographical nature' in the intelligence departments of the British Foreign Office, the Admiralty, the War Office, the Foreign Affairs Historical Section and the War Trade Intelligence Department there was (not surprisingly) little co-ordination between these bodies (*Geogr. J.* **55**, 1920, pp. 309–12).

Four main concerns dominated the work of boundary delimitation. The first need was to define the larger political divisions of the future, and the main consideration appears to have been the ethnic character of the population, though in some cases economic or strategic factors were dominant. Obviously this ethnic consideration was crucial, and was therefore referred to the Supreme Council dominated by the major powers. Next followed a search for the best kind of frontier, necessarily one which could be easily fixed on the ground. The third process was the definition and delimitation of frontiers, which involved legal as well as geographical knowledge: finally provision had to be made for actual demarcation on the ground, a job for survey experts. Working on a general directive from the Supreme Council the Geographical Committee dealt with detail, including such problems as the shifting of river courses, but the final Drafting Committee was composed of lawyers. The British delegation consisted of the chief of the Geographical Section of the General Staff, Colonel Sir Coote Hedley, and two staff officers, Major O. E. Wynne, who had experience of boundary demarcation in Africa and elsewhere, and Captain A. G. Ogilvie, later of Edinburgh (who in fact was the author of the paper). In a pamphlet of 1922, perhaps now rarely read, he gives an analysis of the boundaries of various European states which shows a detailed knowledge of regional geography and of military strategy (Ogilvie, 1922; Freeman, 1967). Much of the teaching on Europe from this time was inevitably political in character but until H. G. Wanklyn's *Eastern Marchlands of Europe* was published in 1941 (by which time events had made the Versailles treaty historic) the main literature on the political geography of continental Europe appeared abroad, with E. de Martonne's *Europe Centrale* in two volumes as a main source. And a much-loved text of the period was Isaiah Bowman's *New World*, which ran through several editions from 1921 onwards.

It was indeed a new world in the 1920s. The British Empire of the Victorian and Edwardian periods was evolving into a Commonwealth enlarged by the addition of several areas held as mandates for the league of Nations, all of them former Turkish or German colonies of which the most notable was Tanganyika in Africa. Article 22 of the Covenant of the League of Nations was designed to provide oversight by advanced nations for these former German and Turkish colonies which could not stand alone 'under the strenuous conditions of the modern world'. Bowman divided the mandates into three groups: the first included the former Turkish possessions of which Syria and the Lebanon were assigned to France, and Iraq, Palestine and Transjordan to Britain; the second consisted of areas in Africa, of which Ruanda and Urundi were assigned to Belgium, Tanganyika to Britain, and the Cameroons and Togoland to Britain and France; the third group, mainly sparsely populated but of some strategic importance, included South West Africa, allocated to the Union of South Africa (on which Bowman prophetically comments, 'It is all very well for the League of Nations to define the status of this former German possession, but what if the Union government ignores it?'), German New Guinea and certain adjacent Northern Pacific islands to Australia, Nauru to Britain, Western Samoa to New Zealand and – significantly – Yap and other former German North Pacific islands to Japan (Bowman, 1928). Within a few years of the Versailles settlement, the German demand for a return of former colonies began and it had become vociferous by the 1930s, notably – among geographers – at the Colonial Section of the International Congress of 1938 at Amsterdam. The designers of the mandate system recognised that Australia and New Zealand had advanced to a status in which they could accept international responsibilities. However, this was never to be a threat to world peace like the allocation of Pacific islands to Japan, already a significant naval power with an increasing, vigorous, able and well-disciplined population easily persuaded that imperial expansion was a mark of national greatness.

China, on the other hand, was once more in the throes of a revolutionary period of its history. Fortunately, P. M. Roxby provided a series of fascinating papers on its geography based partly on his own travels as an Albert Kahn Fellow in 1912–13 (and later) but also on numerous other sources of which the most satisfying was a compilative work by the China Continuation Committee, *The Christian Occupation of China*, published in 1922 at Shanghai. This volume crystallised the local knowledge acquired by missionaries and others. In fact a vast literature existed on China, written with varying degrees of impartiality. Roxby attracted the interest of geographers with a vivid but scarcely impartial article published in three parts on 'The Far Eastern Question in its geographical setting' and in later classic papers (Roxby, 1919–20; 1925; 1934). The work of 1919–20 was a vigorous statement of the major features of political geography with many frank comments on Japan, Russia and China and a clear understanding of the international rivalries in Manchuria, settled predominantly by the Chinese but penetrated also by the Japanese and the Russians, eager to build railways and to acquire commercial power in the last of the world's great prairie belts to be used for modern agricultural settlement. Roxby was a convinced admirer of Chinese civilisation which he regarded as likely to survive all political upheavals: indeed he may well have shocked some of his readers at the time by his sharp comments on the acquisition of German and British bases on the Shantung peninsula at Kiaochow and

Weihaiwei ('the most sinister game of grab the nineteenth century ever played'). Definitely he was not an imperialist. The 1925 paper on population distribution was a fine general summary of the geography of China, necessarily condensed into an article, and it was a source of regret to a wide circle that at that time all his aspirations for writing a book on China came to nothing. There is for example, a comment in the preface to L. H. Dudley Buxton's *China, the Land and the People* (Oxford 1928) that Roxby had withdrawn his offer of collaboration, but fortunately his knowledge of China was still available when the Admiralty *Handbooks* were prepared during the Second World War (p. 143–4).

Russia was an enigma to many students from the revolution of 1917 onwards, as few were able to visit it or to see much if they did so. Reports on its reconstruction were conflicting and in many cases antagonistic. In geographical circles much was lost by the absence of Russian geographers from international gatherings from 1914 to 1952 (except for small groups of two to four geographers at the 1931, 1934 and 1938 congresses) especially as before 1914 their contributions had been of considerable value. Every discussion of Russia between the wars tended to be a mixture of speculation and political argument, especially if (as the present author found out at the Summer School of International Studies at Geneva run by Sir Alfred Zimmern in 1931) the company included one or more articulate communists who saw the only hope for the world in the Russian political and social ethos and practices. Some of the visitors to Russia, notably Mr and Mrs Sidney Webb and Bernard Shaw, saw fine hopes of a future democratic society in the USSR. But Sir Halford Mackinder was not of this company and his extraordinary book *Democratic Ideals and Reality* is described in the preface as 'the outcome of more than the merely feverous thought of war time' and a development of the ideas published in 1904 (Mackinder 1919). Mackinder also claimed that in 1905 he 'gave vogue to the term Man-Power' in which is implicit not only the idea of fighting strength but also that of productivity, rather than wealth, as the focus of economic reasoning. But his book was read at the time by comparatively few people and that is hardly remarkable as much of it consists of political argument, or perhaps more accurately a political monologue not without obscurities.

Nevertheless, many features of world military strategy emerge clearly and some are still of crucial importance. Using a deep knowledge of history from classical times onwards, Mackinder shows that time and time again there has been struggles between the land-based powers and those aspiring to, or in fact possessing, command of the seas. In some earlier epochs this struggle was waged in comparatively small parts of the world, even in Mediterranean peninsulas, but when railways spread across the vast interiors of continents the area of potential conflict became world-wide. The great focus of military power was in the World-Island and before 1914 Russia had become the effective Heartland, 'the region to which, under modern conditions, sea-power can be refused access'. Its apparent possibilities of world conquest were understood, for in Mackinder's view Britain's control of India and her 'knocking at the sea gates of China' were connected with fear of Russia. And if some great military power possessed the Heartland, with Arabia, it 'could take easy possession of the crossways of the world at Suez'. This comment seemed ironic when the Suez Canal was made virtually useless from 1956 to 1974. And when Mackinder wrote, Russia was entering her long period of isolation and reconstruction, so any fear of her outward expansion seemed remote.

Germany, and not Russia, was in fact the power which had exploited the idea of the Heartland. Her pre-1914 strategy had included the *Drang nach Osten* through eastern Europe and the Balkans based partly on the outward movement of German-speaking peoples as far east as the (one-time) German republic around Saratov on the Volga. Over many centuries the success of this eastward movement had been remarkable and it therefore appeared to be the destiny of Germany to go further, to organise and develop Slavonic lands and possibly those beyond the Balkans by building an arterial railway from Berlin to Baghdad. And Germany was strongly entrenched along the Baltic shore, indeed to such an extent that Britain – for all its naval power – was unable to enter the Baltic at any time during the First World War. The Balts, descendants of warlike medieval crusaders, had become an aristocracy of military leaders having an assured, able and enterprising cast of mind. Historically it was from this Baltic countryside that the inspiration of Prussia originally came. What would have happened, Mackinder asks, if Germany had merely remained on the defensive in the west and turned her main forces eastwards into Russia? This is one of the 'ifs and buts' of history as anyone who considers the German campaign in Russia during the Second World War will realise, not to mention the French campaign of 1812. Had Germany won the war, Mackinder (1919, p. 120) notes, 'it was her intention that continental Europe from St Vincent to Kazan, with the addition of the Asiatic Heartland, should have become the naval base from which she would have fought Britain and America in the next war'. To leave Germany in control of eastern Europe would be a fatal mistake and therefore (1919, p. 150):

When our statesmen are in conversation with our defeated enemy, some airy cherub should whisper to them from time to time
Who rules East Europe commands the Heartland:
Who rules the Heartland commands the World-Island:
Who rules the World-Island commands the World.

There are echoes here of Bismarck's comment that Bohemia was the key to Eastern Europe. Mackinder, himself hardly an 'airy cherub', was insistent that there should be a 'Middle Tier' of 'really independent states between Germany and Russia' and these in fact were established with varying political and economic success, as shown in H. G. Wanklyn's book, mentioned on p. 104.

Obviously the vital concern was that the new states of the eastern marchlands of Europe should be 'really independent'. But the weakness of Russia, due to military defeat and internal revolution, combined with the Allied victory, and even the powerful advocacy of two geographers, Romer for Poland and Cvijić for Yugoslavia, made it possible to establish this *cordon sanitaire* between Germany and Russia and to remove the fear that Austria might ever again be imperialist in policy. As it happened the political difficulties of these states, always considerable, became greater when they faced the world economic crisis of the 1930s: equally clearly they were threatened by the Nazi control of Germany from 1933. And it is patently clear that the devastating effect of the world economic crisis in Germany made many of its people, not least its capable but workless university graduates, turn to the Nazi movement as a way of regeneration. Mackinder clearly saw that Germany might rise again to a position of power, even of potential dominance, in Europe and was contemptuous of the view that it was so impoverished that it could do no more harm for a century. Here one can recognise his appreciation of the 'manpower' argument. After the Franco-Prussian War the recovery of France had been swift and it could be so with Germany. Then as now it was difficult to forecast the future and one may smile at Mackinder's confident assertion, widely shared at the time, that within a few years Canada and Australia would equal the 'Motherland' in population. It has often been said that Mackinder's views were used by geopoliticians in Germany, but he is surely not to blame for that, especially as what was anathema (domination of the World-Island by Germany) to Mackinder was to them the inevitable destiny of an inspired and vigorous nation. Naturally Mackinder in 1919 said very little on air power, and equally naturally some of his political views read oddly today. But much that he said is worth pondering.

The visions of peace

Both Mackinder and Roxby came to geography with a background in history and both were fascinated by the interplay of political forces in the modern world. And so too was H. J. Fleure who, from a background in the natural sciences developed teaching of considerable breadth in anthropology and archaeology as well as in geography. The rapid advance of archaeology in the post-war period was a source of satisfaction to Fleure, who in addresses given in the 1930s rather wryly but always generously acknowledged the difficulty of keeping abreast with his reading. Work on physical anthropology had a compelling appeal as a scientific explanation of human qualities and therefore of human societies. As archaeological evidence accumulated it became possible to trace past migrations of human groups, especially as their physical characteristics could be assessed from skulls and other remains.

Fleure applied all the resources of his fascinating mind to the delineation of drifts of people across Europe by land and their movements by sea from the later megalithic period. It was a wonderful story, especially in relation to Great Britain and Ireland, for so long a time at the end of the world, settled intermittently by people having varied physical characteristics from various parts of the European mainland. Each group had its own favoured environment, according to the means of sustenance it favoured; and gradually, as botanists, geologists, climatologists and others shed more light on the nature of the environment before marshes were drained or forests cleared, it became possible to construct – with at least a measure of conviction – a picture of people living on the land at various stages of prehistory. Fleure stated quite definitely at various gatherings that it was the geographer's responsibility to study human life ever since the emergence of his recognisably human ancestors. For most of his long life this was supposed to be a period of half a million years, though it is now known to be many times as long. Everything made this attractive, especially as much material was available through the study of primitive peoples whose direct relationship to environment was readily seen, even though apparently identical environments did not of necessity produce identical societies.

Intrigued by the idea of human regions Fleure expressed his theories both in articles and in his book of 1918, *Human Geography in Western Europe*. His main concept was that regional study should begin with the life of the people, in their accumulated experience of particular areas. This idea was developed in a paper (Fleure, 1919) arguing that observers could recognise regions of difficulty, of privation, of debilitation, of increment, of industrialisation, of nomadism. In a region of difficulty it was hard to make a living, but the challenging character of the environment might itself be productive of human strength and enterprise, illustrated by the contribution Scotsmen made to the building of the British Empire. No region was unchanging in character, for a region of difficulty could be transformed by the use of coal or water power into one of industrialisation. Many coalfields and textile areas in mountain areas came within this category, expressive of a new use of long-unknown or at least unused natural resources. Regions of increment gave marked returns for moderate effort in agriculture, as in the more fertile parts of the Mediterranean or, given water control, riverine lowlands such as those of the Tigris–Euphrates trough or the Nile valley. Excessive heat and humidity, however, produce debilitation inimical to human effort, and excessive cold or aridity could have similarly devastating effects. And everywhere the richer environments aroused the envy of those who lived in poorer environments, so that not unnaturally the nomadic tribes of the world's interior grasslands attacked rich lowlands at intervals, having evolved an efficient social and military organisation. All people had a natural desire for life, for reproduction and for the good life, and it was the extent to which this last was satisfied that distinguished one people from another. Having met the basic needs of food, clothing and shelter, society could move to art, philosophy, literature and learning in general with an advance in civilisation which, to be maintained, must avoid a drift to decadence for every advance in civilisation had its dangers as well as its rewards.

Although Fleure's views aroused considerable interest, they had very little impact on regional geography which, in Britain, continued on much the same progression from the physical to the human aspects that had become traditional. Possibly one reason for this slight impact was the difficulty in mapping regions on Fleure's scheme: no maps at all appear in the 1919 paper and the maps in the 1918 book are unimpressive. In fact, regional writing was not Fleure's *métier* as the chapter on Wales in the compilative volume of 1928 (Ogilvie, 1928) shows, for the essay is an intensely human account of the life of Wales in which the author introduces, and all too briefly develops, many ideas on the relation of the people's lives to the mountains, river valleys and lowlands of a varied land. It also includes many comments on the economic and social history, and even on the religious movements that were influential at various periods. Here, as in the work on human regions, there is a broad sweep through all time, with no general analytic treatment of any distinct and definable regions Wales might possess. And the two illustrative maps are of the distributions of the Welsh language (by Trevor Lewis) and of the distribution of racial types (by E. G. Bowen). Critics of the work of Fleure and of his disciples have been known to complain that they attempted to do too much and to cover, as one of them said, 'everything under the sun'. But the aspiration was to show the unity of the physical and the historical: in 1929 Fleure said that: 'We are in some danger of falling into the fallacy against which General Smuts so earnestly warns us in *Holism*, the fallacy of thinking that, having split the whole, in our minds, into parts we can next take the parts, as our minds conceive them, try to stick them together and so have the whole once more' (Fleure, 1929 p. 13).

Characteristically he at once shows his admiration of Darwin, who gave the world illumination as he made people see 'the unity and order of animate nature' through a study of men in their environments. Inevitably such study must be evolutionary for:

The geographer cannot understand the surface of Scandinavia, the climate of Central Asia, the character of the Congo Forest, the distribution of hoofed animals, the characteristics of human races, or the features of villages, cities, transport, and industry, without digging deep into the past. Nevertheless, if he be a geographer he will study the past for the sake of the present; he is less a chronicler or recorder than a student trying to illuminate the present by an interpretation built upon an appreciation of its evolution (Fleure, 1929, p. 11).

To many young modern geographers, absorbed in a specialism, such views of geography may seem strange, for why should they care about hoofed animals or the surface of Scandinavia when the circulation of transport in cities or the distribution of offices in town centres offers so apparently fruitful a research topic? But to an earlier, if now almost extinct, generation the idea of the unity of the world, of *Holism*, had a powerful appeal. Such an idea may revive again. In some ways it was age-old and in others it was new; and in some minds it was linked with the ideal of understanding all humanity in its infinite diversity and therefore was a contribution to the world peace which it was hoped, with diminishing conviction, could be achieved by the League of Nations. Only as people became citizens of the world could the fear of widespread, even total, destruction be removed: humanity could move forward to prosperity or backwards into barbarism through its own choice.

That geography dealt with numerous topics closely bound up with mathematics, physics, geology, biology, anthropology, history and economics seemed of little consequence to Fleure, who thought that many of these subjects had 'limited their own growth through want of appreciation of such arguments and interpretations as the geographical point of view would develop' (Fleure, 1929, p. 13). Undoubtedly the whole was greater than the sum of its parts, and the human problem was that 'truth has so many approaches that each of us can follow but a few in the course of a lifetime of work'. Why then not recognise that variety of approach was to be encouraged, and admit that differences of outlook could be supplementary rather than contradictory, leading to 'immense advances in knowledge, and especially in understanding'? Much of Fleure's writing shows the breadth of his mind. In a short book published for the Workers' Educational Association (Fleure, 1932), designed for independent students who 'want not to be told what to think but to be helped to think for themselves', Fleure ranges through British life, industrial relations, village and city in Europe, the expansion of modern Europe to China and Japan (which includes a discussion of the then recent Japanese conquest of Manchuria), and finally to early agriculture and social types.

Fleure's work on race attracted considerable attention and was clearly an extension of his earlier work in the natural sciences. To some extent it was based on fieldwork, especially in remote areas such as mountain valleys or isolated coastal villages: some of the new graduates eagerly went out to measure heads, to record hair and eye colour and other physical attributes. Much of their detailed material was published in appropriate journals, but was made available to a wider public in small and inexpensive books (Fleure, 1922, 1923, 1927) which included discussions of other anthropological works such as those of J. Beddoe, V. G. Childe, A. C. Haddon, A. Keith and W. Z. Ripley. Fleure followed other workers in relating anthropological and archaeological evidence and in Europe recognised three main racial types, Nordic, Alpine and Mediterranean, but with a vast range of marginal types. Many of the generalisations prevalent in the 1920s have been contested since then though racial differences certainly exist. In general Fleure was reluctant to be too definite, though on rereading his work one can find some very firm statements, for example:

the rural culture of mid-Europe must not be ascribed exclusively to one race type. We can but say that the Alpine race takes kindly to traditional village life and to industries that have grown out of it, especially such industries as have developed skill in minutiae. The predominance of the areas of Alpine race in the early phases of commercial development of electrical machinery is a significant modern example of the special aptitudes concerned (Fleure, 1927, p. 70).

Fleure had a considerable interest in medical geography but little time for any detailed research, though in his last years he worked on the distribution of blood groups with medical and other researchers. The same interest is seen in this extract, published forty years before his death (Fleure, 1929, p. 41):

phthisis is specially likely to attack those physical types which in particular regions are hard put to it to attain full expression of their powers. Thus, in some moorland areas the acquiescent dark, long-headed type of man, which is such a characteristic element of the British population, accepts a poor diet and risks of infection and suffers severely from young adult phthisis, while the same type in crowded industrial areas puts up a considerable resistance to the disease, thanks to the ease with which, it seems, he there obtains certain types of food. The tall, fair type, on the other hand, with apparently some special sensitiveness to catarrhal infections, suffers severely in a crowded town, but, in the country, he often shows enterprise and is interested in hunting and trapping.

How seriously can one regard such comments? Those who, like the present author, are tall, long-headed and (formerly) fair may agree about the catarrh but have no desire to hunt or trap anything. And, to return to the first quotation, was the industrialisation of certain districts in the Alps really due to the existence of people of 'Alpine race'? There is perhaps some resemblance to ideas put forward by students of eugenics, regarded as rather *avant-garde* in the 1920s. Fleure had an enquiring and experimental turn of mind that he willingly revealed to others, but the enterprise of his thinking was sometimes more apparent than the caution.

Since Fleure wrote these words over fifty years ago hopes that a scientific logical assessment of physical characteristics evolved in varied natural environments would remove 'racial' prejudice, not to mention hatred, have proved vain. Little is generally said of racial characteristics in modern geography teaching, and ascription of particular mental characteristics to actual or supposed racial types, however cautious and tentative, is fraught with social danger. In the 1920s and later the work on race fascinated many students of geography even though numerous pundits said that it was really anthropology: in Liverpool, P. M. Roxby regarded the teaching of racial geography as an essential part of the work in a geography department and was anxious that his students should not only know the main elements of world racial distributions but should also learn tolerance from such a study.

Fleure's breadth of enquiry was notably seen in the series of ten volumes published with the overall title of 'The Corridors of Time' (Peake and Fleure, 1927–56). The series was written in collaboration with H. J. E. Peake, a lifelong student of archaeology and anthropology. The first nine of the ten volumes consisted of a survey of the development of civilisation from the first beginnings of man to the end of the Prehistoric period. Each volume was of some 200 pages, complete in itself, yet related to its forerunners and its successors. Illustrations were acquired from many sources and the authors were obviously familiar with the work of scholars elsewhere, though the American continent was not included. The presentation was effective and many students of the time (here the author draws on his own experience) eagerly read these volumes as they appeared. They showed human progress across the loesslands of the Old World, the advances in crafts and social organisation in riverine lowlands tamed by irrigation in the Nile valley and the Tigris–Euphrates trough, as well as in other 'cradles of civilisation'. The relation of the desert and the sown, epitomised in the Fertile Crescent around Arabia, was a thrilling human story of achievement and struggle and the advances in civilisation made in certain favoured Mediterranean lowlands were equally interesting. And as the reader went from one volume to the next a picture emerged of the gradual spread of settlement across the Old World eventually reaching its coastal fringes and outlying islands. The titles of the books were well chosen: in fact they are comparable with those chosen by a novelist who has a number of devoted admirers, Ivy Compton-Burnett, for each is individual and yet related to all the others.

The authors were frank about their methods, notably in the Preface to volume 9 (Peake and Fleure, 1936) which they saw as 'the concluding volume of our chronological series' which

ends our walk down the corridors of time from the dawn of human life to the periods when written ideas and abstract thought spread far and wide. We have tried to weave into a connected story the facts observed by specialists, not hesitating to advance, in a tentative spirit, hypotheses that may be modified by further study. It seems to us that Grabner's doctrines of the diffusion of culture, and the theories of parallel evolution of culture in different lands, are both of value and that not infrequently both sets of factors are found acting together. Indeed, we think that culture contacts, except when involving complete destruction on one side or the other, have not only provided mutual enrichment by exchange, but have also stimulated fresh developments. Since such contacts have enabled some of the more active minds in the affected zone to rise out of their traditional prejudices, they have raised such minds to a level of objectivity that promotes freedom of thought. This has been a great stimulus to social and cultural development and a most essential tonic for the maintenance of social health.

And so the scene closes, for the two authors, with the transition to historic times in which 'abstract notions, especially in ethics and the underlying social motive power, begin their historic struggle for recognition . . . the day of religious propaganda had begun' (Peake and Fleure, 1936). In fact the struggle to control the hearts and minds of mankind has been a constant feature of human history operating behind all the outward circumstances that can be assessed, measured and recorded.

All this work was absorbing but could one believe it? Careful reading of the Peake and Fleure volumes makes it clear that the authors were feeling their way to an explanation rather than providing an explanation. They were writing at a time when archaeological evidence was accumulating rapidly and when archaeologists were concerned to show the nature of the environment in which people of past ages lived and worked. Gradually the concept that an archaeologist, or a historical geographer, must reconstruct past environments was accepted: it was inherent in the work of J. R. Green (p. 37) and it was a notable feature of Cyril Fox's *Archaeology of the Cambridge Region* (Cambridge 1923) and of J. G. D. Clark's fine works on the Mesolithic Age (Clark, 1932, 1936). In 1932 Fox's *Personality of Britain* was published by the National Museum of Wales and by the Press Board of the University of Wales and at once became widely successful. Although a short work of less than 100 (large) pages but with an abundance of illustrations, it provided a fine summary of the settlement of Britain from the earliest penetration to Roman times. Fox, in this work as in his previous study of 1923, showed that at various stages the inhabitants had occupied areas that were free from forest, such as chalk downlands, while others had their settlements beside rivers.

The main argument advanced was that Britain could be divided into a lowland and a highland zone, and that in the former new cultures soon became dominant while in the highland zone traditions were absorbed more gradually but more permanently (Fig. 12). In short there was more *unity* in the lowland zone, more *continuity* in the highland zone. The boundary between the two zones ran approximately from Teesmouth in Durham to Torquay in Devon. It bears a clear resemblance to the division between the two zones put forward by H. J. Mackinder in his book published in 1902 and in general corresponding to the boundary of the area floored by rocks of the Primary or Palaeozoic era and those of the Secondary (Mesozoic) and Tertiary eras. The aim of the 'brief Essay', the author explains, was 'to indicate the effect of the environment . . . on the distribution and fates of her inhabitants and her invaders', and there lies its fascination for a geographical reader, even if at times heavy generalisation was apparent. Surely, for example, it was misleading to regard the term 'highland zone' as adequate, when in fact much of the settlement within it was on coastal lowlands and the valleys by which it is penetrated? And if the idea of a highland zone is extended to Ireland on a basis of the age of the geological strata, only the extreme northeast is 'lowland' and all the rest, including the whole of the central lowland, is technically 'highland'. Nevertheless, the theories of Fox brought out very clearly the position of the English lowland as the area

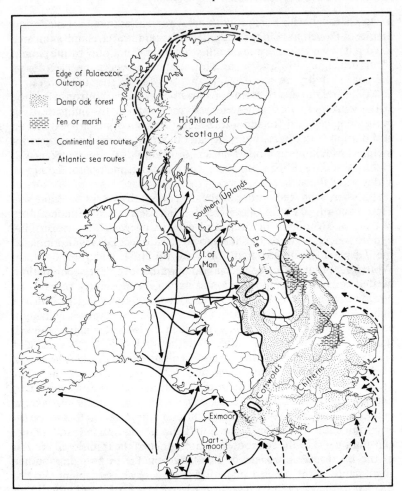

Fig. 12 The highland and the lowland.
Sir Cyril Fox's *Personality of Britain* was written partly as a guide to the excellently arranged archaeological section of the National Museum of Wales at Cardiff. His work showed a clear appreciation of the relationship between settlement and the physical environment and many geographers studied the new book with interest. Revised and modified later, it achieved a wide circulation. The division between highland and lowland Britain, shown here, was in line with the view of H. J. Mackinder, though Fox went further by arguing that essential cultural characteristics were associated with the lowland and the highland. The modern emphasis on 'diffusion' is really the same idea. It is interesting to observe that J. R. Green (cf. Fig. 3, p. 38) also had the idea of mapping woods and marshes in his studies of early settlement. Redrawn from map given in Fox, C., *The Personality of Britain* (Cardiff), 4th edn, 1943, opp. p. 28.

in closest touch with Europe, both before and after the emergence of the Straits of Dover and of the remainder of Britain, with Ireland, as an area having its own cultural individuality, populated not only by movement from the English lowland but also by immigrants who came by sea along the coasts of Britain and Ireland and even along the stormy western coasts of Ireland and Scotland. At least from the early Bronze Age the Atlantic routes were followed and there are many indications of movement between Ireland and Britain. Fox's work is crisply written and backed with interesting material, but strangely enough he does not mention Mackinder's (somewhat cautious) use of the terms 'highland' and 'lowland' (p. 81) nor the use of the term 'personality' for France by Vidal de la Blache.

To many who know little of the time when the works of Peake and Fleure and of Fox were eagerly read, it may seem that the geographers were then swimming in deep and even dangerous waters. But any hypothesis put forward was likely to be questioned: Fox, for example, in the *Personality* showed that the view of H. J. Fleure and W. E. Whitehouse that there had been a 'valleyward movement of population' needed considerable modification as in fact the movement revealed by new discoveries after 1916 was 'from poor soil to rich soil, from open or lightly forested land to densely forested land . . . it was a change in economic outlook, rather than a change in the level at which man lived' (p. 83). This same idea was inherent in the work of S. W. Wooldridge† (1900–63) and D. L. Linton† (1906–71) discussed on p. 126. The appeal of Fox's work lay in its revelation of where men lived in many prehistoric periods and of how their movements were influenced by natural barriers and natural routeways. Within its range it showed the adaptation of early settlers from different homelands to the varied environmental conditions found in Britain and Ireland and of the continuing use of the sea routes. It strengthened the traditional interest in the historical approach, or rather widened it by bringing out the significance of the prehistoric period in the story of settlement. And all this led to the view, so strongly argued by P. M. Roxby and others, that the homeland was an end-product, moulded by successive generations who had pastured flocks and herds, cleared woodlands, drained marshes and in countless other ways made and developed the landscape.

Man and the earth

The geographer's concern with the underlying problem of the relation of man and the earth was thoughtfully discussed in an address by P. M. Roxby who noted that the Ratzel school laid the main emphasis on the control of human activities by natural conditions, on the permanency of the stage, 'always the same and always situated at the same point in space' (Roxby, 1930). Vidal de la Blache and his followers laid considerable emphasis on 'the creative power of human groups to adapt themselves to and, within limits, to mould the natural environment, to leave their impression upon it, and thus in the course of generations to transform it, and give it a personality which is the outcome of the interaction'. Roxby commented on the detailed regional work of the French geographers and of many modern German geographers, including Hettner, whose work seemed to be animated in many cases by conceptions similar to those of Vidal de la Blache and the French school. And he was deeply appreciative of A. J. Herbertson ('my honoured master') whose work on natural regions was 'the work of a man who had deliberately trained himself for his task by severe discipline in many branches of analytical science'. To regard an area as 'always situated at the same point in space' is accurate in terms of latitude and longitude but in no other way for, as Mackinder had pointed out in 1902 (p. 81), the effective human position of Britain in the world was changed dramatically in the Age of Discovery. Human geography was concerned with the adjustment of human groups to their physical environment but also of their inter-regional relations, which obviously were subject to constant change.

Human geography was a term of recent origin in 1930 and 'liable to a more than ordinary degree of misconception'. In Roxby's view its four principal aspects were racial, economic, social and political. Well aware of the pitfalls of dealing with race, Roxby argued that racial geography was as much a part of the subject as geomorphology, for the geographer was closely concerned with the relationship of climate and other physical factors to race in a region. There were in the world some regions, such as China or the Mediterranean lands, where certain dominant racial types were in effective possession and any new racial element was unlikely to become significant: indeed these regions could almost be described as 'closed' human associations. But regions less densely, or even sparsely, settled such as tropical Australia, much of central and eastern Asia, Malaysia or southern Brazil, might perhaps be partially settled by immigrants having vastly different racial characteristics from the natives. Could one agree with General Smuts that the advance of the native African could only be achieved by introducing white settlers in the highlands of East Africa which stretch in an unbroken belt, hundreds of miles broad, from Kenya to South Africa? Clearly Roxby was on controversial ground, but he was not a man to be deterred by that. In fact discussion of white settlement in Africa and elsewhere was of interest to many geographers in the 1930s and, for example, was thoroughly discussed at the meetings of the Colonial Section during the Amsterdam Congress of 1938.

Economic geography in Roxby's view was inseparable from social geography and therefore meant much more than a mere study of products and manufactures. Based on the investigation of agriculture and industry and on the exchange of commodities – commercial geography as normally understood – it should be related to other aspects of human adjustment to the physical environment. On a world view there were nomadic, pastoral and other societies such as settled agriculturalists, all of which had evolved their own way of life that in varying degrees depended on trade. Through the centuries various societies had evolved some kind of equilibrium in relation to their environment, but problems arose for many of them 'so suddenly and so tragically drawn into the maelstrom of modern commerce'. Roxby may well have had a picture of some primitive societies that was kindly rather than realistic, but world commercial and political expansion had far-reaching effects. Some nations had made a profitable adjustment to changed economic circumstances, such as Denmark for whose achievement in co-operation Roxby had the warmest admiration. But the future of Africa appeared to raise many economic and social problems and a committee on the human geography of tropical Africa, set up by the British Association in 1926, was already collecting information from local African sources on its human geography. Roxby was chairman of this committee and A. G. Ogilvie the secretary: although its fruits were not remarkable on a superficial view, it gave direct or indirect encouragement to many people who were interested in research on Africa, of whom some, including S. J. K. Baker, presented papers at various conferences on their work. In time the African universities carried on this same work and a number of British geographers maintained friendly contacts with African colleagues.

Political geography was also in Roxby's view part of the responsibility of a human geographer. To him it was a source of endless fascination, to be followed by daily study of the Press and the radio: in short, a geographer must be a good citizen. He was clearly concerned by the dangers already apparent in the New Europe of Versailles and subsequent treaties, and appreciated the difficulty of defining states in which all 'geographical realities' could be acknowledged, for these included not only 'considerations of physical and economic geography' but also 'culture and language'. How could one define a state in which culturally related people would be included and in which at the same time there would be no interference with the flow of trade along natural entries or between regions economically interdependent? He feared the growth of a 'Mittel Europa' view among some German geographers and yet recognised the dangers confronting small states which, he suggested, could only survive in some form of a federation under the auspices of the League of Nations. Obviously this did not happen, but the various federations of European states for economic and defence purposes after the Second World War embody the same idea. Within states there could be local loyalties such as those to Kent or East Anglia, but these were merged in a wider national patriotism. Like Mackinder and – more recently – C. B. Fawcett (p. 135), Roxby saw that the county boundaries in Britain were obsolete and suggested that they might be superseded by larger administrative entities more in harmony with the modern economic regions of the country.

Human geography as Roxby viewed it was a study of great breadth, for it included all that has been discussed in a historical as well as a contemporary setting. And it also involved detailed study of the entire world and of co-operation between historians and geographers. There would be, in Roxby's view, the development of specialist studies on various parts of the world on a regional basis as well as on the various systematic aspects such as geomorphology, climatology or economic geography. That Roxby apparently regarded regional studies as more likely to be fruitful does not mean that he condemned systematic studies. In fact he was tolerant of differences between one department of geography and another. Unfortunately he did not live long enough to see the vast expansion of the universities that followed the Second World War, but Fleure did and in various speeches towards the close of his life he made it clear that he was happy to see many new developments in the subject. By the 1930s there were many ideas in active circulation, and the test of their validity could come only by detailed research for it was not possible to live permanently in a state of euphoric expectation that light would dawn without it.

Whatever criticism might be made of the broad sweeping judgements, the reliance on eloquently presented hypotheses – even it seemed on intuition – of the time, the plain fact is that much of the teaching given in the early years of the honours schools in Britain was attractive to the students. It opened a new and vivid world scene, in which the geographical influence on historical progress seemed to be, if not compelling, at least crucial. And the emphasis on societies and their development through prehistoric into historic times appeared to be the culmination of an evolution that, in its geological aspects, had been emphasised in Darwinian thought. Naturally this led at least some students to speculate and argue on such matters as the relation of science and religion, or on issues of international politics such as the hope that the League of Nations could achieve a world human unity of purpose that could result in peace. Behind all this lay the view that human enterprise had opened the world as never before in history and that it should be possible for prosperity to become widespread. Phrases like 'unity in diversity' matched with 'diversity in unity' appeared to have a deep significance, for they implied that all men could contribute to the common good. To those who enjoyed the stimulus of large ideas it was a golden time. But the prospects of a golden age were never bright and by the early 1930s they had diminished almost to extinction with the spread of unemployment and economic depression through Europe and America, the decline of world trade and the consequent increase of tension, largely through economic circumstances, among minority communities in Europe who could be persuaded that their difficulties were due to the injustice of the Treaty of Versailles. By the middle 1930s many students of Europe were convinced that the danger of war was grave and inexorably the progress towards the Second World War became clear. Nevertheless the work of the universities continued, with the salutary realisation that after 1918 the Allied nations had won the war and then failed to win the peace.

Chapter 7

Specialism in the inter-war period

To give a world view was a major aim of geography teaching during the inter-war period, in universities, colleges and schools. The world had been revealed by discovery, mapping, economic penetration, the accretion of empires and – for the student – even the publication of textbooks on its continents for use in classrooms. Underlying the wish to know the whole world was the Darwinian emphasis on the unity of nature and the so-called 'social Darwinism' of Herbert Spencer, crudely represented as the 'survival of the fittest' in the evolutionary struggle. The League of Nations was seen as a means of fostering human unity and avoiding devastating world conflicts. Only with world peace could economic progress be assured on a long-term basis and this inevitably depended on the growth of understanding between peoples of different cultures and traditions. The scientific advances of the previous century had meant that areas of the world had been developed as never before, many of them by migrants who became permanent settlers creating new societies of growing economic power, conspicuously in the United States and Canada, but similarly in South Africa, in the Atlas lands of Africa, in Siberia by the Russians, in South America and in Australia and New Zealand. Industrialisation had transformed the life of many countries, especially in Europe but not less in Japan. Geographers were living in a time of opportunity, for they could offer knowledge of many parts of the world in their regional work, to be maligned at a later time for an inadequacy that was to some extent inevitable. There were, however, many contributions of value to an understanding of the world, for it was realised that detailed study, regional or systematic, must be the basis of generalisation.

The trouble was that much generalisation was based on inadequate foundations. This meant that the contributions of systematic geographers became of immense significance. Geomorphologists sought an explanation of the physical environment more satisfying than its elementary regionalisation; climatologists – though hampered by inadequate data – sought more understanding of the exceptional as well as the general characteristics of the seasons affecting people not only in agriculture but also in other aspects of experience; historical geographers sought to explain how the human environment had evolved, using period studies as one method likely to be productive; economic geographers considered various industries, power supply, mining, farming and other activities as basic to the support of human communities, many of them much more aware of the social welfare of people than is believed by some geographers of a later time. In the systematic aspects of geography, the possibilities of research were apparently endless and the view – sometimes aggressively expressed – that regional geography had failed to be academically satisfying arose from the disillusion with its broad generalisations that came naturally to workers specialising in detailed studies.

In this chapter consideration is given to studies of a detailed character by geographers in the twenty years of the inter-war period and the story finishes with the first clear indications of the use of geographical material in replanning Britain. All through this period the breadth of views described in Chapter 6 impelled some scholars (and others) in various subjects to ask whether such vast aspirations were in fact practicable. Could one, for example, range over all human history or over all the world distribution of population or of climate or landforms, or – as Mackinder attempted to do – over global strategy in peace and war, or again with Fleure, over archaeology and anthropology as well as of geography and even sociology, except by making superficial judgements and intuitive generalisations? Uncertainty arose too about what Carl Sauer has called 'the attempt to devise a natural science of the human environment' in which, he notes, the relationship was 'gradually softened from the term "control" to "influence" or "adaptation" or "adjustment", and finally to the somewhat liturgical "response"' (Sauer, 1941). In general, however, geographers did more to show the value of their work by doing it than by arguing about it, and for many of them the first and most obvious need was to go out into the field and see for themselves. But see what? The ability to observe is not in itself a natural endowment, even of geographers, and actual training in fieldwork can only train a student to observe for himself. In some universities this was so inadequate that one had to rely on one's own physical and intellectual stamina. But some of the most interesting detailed contributions to geography of this time were obviously based largely on fieldwork: they are now considered under the broad headings of physical, historical, regional and human geography.

Physical geography

Vigorous personalities found great satisfaction in the study of physical geography at this time, including geomorphology, climatology and – to a regrettably lesser extent – biogeography. Before the Second World War there was little sign that physical geography might be left to the geologists, as it had been by some American geographers, for the essential connection of geography with the field sciences was widely accepted. More controversial was the type of physical geography to be studied, for some geographers in their regional writings apparently thought that physical geography was merely a summary treatment of the geological history of the area they were studying. To others an analysis of existing landforms was the first stage of enquiry and observation, but only the first stage, as from what could be seen, photographed, mapped, mathematically analysed, inferences would be drawn on the origin and evolution of the physical landscape. As so many geomorphological processes take thousands or even millions of years to show any perceptible results, special interest was centred on processes that could show developments over a few years, or even months, such as changes in sand dunes and other coastal features. For this reason the work of the Cambridge University Field Laboratory – beside Scolt Head Island on the north coast of Norfolk – from 1930, was of special interest (Steers, 1934). Glaciation, studied in various countries outside Britain, also showed the impermanence of physical phenomena as glaciers and ice-sheets retreated – or advanced – but as in Britain there was no permanent snow except possibly for a few patches on Ben Nevis the interest of studying glaciation lay in discerning how it had moulded the British landscape and that of Ireland. The question that geomorphological workers tried to solve was why the landscape had its present form, and in fact such an analysis proved to be fruitful in regional study for many glacial landforms had influenced the pattern of fields, roads or railways, and the soils derived from drifts had particular qualities that were of obvious agricultural significance. Larger questions such as the distribution of peneplanes or surfaces of erosion inevitably involved geological history for their explanation though their mere recognition was itself an advance in the analysis of the physical landscape: not for one moment could the devoted geomorphologists of the time be satisfied with mere recognition.

Of the various detailed studies made during the inter-war period, those on coastlines had a special appeal, both to people with an interest in field sciences and to those who could merely claim to be naturalists or bird watchers. There are also periodical scares about coastal erosion, usually due to sensational newspaper reports with dramatic illustrations, for few people realise that the country's area is expanding rather than contracting due to reclamation of marshlands or of mud-flats in river estuaries. Material of some significance was published in the reports of the Royal Commission on Coast Erosion, of 1907, and twenty years later J. A. Steers gave the first of several papers on 'The East Anglian coast' based on four years' study (Steers, 1927).

In the discussion following the presentation of the paper at the Royal Geographical Society, Professor F. W. Oliver said that: 'It is a singular thing that Mr Steers should be the first person who has ever, to my knowledge visited Blakeney Point for study other than as a bird man, a botanist, or a biologist.' He goes on to express the view that 'geological colleagues' might advantageously have done so to see physical processes in action but they declined and 'continued to bore holes in the ground'. How the varied forms evolved was controversial, but at least the problem of the influence of longshore currents and of weather conditions could be experimentally observed as it was in later years, especially by a succession of workers on the north Norfolk coast. In 1934 J. A. Steers edited a book on Scolt Head Island which gathered together observations by a variety of workers (Steers, 1934). To the coastal geomorphologist, and indeed to others, this book provides fascinating reading, but here one can merely note that for the geographer, as indeed for the student of marine fauna and flora, an analysis of one coastal area in detail over a considerable number of years was of value as a commentary on the generalisations available in standard texts, of which D. W. Johnson's *Shorelines and Shoreline Development* (New York, 1919) was the main general contribution on coasts.

Controversy is the meat and drink of geomorphologists, as those who read the discussions that followed the presentation of papers to the Royal Geographical Society will appreciate. Several were written by W. V. Lewis† (1907–61), of which the first (Lewis, 1931) dealt with 'the more important shingle formations' of the south coast of England and especially with Hurst Castle spit and Chesil beach, on which Lewis collected data never published owing to his early death. Later papers dealt with Dungeness foreland (Lewis, 1932; Lewis and Balchin, 1940). This area has been built out mainly since Neolithic times and that there had been considerable reclamation of land at least from the eighth century and probably from Roman times as the sea-level then was 5 to 6 ft lower than now. Changes of sea-level were also noted in a study of the Culbin Sands by J. A. Steers (Steers, 1937) but there, as on other coasts, the vast erosive power of sudden storms such as that of 1694–5 had become a legend perhaps exaggerated in terms of actual physical geography.

Another study followed up by later work was based on observations of the Lancashire coast from Southport to the Liverpool dock belt by R. K. Gresswell (1905–69) (Gresswell, 1937; 1953). Partly concerned with the sand dunes, this paper also contains material on the wave-like form caused by a number of undulations on the foreshore: this probably seemed at the time to be merely a piece of interesting observation, but in fact it proved to be of military significance, for when the invasion of continental Europe was planned observations were made of the development of beach ridges as they were known to be a possible danger to landing craft. Study of the coast carried out as a purely geomorphological investigation has considerable relevance to a variety of human affairs, including the preservation of beaches at resorts and the provision of access for the public who, for example in southwest Lancashire, had accelerated some of the dune movement by preventing the growth of stabilising vegetation. In time, especially through the work of J. A. Steers and Vaughan Cornish, the need to control coastal development by deliberate planning became appreciated (Goudie, 1972).

Interest in the long-term evolution of landscape was shown in a number of papers during the inter-war period, for field studies revealed many surfaces of erosion, or peneplanes, in various countries (Beckinsale, 1972): at the Cairo Congress of the International Geographical Union in 1925 a commission was appointed to study Pliocene and Pleistocene terraces, and at the Paris Congress in 1931 a further commission on the mapping of erosion surfaces was added. These two commissions were combined at the Washington Congress of 1952 and the new commission, on erosion surfaces around the Atlantic, was terminated at the London Congress of 1964. In Britain various geologists had commented on the form of landscapes and made suggestions about former river courses (as indeed Mackinder did in his *Britain and the British Seas* of 1902), though the main inspiration came from American workers, notably W. M. Davis and D. W. Johnson, whose *Stream Structure on the Atlantic Slope* (1931) was hailed as 'the great masterpiece of denudational chronology'.

Surfaces of erosion were regarded by some workers as an essential key to regional geography: for example, A. G. Ogilvie, in his essay on central Scotland in the 1928 volume, *Great Britain: essays in regional geography*, recognises four surfaces: plains of raised beach and alluvium; the 'lower lowland' peneplane; the 'higher lowland' peneplain; and finally the upland plateaus. Of the two lowland peneplanes, the lower lies mainly between 100 ft and 500 ft and the higher between 500 ft and 750 ft though over the east coast it falls to 400 ft and around the hills rises to slightly above 1,000 ft. Ogilvie, however, regarded this work as tentative only, as a hypothesis to be tested by further research, but it certainly provided a splendid underpinning to his essay on regional geography, especially as the surfaces are clearly visible in the area. Nevertheless many questions remain. Many rivers have curious courses, explicable only by elucidating their geological history as well as the Pleistocene history, and the varied resistance offered to erosion by different rocks – by no means a simple matter of 'hardness' and 'softness' as people frequently supposed (p. 59) – posed further problems, even though W. M. Davis postulated that a peneplane could equally truncate rocks of varying resistance to erosion (Davis, 1899). He said that 'whatever the uplifts of youth, whatever the disorder and hardness of the rocks, an almost featureless plain (a peneplain), showing little sympathy with structure, and controlled only by a close approach of base-level, must characterize the penultimate stage of the uninterrupted cycle; and the ultimate stage would be a plain without relief'.

Erosion surfaces in the lowland area of South Wales appeared to exist at levels of 600 ft, 400 ft and 200 ft and at similar altitudes in south and central Ireland where, however, they are in many areas marked by drift deposits of varying depth. A. A. Miller† (1900–68) worked on Pembrokeshire and Carmarthenshire and agreed in general, though not in detail (Miller, 1937), with K. L. Goskar and A. E. Trueman who had published a paper on the 'coastal plateaux' of South Wales (Goskar and

Trueman, 1934). In his paper, Miller reaches the view that the 'so-called 600 ft platform' owed its form mainly to subaerial erosion, having been graded to a 400 ft sea-level, which had remained constant for a considerable time, producing a widespread erosion surface and cliffing the coastline which lay to the north. The sea-level then fell gradually to 200 ft and the rivers extended their courses over the emerged coastal plain and cut it up into isolated plateaux. Later the sea fell abruptly to a level below that of the present day and later rose, making estuaries and drowning river valleys. And throughout this time the cliffs that so notable a feature of South Wales developed. The surfaces of erosion seen in South Wales appeared to be similar to those in Cornwall and in the south of Ireland, but this was not unexpected as the Irish Sea was a feature of no great geological antiquity and both Britain and Ireland lay within the same geological province of Europe.

What Ireland possessed to a remarkable degree, however, was a series of east–west ranges of mountains and ridges in the south and southwest, finishing in a series of peninsulas battered by Atlantic gales. This exceptionally fine area of Armorican folding, in which generally the Devonian Old Red Sandstone formed the uplands (though with inliers of lower ground marked out in older and less resistant rocks) and Carboniferous shales and limestones occurred in the valleys, appeared to offer a fine example of anticlinal ridges and synclinal valleys drained by rivers that flowed securely through their valleys and then turned sharply at right angles to cut gorge-like passages in the anticlinal ridges. The relation of these river courses to the physical layout of the country had inspired the famous Jukes paper of 1862, notable for its use of 'consequent' for streams developed on an initial surface and 'subsequent' for those that emerged in valleys worked out in less resistant rocks through long-continued erosion (Jukes, 1862). In the south of Ireland the original consequent drainage probably developed on an initial Cretaceous surface since removed by denudation. These original consequent lines are seen in the courses of some existing rivers such as the upper Suir, and in the north–south reaches of the Blackwater, Lee and other rivers further south, though the subsequent rivers in the Carboniferous Limestone valleys have become the major drainage features.

In 1939 A. A. Miller published a paper in which he accepted the main lines of Jukes's argument that the original consequent drainage was from north to south in Kerry and Cork and from northwest to southeast in Waterford and Wexford (Miller, 1939). Many detailed local observations in Miller's paper are of interest, such as the possible sequence of events which led to the development of the remarkable 'elbow of capture' in the river Suir's course. To Jukes later workers owe the concept of 'antecedent' drainage by which a river may retain in part, if not in entirety, its course through many periods of geological history. Theorising about the past course of rivers had obvious fascination for a number of workers and the special problems of Scotland were studied by

D. L. Linton with interesting results (Linton, 1933, 1934, 1940). But it is a complex subject and may well involve the entire history of the Tertiary era, not to mention the earlier changes in the distribution of land and sea.

S. W. Wooldridge, in collaboration with others, gave some fascinating contributions on southeast England including the London basin which showed the relation of geomorphology to human settlement, especially in the Saxon period. Of these the first, written with D. J. Smetham in 1931, was a study of the drifts of Essex and Hertfordshire based primarily on fieldwork (Wooldridge and Smetham, 1931). The argument is that the area covered with London Clay offered such difficulties for agricultural settlement that both the Romans and the Saxons in their early period found the drift-covered areas more attractive, though as expansion continued there was some occupation of the London Clay areas. Much of the argument is based on place-name evidence. In 1933 S. W. Wooldridge with D. L. Linton challenged the views of some archaeologists on the early settlement of England in both prehistoric and early historical times (Wooldridge and Linton, 1933) and showed that certain soils, notably the loam-terrains, were favoured; Saxon settlement was further considered by the same two authors in a paper published two years later (Wooldridge and Linton, 1935). All this, with much more basic work on geomorphology, was treated in one of the six monographs published by the Institute of British Geographers before its inevitable but regrettable virtual suspension during the Second World War. *Structure, Surface and Drainage in South-east England* (1939) rests on an analysis of Tertiary geology and shows the significance of various geological outliers such as those of Pliocene age on the North Downs or deposits of glacial origin further north. For many readers the interest of this monograph, in time sold out and republished, lies in the geomorphological methods employed, but it is obviously of deep significance as a basis for regional and human geography, as its authors argue in their final paragraph from which these comments are extracted.

It would be possible to multiply almost without number, and certainly without profit, individual instances of correlation between physical history, land-form, and human use or occupancy. But the case for a thorough study of landscape evolution must rest on broader grounds than these. The terrain must be appreciated as a complex *whole* before we can hope to perceive the nature of its reactions with man. . . . Our study of the general Land–Man relationship must surely take account not only of the qualities and differences of land realized in the present, but also those operative in past phases and potential in respect of the future.

Interest in the former distribution of woodland, fen and marsh was abundant during the inter-war period and the work of J. R. Green (pp. 37–40) was admired, not for its accuracy but for its pioneer quality. The *Map of Roman Britain* published by the Ordnance Survey, followed by the map of *Britain in the Dark Ages*, included information on the distribution of vegetation, some of it heavily criticised in the work of Wooldridge and Linton (1933, 1935). R. G. Collingwood and J. N. L. Myres, in *Roman Britain and the English Settlements* (Oxford, 1936) include several maps showing distributions of places and finds in relation to the presumed vegetation of the time, and similar correlations appear in the works of Cyril Fox, *Archaeology of the Cambridge Region* (Cambridge, 1923) and *The Personality of Britain*, first published in 1932 at Cardiff and reissued several times since (P. 114). Consideration of the conditions of the time is also seen in the fine works of J. G. D. Clark on the Mesolithic era (Clark, 1932, 1936). Recreation of contemporary environments became a favoured enterprise among archaeologists. It was, however, not only in long-past ages that the relationship between settlement and physical environment could be discerned, as Alice Garnett convincingly showed in work now to be considered.

Visitors to the Alps often comment on the apparently incomprehensible siting of pastures and crops, with vines clinging to precipitous and high-lying fields. The contrast between the *adret* or sunny south-facing and the *ubac*, a commonplace of geographical writing, is clear in many valleys, but this is merely a generalisation that has normally been illustrated by a few well-chosen examples. In the 1930s Alice Garnett carried out several field investigations in the Alps, including the Val d'Anniviers oriented from north to south, and also in various Austrian valleys oriented in differing directions (Garnett, 1935; 1937). Shadow areas were mapped at hourly intervals for the midwinter solstice and for the equinoxes and these, with other climatic data, were related to field observations on crops, pastures and other vegetation. The conclusions with some suggestions for further research are of great interest. Each valley is an individual unit having a variety of climatic units, affected by the chance position of distant peaks and ridges, or of local shoulders in relation to the form of valleys or the direction in which the valleys are set within the relief as a whole. The Val d'Anniviers, for example, has areas where cereals ripen up to 1,900 m near St. Luc and Chandolin, but these have 90–100 per cent exposure to sunlight at the equinoxes: at much lower altitudes with exposures of less than 50 per cent almost all the land is left to forest or alpine pastures, according to altitude. Duration of sunlight appears to be of more significance than intensity, and early morning or late afternoon shafts of sunlight may be advantageous to growth, especially as the most rapid increase in the rate of assimilation takes place with the gradual increase of weak light values, that is when sun altitudes are low. The assimilation curve flattens when high sunlight intensity is reached so there are obvious disadvantages to plant development and assimilation processes in a site robbed of weak direct sunlight until the sun has risen high in the sky, or a site from which the sunlight in the late afternoon is suddenly cut off. Dr Garnett's monograph contains many other fascinating observations and has often been in the present author's mind during mountain holidays in Switzerland and even in England: certainly it is notable that at Findelen, above Zermatt, cereals are grown at 2,100 m, the highest in the Alps, while on the opposite site of the valley there is tundra vegetation. Within 1 km there is a contrast equivalent to a 30–40° range of latitude. And in Val d'Anniviers the complex land use obviously needed some explanation of the type given by Garnett even though many of the mountain pastures were no longer used by 1973 (personal observation).

Unfortunately, few contributions of note were made to biogeography at this time by geographers, possibly because few of them had an adequate knowledge of botany. This was perhaps a source of regret, though the progress made in the study and mapping of vegetation was made clear by the publication in 1939 of A. G. Tansley's *The British Islands and their Vegetation* at Cambridge. Sir Arthur Tansley's book gathered into some 900 pages the fruits of a lifetime's work in what had become known as plant ecology, some of it published in the *Journal of Ecology*. Readers of this classic work will see that the debt to geographical studies is fully acknowledged, and it is also good to see a generous acknowledgement to a fine but much neglected book, E. G. Bilham, *The Climate of the British Isles* (London, 1938). That the study of plant geography in its entirety involved the study of the whole environment in the field is made abundantly clear in Tansley's writing. It involves not only climatology, but microclimatology, that is the study of the habitat of each individual plant, in association with other plants. Indeed the idea of plant associations, and of the evolution of vegetation through the changes and chances experienced in time to a climax association that might never be achieved, gave fascination to this study.

In practice, as E. W. Fenton showed in his study of Boghall Glen in the Pentlands, the existing vegetation had been greatly influenced by human activity, notably by using the valley for grazing sheep instead of cattle or by burning the vegetation to encourage new growth, in some cases with disastrous results as the peaty soil might be partially or even completely destroyed and erosion may ensue (Fenton, 1933). That many areas of peat on mountains in Britain and Ireland are showing rapid disintegration is well known to those who climb them, but the full explanation is controversial. Behind Tansley's work, and that of various plant geographers who were pioneers in such studies as R. Smith (pp. 61–2), W. G. Smith (p. 85) C. E. Moss (p. 86) and others, lay the view that environment must be studied as a whole, in its physical and human aspects. Behind it also was the concept of the evolutionary process in which all life is in association, having at one and the same time its individuality and its place in a community, even at the humblest levels of flora and fauna.

Historical geography

For much of the inter-war period in Britain geography was closely allied to history. Several of the teachers of the subject had graduated in history and the inspiration of the French school of geographers, especially through the work of the Vidal de la Blache, was strongly felt in a country where French was normally the second language. The emphasis of many French geographers on the long-continued evolution of the human landscape had an instant and challenging appeal. Europe had cities of Roman origin, built, destroyed and rebuilt through many centuries, rural landscapes tamed and developed by the patient work of engineers and farmers, lands wrested from the sea and attacked by it in catastrophic storms, ports that had silted up while others had risen to greatness: it needed little imagination, though more than many British geographers possessed, to experience the appeal of history in the towns and the countryside of Europe. And to many this gave an immediate challenge to unravel the story of the evolution of so fascinating a human landscape. But the task was not easy.

In 1932, E. W. Gilbert wrote a paper which summarised the meanings – for there were several – of historical geography (Gilbert, 1932). These fell into five main categories, of which the first was followed by E. A. Freeman (p. 37), the historian whose concern was to show the boundaries and the territorial expanse of states that had existed in the past. This was obviously a useful service, if limited in aim. The second purpose, especially associated in England with the Hakluyt Society, was to study the history of geographical discovery and exploration. This included much material of high literary quality and very considerable interest, not only geographically but historically, and led some geographers, notably E. G. R. Taylor into fascinating if somewhat esoteric studies such as the history of navigation. Obviously it is the type of study that will appeal only to a limited number of people, but it demands austere standards of scholarship and is generally of great significance to students of the historical geography of many areas of the world. For student use, a text on the history of discovery was published by J. N. L. Baker† (1893–1971) (Baker, 1931). The third need is to study the history of geography itself, which obviously needs no defence as other subjects recognise a comparable need to review their own distinct contribution to the history of learning. In the case of geography there is the attraction to many people of the history of cartography, including both maps and surveying instruments, and also of the concepts of writers in many periods of history. Reference has been made on pp. 36-7 to the work of E. H. Bunbury, and during the inter-war period a major contribution was the two works on Tudor and Stuart geography by E. G. R. Taylor (Taylor, 1930, 1934).

There was also a searching for an assessment of the influence of geographical environment on the course of history, which Gilbert notes as the fourth line of enquiry. This led in many courses to the cult of the large idea, even of sweeping generalisations in some cases such as those discussed on pp. 108-19. But the courses of the time given on topics labelled 'human', 'historical' or in other broad terms, were certainly interesting and induced students to think of world human problems and to discuss argumentatively such issues as the climatic determinism of

Ellsworth Huntington, the 'environmental' determinism of Ellen Churchill Semple or even the 'stop-and-go' determinism of Griffith Taylor as compared with the 'possibilism' which Lucien Febvre recognised in the work of Vidal de la Blache. Emotive phrases like 'geographical control' were in circulation and the global strategy of H. J. Mackinder stimulated considerable thought on political geography. Much of this came from a desire to understand the world, meaning the whole world and perhaps the sheer impossibility of doing so should not condemn well-intentioned and high-minded effort. But it was the fifth and the last theme of Gilbert's paper, 'the reconstruction of the regional geography of the past', that called forth a response of immense significance, now to be briefly considered.

The publication of fourteen essays in a volume edited by H. C. Darby, *An Historical Geography of England before A.D. 1800* (Cambridge, 1936) was widely welcomed. Though the eleven authors adopted different methods of approach, partly conditioned by the nature of their material and of the periods on which they wrote, in general the pattern followed was in accord with that suggested by Gilbert. Seventeen years later, Darby pointed out that this was not the only possible approach for the data could have been organised 'not in terms of horizontal cross-sections but vertical themes – the clearing of the wood, the draining of the marsh, the reclamation of the heathlands, changes in settlement, and so on ... both (methods) ... are permissible, and even desirable' (Darby, 1953, p. 8). Neither the 'vertical' nor the 'horizontal' method gives a whole developing picture but either could be helpful. On the relation of economic history and historical geography, Darby comments that if economic change is part of historical study, than the treatment of it is historical: similarly if an understanding of landscape is part of geographical study, then the treatment of it must be geographical. But many – certainly the present author – would agree with Darby's view that tariff walls around academic subjects are unnecessary and unprofitable, especially as so many fascinating research enquiries lie in borderlands. The difficulty, however, at times has been that geographers have underplayed their hand by leaning too heavily on the material provided by historians and saying little of the landscape as it existed at any particular period.

That the reconstruction of past landscapes is a difficult task needs no emphasis. For recent periods, in effect from Victorian times, Ordnance maps give material capable of careful analysis that is at least a contribution to the reconstruction of the landscape, but for earlier periods maps give far less definite information, though more than is perhaps commonly supposed. Analysis of soils, of former river courses, of topographical detail, of accounts of agricultural activity, forest planting or clearing, the observation of travellers, and much more in contemporary records – all may be of assistance. Already by the inter-war period the value of air photographs in showing former field boundaries and other long-hidden features of past landscapes was demonstrated. In one of the two essays he wrote in the 1936 book, H. C. Darby showed how the Fenlands had been drained and brought to their great agricultural productivity and this theme was further developed in two books (Darby, 1940a, b). Meanwhile the study of Domesday Book by Darby and others, eventually to be published in a series of volumes, from 1952–1975 had begun. For the Roman period, excellent material was available, as E. W. Gilbert showed in his essays; and for Anglo-Saxon times S. W. Wooldridge used place-name evidence and detailed topographical work to demonstrate the distribution of population. Wooldridge quotes with approval the statement of J. R. Green in 1882 that: 'The ground itself, where we can read the information it affords, is . . . the fullest and most certain of documents. Physical geography has still its part to play in the written record of that human history to which it gives so much of its shape and form' (Green, 1882, vol. 1, vii in 1897 edn). That many of the landscape reconstructions of Green, and much of his history, have been proved to be wrong does not mean that his aims are also to be dismissed as wrong-headed. Happily, place-name study has steadily advanced and it is interesting to note that the acknowledged international expert of the time, Eilert Eikwall, contributed an essay on the Scandinavian settlement of England to Darby's (1936) volume. E. G. R. Taylor contributed two essays on Tudor England, based partly on the work of John Leland, who died in 1552, and William Camden, born about the time that Leland died, who travelled widely through the country in the last thirty years of the reign of Queen Elizabeth I (1558–1603). Literary sources may reveal an observant traveller's critical appreciation of a landscape, its farming and towns, and almost always its roads: such works may be artless in that they record what was well known at the time of writing. Centuries later they may evoke a vanished world. Wherever possible one source should be checked against another: before the age of exact topography maps provided only a limited measure of certainty, but from the nineteenth century they are splendid source materials, not always adequately appreciated.

Other travellers who left material of considerable interest include Arthur Young (1741–1820) who appears to have been in a state of almost perpetual motion for some forty years from 1767 (partly to escape from Mrs Young) when the first of his numerous works appeared. Essentially he was an agricultural reformer and it matters little that his own efforts at farming had been unsuccessful or that, as A. W. Hutton pointed out in the introduction to his edition of Young's Irish travels, his writing is 'too artless to allow his works a place in literature as such'. Though it adds to the value of his writing for posterity, it may discourage some readers to find that 'he is apt to intercalate, even into his most brilliant passages, statistics relating to such homely details as manures' (Young, 1770; Hutton, 1892, xi). And there are many fascinating contemporary sources, including the *Tour Through the Whole Island of Great Britain, 1724–7* of Daniel Defoe (Cole, 1929) – to be used with caution no doubt but nevertheless of value. The final essay of Darby's (1936) volume, O. H. K. Spate on 'The growth of London, A.D. 1660–1800', has been widely praised for its content and presentation. In this case material was abundant, almost embarrassingly so, and included some fine maps produced by cartographers and published by commercial firms of the time. W. G. East's essay on England in the eighteenth century ends with the statistical material available in the 1801 Census, clearly more reliable than the various estimates of population that are given in the book for earlier times. It is strange that comparatively little was written on the historical geography of the nineteenth century until recently. So much source material exists and not all geographers would willingly accept H. C. Darby's comment (in 1936) that 'the geography of the nineteenth century has been covered in certain chapters of Dr Clapham's *Economic History of Great Britain*' (Clapham, 1926–38). In fact, the *New Historical Geography of England* (Cambridge, 1973) includes important contributions on the nineteenth century (p. 183).

Regional and human geography

As the teaching of geography developed in the universities, many students in the honours schools wrote essays based on fieldwork covering areas of varying extent, in some cases of 50 or more square miles. There were undergraduate exercises through which many students discovered the problems of fieldwork and its presentation. Generally the pattern was to give an account of the structure, physical features, climate, vegetation, historical development, agriculture, industries, communications, rural and urban settlement. To many students of a later time this will seem to be a laudable enterprise but one of superhuman ambition, so that inevitably much of the material would be superficial, derived uncritically from the work of others, or even irrelevant. But the aim was to show man in his relation to environment and at least such exercise made students appreciate the complexity of the environment. In the geographical journals, notably the Scottish journal, interesting local studies were published, dealing with small areas. Many British geographers looked enviously to France, where the regional monographs written as exercises for higher degrees included some work of admirable quality and where Vidal de la Blache's *Tableau de la géographie de la France* (1903) had shown the relationship between agricultural life and the physical landscape vividly and convincingly. British geographers who read it carefully would probably agree with the remark of Philippe Pinchemel that the *Tableau* is 'a masterpiece which will never be superseded'.

A challenge to produce a regional geography of Britain, in some detail, came in 1926 when the National Committee decided to issue a volume of essays for the International Congress of 1928 in Cambridge: this appeared as *Great Britain: essays in regional geography* by twenty-six authors, edited by A. G. Ogilvie and was a book of almost 500 pages.

There are two general chapters, one dealing evocatively with landscape and agriculture by Sir E. John Russell, who was then director of the Rothamsted Experimental (Agricultural) Station (see also p. 86) and another on climate by H. R. Mill, who had been for many years director of the British Rainfall Organisation, on the climate of Great Britain. No summary of the whole was given, nor was any map provided of the bounds of the various regions as some of the boundaries were 'quite arbitrary', 'open to criticism' and 'would mislead' if used in 'elementary text-books'. Oddly enough the Isle of Axholme was discussed twice, in chapters on Lincolnshire and on the South Yorkshire coalfield. For the student of the time the regional essays of this volume gave a far clearer picture of Britain than anything available before. With few exceptions the essays were written by university teachers on the areas in which they worked. No standard method of presentation was adopted, though in general there was a conscious effort to show how features of the human landscape were related to physical features. Two contributions differing greatly in method of presentation by A. G. Ogilvie and H. J. Fleure have been discussed on pp. 110 and 124.

One of the more successful essays, by P. M. Roxby on East Anglia, showed that a clear relationship existed between the various 'sub-regions', each with their distinctive type of soil, and agriculture, though this had been gradually developed as economic circumstances had changed. The 'great increase of regional specialisation made possible by the Agrarian Revolution' (from the eighteenth century), Roxby notes, is 'strikingly shown . . . by the varied response of the different sub-regions within East Anglia'. In other words, the modern demand for farm produce may induce farmers to specialise in such a way that the agricultural landscape reflects the physical qualities of the soil more and more, however great may be the unifying effects of scientific fertilisation and the introduction of new crops. Roxby conceded that further adjustments to economic demand would be necessary, for when he wrote the import of cheap grain and meat had (as indeed since 1875) been unfavourable to the East Anglian farmer but there were already signs of a transfer of activity to dairying and experiments were in progress on growing sugar-beet. A great admirer of Denmark, Roxby suggested that a development of intensive dairying with feedstuffs grown on the farms might be profitable. Another stimulating essay, which owed much to its illustrations, by C. C. Fagg and G. E. Hutchings on the southeast showed that there 'physiography, varied vegetation, and history as a human environment are very definitely related to its geological structure'. A brief essay by F. Debenham gives a fascinating picture of the Fenlands, on which further light was shed later by H. C. Darby (p. 131). Some of the essays in this 1928 volume were far less successful than those mentioned here, and possibly this illustrates the view that the writing of regional geography demands an artistic appreciation of landscape combined with the ability to select from a mass of materials those that are of relevance to its life.

North
England

Yorkshire

Lancashire

Peakdon

Trent

W
a
l
e
s

East

Severn

Central
England

Anglia

Bristol

London

Wessex

Devon

Boundaries of
Administrative
Counties

0   50
Miles

Nothing is easier than denigration of regional geography, and it would be easy to describe one's agonising efforts to become interested in some of the standard regional texts of the 1920s that, reread, seem even worse now than they did then. Oddly enough some generally forgotten books stand out as offering some light in darkness, notably S. W. Rider and A. E. Trueman's short but vivid *South Wales* (London, 1929) and a few other works that dealt with part of Great Britain. Though not written as a regional text, C. B. Fawcett, *The Provinces of England* (London, 1919, reissued in 1960) introduced ideas of regional 'devolution' (Fig. 13). This idea was not new, and had in fact been suggested for France by Vidal de la Blache as early as 1910 (Vidal de la Blache, 1910; *Geogr. Rev.* **7**, 1919, pp. 114–18), but at the time it seemed to be an interesting if unlikely development, though the idea was revived when the need for a new administrative structure was considered by a Royal Commission in the 1960s (p. 177). Another piece of work by C. B. Fawcett on the conurbations of Great Britain, published in 1932, recognised the significance of the major towns and especially those that had grown into one another to provide a continuously urban area (Fawcett, 1932). Just as J. F. Unstead (p. 193) in his primary physical regionalisation (Unstead, 1933) found that Greater London by its very presence must be given some status as a regional entity, so Fawcett saw that in the West Midlands, Merseyside, the Manchester area, West Yorkshire and Tyneside, to take the major examples, there were continuous urban areas of considerable size which had particular problems and were therefore worthy of special study. But this paper, though studied widely, had no immediate practical fruits until after the Second World War when the conurbations were officially defined for the 1951 Census and became the basis for the metropolitan areas of the 1970s. Geographical bread cast on the waters may return after many days, even forty years or more. Fawcett acquired the term 'conurbation' from Patrick Geddes, who in *Cities in Evolution* (1915) coined the word to deal with continuously built-up areas of considerable extent.

Dudley Stamp's advocacy of the Land Utilisation Survey was a constant feature of the 1930s and markedly successful, for the whole of Great Britain was mapped by voluntary workers within little more than ten years. It had a sixfold classification of forests; meadowland and

---

Fig. 13 Fawcett's provinces of England.
C. B. Fawcett took the view that counties were archaic units of little value to the smooth administrative running of England and that sooner or later a more modern definition would be needed. He therefore suggested these regions and later modified them slightly, mainly by dividing 'Peakdon' (based on Sheffield) between Yorkshire and 'Trent', which he renamed the East Midlands. He also added Northamptonshire to the East Midlands. Reproduced from Fawcett, C. B., *The Provinces of England* (1960), (revised with a new preface by W. G. East and S. W. Wooldridge), (London), p. 162.

permanent grass; arable (tilled) land, including market gardens; heathland, moorland, commons and rough hill pasture; unproductive land. Each of these categories could be inserted by any observer who could read a 6 in. map in the field, but those willing to provide more information were encouraged to do so, both on the map and in the margins. The story of the survey's vicissitudes is told in the first chapter of Stamp's *The Land of Britain: its use and misuse*, first published in 1947. This is a summary volume covering the entire survey of which the first three chapters deal with the planning of Britain, on which work had begun before the war, especially on the location of the industrial population and on land utilisation in rural areas: the Royal Commission on the former and the Committee on the latter published the Barlow (1940) and Scott (1942) reports (Royal Commission, 1940, 1942), which together gave a basis of discussion for post-war planning.

The great achievement of the Stamp survey was to give a factual demonstration of the land use of every acre of Britain, enriched by the publication of ninety-two reports which, it was said, had only been read from end to end by two people, Stamp himself as editor and James Fairgrieve who reviewed in *Geography* each part as it appeared and in time acted as an honorary editor. The enterprise has been compared to a modern Domesday survey and undoubtedly it is of great significance for future workers on the history of agriculture in Britain and a source of fascinating relevance for historical geographers of a future time. As Stamp points out in his chapter on 'Wartime changes in land use, 1939–45':

The maps refer essentially to pre-war conditions, and the County Reports described the conditions of land use and agriculture as they were in the nineteen-thirties . . . at a very distinctive period . . . when for various reasons agricultural use of land was at a nadir, when the proportion of the surface under the plough had reached the lowest ever recorded since statistics were first collected in 1866 and undoubtedly lower than it had been for over a century and a half. Much of the poorer land had become agriculturally submarginal and was being abandoned. There was widespread neglect of such essential forms of maintenance as hedging and ditching . . . for many farmers the only profitable crop was a crop of bungalows, which destroyed the balance of the very farm on which they depended ultimately for their existence (Stamp, 1947, 404).

The British agricultural landscape was changed virtually beyond recognition from the Second World War onwards and an immediate effect, with little overall increase in the labour force (and in time its diminution) was a rise from a pre-war production of between 35 and 40 per cent of the nation's food to almost 75 per cent.

Quoting reviewers of his books, Dudley Stamp gleefully recalled one who said he had 'a passion for facts and a tidy mind'. But as the quotation given above shows generalisations could be made and the work of the Land Utilisation Survey was an obvious basis for replanning Britain. It was also controversial, for Stamp had stated that 38 per cent of Britain was 'good agricultural' land which should be reserved for agriculture unless the circumstances were exceptional, and that as far as possible national parks, forests, main highways, water supply and power schemes, even green belts, should be restricted to poor lands: the comment on green belts was rather odd as they commonly consist of intensively farmed land around cities, including market gardens and highly capitalised dairying enterprises. Realistically, he advised that sites for 'garden cities and satellite towns' should be found on land of intermediate quality, as only in some areas (as planners were later to discover) were areas of poorer soil likely to provide suitable sites, and in any case poorer land might not give appropriate locations for heavy industry. In some ways these suggestions were a dream incapable of realisation, and partly induced by the demonstration of E. C. Willatts in his classic county report for Middlesex that the spread of London from 1919 had absorbed thousands of acres of excellent farming land and even of market gardens (Willatts, 1937). Undoubtedly the survey provided a basis for the argument about the replanning of Britain that was to continue into an indefinite future. In the post-war period the survey, and Stamp as its director, figured prominently in planning enquiries dealing with urban expansion. For historical geographers of the future, the survey provides source material of incalculable value.

Settlement study, especially of villages, attracted several workers during the inter-war period and were encouraged by a commission of the International Geographical Union appointed at the Cairo Congress in 1925. The initial advocacy came largely from Albert Demangeon (1872–1940), the distinguished French geographer who had written the first volume of the *Géographie Universelle* on the British Isles (1927). The idea was to collect data from a number of countries on dispersed and nucleated settlement and if possible to prepare a map showing the prevalence of villages and individual farmsteads in various countries. Clearly there were many explanations for the sites of villages, including the availability of spring waters and of dry ground for building sites. Much work was done on the Continent, notably in Belgium and France, and Demangeon crystallised many of the research findings in a summary article published in the *Annales de géographie*. But as the work proceeded in Britain it became clear that the problem was one of infinite complexity and that a solution could only be found by detailed researches with intensive fieldwork. Apart from the possible influence of soils, drainage and water supply, or communications, even the need for defence against natural hazards such as avalanches in mountains as well as against enemies, much depended on the local agricultural practice. Some of the early hypotheses, such as an association with ethnic groups, were exploded by later investigations but C. B. Fawcett, reviewing the long continued work in 1938, reached the conclusion that: 'Within the limits of the physically possible the type and distribution of habitat is mainly dependent on the type of rural economy and the stage of its development' (*Geogr. J.* **93**, 1938, pp. 152–5). However, even this cautious statement could be contested. Although much interesting work was done in 1938 the Commission on the Rural Habitat became part of a Commission on Population. Unfortunately the war interrupted the work and despite some interesting contributions made later, notably by the economic historian M. Beresford on forgotten and abandoned medieval villages, a great many mysteries still remain.

The outlook in 1939

By 1939 geography in Britain, as indeed elsewhere, was in a stage characterised by experiment and enquiry into a vast range of problems and topics. Notable work had been done in geomorphology, and also in historical, regional and human geography, while political aspects fascinated Mackinder, Roxby and many humbler workers of the day. In the teaching of historical geography the broad sweep through the ages fascinated the students of Roxby, while those who wanted a firmer, indeed a more austerely scholarly, approach turned with satisfaction to the period studies in Darby's volume of 1936 and his later work. In economic geography the need for a thorough local treatment was met by the publication of *The British Isles: a geographic and economic survey* by L. D. Stamp and S. H. Beaver in 1933 which, like Chisholm's classic *Handbook*, was revised and reissued on several later occasions. The concern was to combine generalisation with adequate local study, to be critical of the attractive hypothesis that was based on flimsy evidence or at times was little more than a 'hunch', however eloquently and persuasively presented. Wisely in 1934, C. B. Fawcett, drawing attention to the variety of topics that geographers studied, said that: 'We are as yet in the early stages of investigation of the many problems of human geography, and have not reached well-established generalisations. The study is in the stage of collecting facts, and framing and establishing hypotheses, most of which can only mark stages in its development' (*Geogr. J.* **84**, p. 427).

Fortunately, most of the leading geographers of the time were tolerant and eager to encourage research in any aspect of the subject. The experience of attending conferences both in Britain and abroad, notably in the international congresses, was apt to be bewildering as one was rapidly whirled from one area and one aspect of any branch of geography to another. It was indeed an academic variety show. There were so many papers that had their own interest but little relation to any others. And this was naturally reflected in the journals. For example, two papers by Arthur Geddes showing the relationship between increases and decreases in population movements in India to health, famines and diseases undoubtedly broke new ground but they stood alone (Geddes, 1937, 1941). However, many doors were open for those who cared to go through them, possibly more than people appreciated at the time. It seemed that a war might set back progress for many years and it had its academic casualties, such as the loss, after a short but spirited life, of the

Journal of Geomorphology, published from 1938 to 1941 under the care of an international editorial board. But the harvest of much patient pioneering was to come, even though ten bleak years lay ahead in 1939.

The involvement of British geographers in current affairs was seen in 1938 when more than forty pages (22–40, 499–526) of volume 92 of the *Geographical Journal* were given to a discussion of the distribution of industry in Britain. Eva G. R. Taylor introduced the theme with the comment that the Royal Geographical Society had been asked to assist the Royal Commission which later produced the Barlow Report. Much that was said then would not be accepted now, for the basis of the argument was that only a limited part of the country was suited to industrial growth, especially as many areas – including 'the textile towns of the South Pennines' – were 'poorly accessible from London by rail' and 'marginality of position' could impede development at Liverpool, Newcastle and – especially – Swansea. The 1931 Census had revealed a concentrated industrial belt following an axis from southeast to northwest 'and broadening as it gets farther from Greater London'. The 'sea-entries' dominating England's external trade were at the extremities in Liverpool–Manchester and the Port of London, which together handled two-thirds of the imports and exports. This became known as the 'coffin-shaped belt' (p. 152), an unhappy term, but it was more discreetly described in the evidence sent to the Barlow Commission. 'The major pools of skilled and semi-skilled labour are to be found in an axial belt covering approximately 14,500 square miles or 39 per cent, of the total area of England and Wales, which runs from Greater London in the South-east to South Lancashire and the West Riding in the North-west.' The remoter areas, the Northumberland and Durham coalfield, west Cumberland and South Wales, were all facing acute problems of unemployment and had become Special Areas. A comparable study for Scotland, drafted by D. L. Linton, showed that there, too, industry was concentrated, indeed to such an extent that 30 per cent of all the industrial workers were in Glasgow. Consideration was given to climatic hazards, on which Gordon Manley (1902–1980) wrote with his usual mixture of hard fact and charm, especially for the Pennines.

By the time the Barlow Report appeared, Britain was at war and therefore the debate about industrial development in various areas was postponed, though it became a main issue of post-war planning. And much else was postponed, notably the hopes of compiling a National Atlas comparable with those available for numerous other countries on which Eva G. R. Taylor introduced a discussion at the Royal Geographical Society in December 1939: the suggestion that such an atlas should be published was first made at the meeting of the British Association at Cambridge in 1938 (*Geogr. J.* **95**, 1940 pp. 96–108). It failed to attract government financial support. Another farseeing article of 1939, on 'Practical regionalism in England and Wales' by E. W. Gilbert, showed the vast variety of divisions made by government departments such as the Post Office, the Central Electricity Board, the Ministry of

Labour, the Registrar-General for the Census, and notably the Ministry of Agriculture which had different areas as their advisory provinces from their agricultural divisions for statistical purposes, which had no apparent relation to the 'regions' of the milk marketing boards. The twenty-six divisions given by Gilbert included the regions of the Automobile Association, the sales area of a chocolate firm and the dioceses of the Church of England. But the most interesting of all was the Civil Defence Regions which, with modifications, became the Standard Regions in 1946. These were based on the grim possibility that in wartime part of England and Wales might be cut off from the Central Government in London so that major decisions would have to be made locally by regional commissioners, described by detractors as 'dictators' and compared with Cromwell's eleven major-generals! Fortunately at no time was communication with London, or from one part of the country to another, paralysed either by invasion or air warfare so the ultimate value of this regionalisation was not shown directly to the population of Britain. It meant much more to those involved in government, and especially in civil defence (Gilbert, 1939).

Only hours before the war began, Alexander Stevens† (1886–1965) of Glasgow gave a presidential address at the British Association which challenged the widespread faith in the 'natural region' (Stevens, 1939). He regarded a 'natural geographical region' as an organised, man-made region, conceivably with boundaries that might cross a mountain range, partition a river valley or even divide a coalfield. The geographer was 'concerned with physical and biological nature only in so far as it may be regarded as human environment, and only with man in so far as he had demonstrable relationships with the environment'. The natural geographical region was best seen in the nation-state, revealed in Europe in its maturity, though the USA, Soviet Russia and other countries were striving towards a similar achievement. In Stevens's view man was not merely as Herbertson said, the 'nerves of a natural region' but rather the 'living principle'. In the course of history, men made their own boundaries. These might cut through a physical unit as well defined as the Rhine valley, in Roman as in modern times, and might intersect a coalfield, as between France, Belgium, Holland and Germany. The possibility of drawing political inferences from such views is clear, especially in a historical perspective. Less controversial was the observation that in both lowland and highland Scotland regional names existed which expressed some consciousness of local identity and therefore of regionalism, rarely if ever studied. Nor is this unique to Scotland, for it obviously exists in such units as the Pennine dales, Holderness, the Vale of Belvoir, the Vale of Glamorgan, the Fenlands and many more. That these had a physical basis is obvious, but economic developments, for example in mining, may make new local regional boundaries as in the Pennines or the Clyde basin. Stevens was taking a cool hard look at the whole regional concept and possibly the derivation of some of his ideas, in part at least from Ratzel and other

German geographers, did not commend them in the intellectual climate of 1939. Even so, the regional concept was acquiring a new complexity in geographical thought and Stevens's address, though expressing and indeed crystallising many of the misgivings of works of its time, did not attract much comment for people were much more concerned with the war and the contribution that geographers might make to current needs. At first the possibilities of using geographical knowledge appeared to be slight, but in time geographers were in great demand and the contribution made both to the war effort and the post-war replanning of Britain was considerable.

Chapter 8

Geography in war and peace

War gave most geographers a clear task which they readily accepted, generally under some form of direction so that they had to make few personal decisions in their work. In the Admiralty *Handbooks*, for example, a clear directive was given on the form each book should take and the services of draftsmen and others were provided. Those in the service departments had duties far more explicitly defined than in the normal life of a university. Geographers certainly showed that they could meet the demands of such work, but with varying success from one person to another. Peace brought the challenge of freedom and controversy about the nature and purpose of geography flourished once more. The sharply worded defence by Wooldridge and Linton of geomorphology (p. 147) was an attitude developed from the fear that preoccupation with economic and social aspects of geography, clearly of relevance to planning, might become dominant: nor was that all, for the modern progress of geography had been based on field study of the physical as well as the human aspects of landscapes. The work of Stamp and his numerous associates showed this decisively, for land-use study invariably raised questions of the physical quality of the landscape, and obviously of soils and drainage conditions. In the comments of C. A. Fisher (p. 149) one may recognise the anxiety that geographers should still be conscious of the whole world as well as of their own homeland, their own specialism. Also represented is the idea of geography as a study of some breadth along with its concern for detail. Also growing at the time was a disenchantment with regional geography, so strongly entrenched before the Second World War and an increasing expectation that systematic study would prove more productive. There was no universality of outlook and the tensions apparent in the immediate post-war years were to become more marked later.

In 1947 Eva Taylor spoke of 'the sudden rise of geographical prestige which occurs in war time' when 'geographical intelligence of every kind . . . becomes vital' (Taylor, 1947). Regrettably no comprehensive survey was made of the work of British geographers from 1939 to 1945, for the warning was given that little should be said about work for the Government, however non-military it might appear to be. Secrecy soon became a habit, but in 1946 an American, L. S. Wilson, wrote an article in the *Geographical Review* that was remarkably informative about wartime activities in Britain (Wilson, 1946). Much of the co-ordinating work for the invasion of Europe was done in Manchester College, Oxford, and the Admiralty photographic library was housed in the Bodleian Library close by. Many geographers worked in various Admiralty departments scattered through the country and in the headquarters of the Geographical Section of the General Staff, located in an outer London suburb. Some geographers worked as meteorologists, and as instructors for airmen. Others again were concerned with the analysis of air photographs of enemy-held territory, of obvious significance for aerial attacks. Many other responsibilities were accepted by geographers, including the provision of lectures for men and women entering the armed services and the maintenance of courses for the much reduced number of undergraduates.

One wartime enterprise was the publication of the Admiralty *Handbooks* by the Geographical Section of the Naval Intelligence Division. This followed the precedent of the First World War, when similar *Handbooks* were produced (p. 103). If any doubt existed about the fruits of university teaching and training between the wars it would be abundantly resolved by comparing the two sets of *Handbooks*. Over thirty countries were treated in considerable detail, some in as many as four separate volumes. The work began effectively in 1941 and the staffs consisted mainly of geographers drawn from universities, though they also included anthropologists and others whose research work was based on distant parts of the world such as the Pacific islands. There were two centres, at Cambridge and Oxford, and the books were published by the university presses. The Oxford centre was closely associated with the School of Geography and located inside it with Professor Kenneth Mason as its director, but at Cambridge the centre was in the Scott Polar Institute with Mr (Sir) James M. Wordie as director and Dr H. C. Darby as editor-in-chief. The link with the University was therefore more apparent in Oxford, where several of the volumes were written by members of the teaching staff, while at Cambridge the contributors were drawn from several universities. In both centres a number of visiting contributors assisted, either as part-time workers in university vacations or as occasional visitors who wrote particular chapters. The intention was that volumes should be useful to military, naval and other government personnel both during and after the war, including the Diplomatic Corps. It was not the intention to duplicate material provided in other governmental books such as the Admiralty *Pilots* so well known to mariners. In effect the books as a whole provided a kind of universal geography relating to conditions of the 1930s: most of them are excellently illustrated and much is owed to the work of the cartographers, many of whom had no previous knowledge of such work though they had qualified in some of the leading art schools of England. The enterprise they showed in what was to them a strange, and perhaps not entirely welcome, type of work was beyond praise. Wilson (1946) said that '. . . the high standard of workmanship and the excellent selection of material make the series one of the most outstanding and lasting contributions to the geographical literature that has resulted from the war.' In time these books were derestricted and sold on the open market: complete sets are available in most university libraries.

Meanwhile the work of the Land Utilisation Survey, originally begun in an effort to find the use actually made of every acre of Britain and owing much to the example of various detailed local surveys made by students and others at various times, acquired national significance in wartime. Its director, L. D. Stamp, wrote that in 1939 officials in several counties asked for sets of the original field maps on the 6 in. to 1 mile scale as a basis for the 'planning the ploughing' campaign (Stamp, 1947). The publication of the 1:63,360 maps continued steadily and all the county reports were published by 1946 (in ninety-two parts). The secretary of the survey, E. C. Willatts, was transferred to the new Research Section of the Ministry of Works and Buildings in 1942, from which the new Ministry of Town and Country Planning developed in 1943. The Ministry published several of the 1:625,000 maps which were based on the survey work, such as those on vegetation, land classification, types of farming and general land utilisation. L. D. Stamp became the chief adviser to the Minister of Agriculture on rural land use in 1942 and the Land Utilisation Survey maintained this mutually helpful association through the war.

Apart from the obvious value in planning the food production of Britain, so substantially increased, the survey's work had certain planning implications for post-war Britain. The first major principle was to direct new developments in housing, industry and other non-agricultural features to the poorer land where possible: that this was not possible everywhere was clear, however, as the need for a new first-class airport (Heathrow) for London might involve (as in fact it did) the use of some excellent land. Secondly, industrial developments and associated housing should not be spread indiscriminately through the countryside, as farming might be adversely affected by such developments. Thirdly, a farm was normally one unit, and the removal of even a single field might affect its life adversely: this proved later to be a severe problem, especially when motorways were built, but at least it prevented the casual sale of fields for building land which had been so marked a feature of the inter-war period. To those old enough to know Britain before and after the war, the general effect of wartime agricultural improvements was to change the rural landscape almost beyond recognition and to develop a productivity not known before. In some parts of the country prisoners of war laid new drains and carried out permanent improvements. One of the most valuable principles that emerged, partly through the work of the survey, was to make an 'urban fence' as a suitable limit for future building and also to define a 'semi-urbanised area' within which land could only be used for building under certain controls. Village expansion was not precluded, but any growth should be near the heart of the village and any new houses should be architecturally harmonious with those that existed.

The work was a classic example of Patrick Geddes's dictum 'survey before action' and contributed to the widespread conviction that agriculture should never sink to the depressed level of the inter-war period and that the indiscriminate sprawl of suburbs should be prevented. The Land Utilisation Survey was done in the field by voluntary workers of whom Stamp (1947, p. 19) wrote: 'The use already made of their work in the great war effort, in the plans which are being made and the foundations which are being laid for a better Britain of the future, as well as in the creating of a new Domesday Book, can scarcely fail to thrill those volunteer surveyors of 1931–34 . . . who made the whole work possible.' It was a well-timed enterprise. Already before the war the interest in planning was growing, stimulated by the necessity of providing some employment in the depressed areas such as those coalfields which appeared to be dying or mortally wounded, and also by the need to achieve a new distribution of industry that would reduce pressure on favoured areas such as Greater London with its outlying fringes, and the West Midlands. Then there was also a need to prevent the indiscriminate spread of housing into the rural areas of Britain, so apparent in the ribbon development of the inter-war period. These and many other matters of planning concern were discussed in the Barlow Report of 1940 on location of the industrial population and the Scott Report of 1942 on land utilisation in rural areas (p. 136). In wartime controls could be imposed that would be politically unacceptable in peacetime, but the need for some form of planning was generally recognised, though with varying degrees of enthusiasm. Most people saw this in terms of their own immediate environment, and even in terms of past mistakes. Coventry might welcome the expanding motor industry but should it also be located at Oxford? One interesting paper showing concern on this question was E. W. Gilbert's 'Industrialisation of Oxford', written, however, when he could only deplore what had already happened (Gilbert, 1947).

However recognised and whatever its ideological basis, planning for the future was a need of the time in the late 1940s. Rebuilding of devastated cities, provision for the new houses required by many thousands of people (even in some countries for millions), the creation of New Towns to accommodate people from the conurbations and thereby to limit their growth, the preservation of the countryside from the indiscriminate 'development' that had been seen in Britain and many other countries during the inter-war period – all were problems for the future, and indeed the immediate future. Books with titles like 'When we build again' were avidly read, and so too were many of the numerous books on town planning, such as those on London, Manchester and Birmingham (the latter splendidly discussed in the West Midland Group's *Conurbation* (West Midlands Group, (1948)). Unfortunately, as

Eva G. R. Taylor showed in her 1947 address to the British Association, far less work had been done by geographers on towns than on rural areas: in her view there was a need 'to obtain a much firmer grasp of the anatomy and growth of towns as functioning organisms, reflecting the circumstances of place'. There had in fact been 'no co-ordinated over-all study' (Taylor, 1947). In spite of many useful individual efforts, geographers at that time had less to offer planners on urban than on rural land use, and consequently many of them looked elsewhere for inspiration, even to statisticians of whom some had the quaint idea, happily long since discarded, that each town as defined by the Census should have the same proportion of people within the various social classes and occupational groups as the national average.

While the tendency to seek some easily recognisable principle to be followed in town reconstruction and development was natural, it soon became clear that a primary need was to study what was physically present on the ground, a task which in many towns was done later by geography students, with others, as a vacation job preparatory to the compilation of town development plans. As time went on urban geography attracted a large number of eager workers well versed in methods pioneered in other countries, and especially in the USA. British work on urban geography at this time owed much to the work of Walter Christaller of 1934, translated by C. W. Baskin (Christaller, 1966) but earlier made known through the publications of R. E. Dickinson (Dickinson, 1947) and others. Christaller's grading of towns in an urban framework where all were related led some workers to a close study of transport (Green, 1950, 1951; Carruthers, 1957) as well as to more general studies (Smailes, 1953). Mr Carruthers as a civil servant made a notable contribution to the work on Greater London which led to its redefinition (Royal Commission, 1961): this led to the conclusion that some of the local centres within the Greater London conurbation were comparable in commercial strength to major provincial centres such as Leicester (Smailes and Hartley, 1961). Another profitable line of enquiry was developed in *A Social Geography of Belfast* (Jones, 1960).

The new academic freedom

During the war years many geographers had been obliged by circumstances to follow particular lines of enquiry, or to meet immediate needs laid down by their employment. Now they could do what they liked. However, there were dangers in such a situation and of these one was that the social pressure of the time would lead to a preoccupation with planning, with the application of geography to the exclusion of fundamental or pure research. Contemplation of the history of the Land Utilisation Survey shows that what began as pure research eventually had its clear and nationally significant application, and the needs of wartime had shown that detailed geomorphological work might be of considerable significance in military operations. To quote Eva G. R. Taylor yet again, 'There can of course be no applied geography unless there has first of all been an adequate pure geography' (Taylor, 1947). But the range and scope of geographical study was avidly debated, especially as many geographers looked towards America and saw that there geomorphology had been increasingly incorporated with geological teaching: fears were expressed that similar developments might follow in Britain. But did this matter?

S. W. Wooldridge and D. L. Linton undoubtedly thought that it did, for they responded vigorously to a letter in the *Geographical Journal* criticising the R.G.S. for including a paper by K. M. Strøm, Professor of Geography in Oslo University, on the origin of Norway's remarkable upland surfaces, apparently evolved in Tertiary times. The correspondent (of high military rank but also in his first year as a student at Cambridge) argued that the lecture 'ought to have been read before a society of geologists or geomorphologists . . . of what use is a knowledge of the Middle Tertiary phase in the evolution of the Weald to a geographer concerned with the present reality of the area as regards relief?' (*Geogr. J.* **111**, 1948, pp. 147; **12**, 1948, pp. 19–27, 125–7). Wooldridge argued that 'it was only possible to understand the existing relief by reference to its origins' and made effective use of W. M. Davis's comment that: 'To look upon a landscape without any recognition of the labour expended upon producing it, or of the extraordinary adjustment of streams to structure and waste to weather, is like visiting Rome in the ignorant belief that the Romans of today had no ancestors.' There are obvious signs of a demarcation dispute here, but any serious student of the geography of Norway would be intrigued by the paper by Strøm. Linton argued that 'such acknowledged masters as Vidal de la Blache and Hettner' were concerned with 'the study of areas of the earth's surface', with 'the recognition in any area of the elements – whether of terrestrial, cosmic or social origin – that have given any area its unique character, with the inter-relations of these areas and their mapping'. He was on even more controversial ground in arguing that 'geography is not concerned with the study of phenomena in relation to man and still less . . . with the study of man in relation to his environment'. In Linton's view, this was 'human ecology', a vogue term of the time now rarely used in Britain.

Controversy about the nature and content of geography was a sign of vitality. The prospects were bright for the number of students, and the range of careers they entered sharply increased. Both during and after the war there was a growing demand for books, especially for those moderately priced. The geographical societies looked forward to a brighter day when they could increase the size of their publications, though the Royal Scottish Geographical Society never achieved the strength it had known before the war and the Manchester Geographical Society issued only occasional journals and eventually ceased publication altogether. The Tyneside Geographical Society, having had a brief but interesting period of publishing before the war, failed to revive afterwards except at an annual social gathering. But the Royal Geographical Society continued to publish its journals and under its new director, L. P. Kirwan, to welcome a somewhat wider range of articles than those that had appeared earlier. From 1946 the Institute of British Geographers, originally founded to publish monographs, began to publish articles. Apparently the supply of suitable monographs was slight and few were published after the war.

Although it was not a propitious time for the founding of new journals, an enterprising group of young geographers published *Geographical Studies* from 1954 to 1959: it was described as 'an independent journal which has been started in the belief that greater facilities are needed in Great Britain for the publication of geographical articles, notes and discussion'. Heavy criticism was given to the assumption in the initial editorial article (by C. A. Fisher) that the younger geographers of the day represented 'the third generation' of British geographers (Fisher, 1954), especially by J. N. L. Baker who pointed out that British geography had a centuries-old tradition of achievement that long preceded the pioneer work of H. J. Mackinder and other teachers who began the modern revival of the subject in the universities. Two journals of a more definitely regional character must be mentioned. Of these the *East Midland Geographer*, issued from the University of Nottingham since 1954, is a valued source of papers on the area it serves and *Irish Geography*, first published in 1944, has from its inception concentrated on the presentation of material on Ireland. The *Geographical Magazine*, founded in 1935, has been successful in reaching a wide public of varying academic standards. It is perhaps regrettable that opportunities for the publication of papers by geographers have been limited, but some have found welcoming editors in other journals, including *Urban Studies*, the *Town Planning Review*, local journals of historical and field scientific societies, or those published in the United States or continental Europe, with many more. Others have appeared in reports of various conferences and symposia. Enterprise has been shown by many student geographical societies which have published an annual journal and given many young writers their first (and probably their last) appearance on a printed, or at least a cyclostyled page.

In the immediate post-war years many tensions developed among geographers, some of which were a sign of progress. In the *Geographical Studies* editorial noted above, C. A. Fisher argues that the 'world view', proclaimed by Mackinder and other pioneers must be maintained and that inside a geography department there should be people of widely different interests who, in their pursuits of specialist researches, may have learnt such crafts as pollen analysis or the deciphering of medieval manuscripts (Fisher, 1954). Obviously a student of Domesday geography can only work effectively if he appreciates – as fully as any professional historian – exactly what the Domesday Book says: equally obviously much light may be shed on landscape evolution by the study of pollen. And every encouragement should be given to those who still possess the will – and more practically can acquire the opportunity – of studying remote areas, for the whole world matters. A danger against academic retreat into a safe haven in noted by C. A. Fisher.

To narrow down our field of study to some pseudo-scientific specialism and to burst forth into an exuberance of jargon which is nothing more than the secret language of an academic trade union will deceive no-one, not even ourselves. And likewise if, instead of taking the world as our parish we make our parish the world, we shall not be true to our calling. It would be tragic indeed if the tendency to little Englandism in our national life were to be reflected in an excess of parish-pump geography among the heirs of Mackinder and Herbertson (Fisher, 1954, p. 2).

Unfortunately, in the immediate post-war period it was clearly revealed that geographers had neglected the opportunities of studying their own immediate parishes because they did not realise how interesting and rewarding such work could be.

And this applied especially to towns. Whether people liked living in towns or not scarcely mattered, for in fact four-fifths of the population of Britain did so and therefore the social welfare of the nation depended on the urban environment they know from birth to death. Lewis Mumford and other prophets of a new age could fulminate against 'the insensate town' and say that no place should grow beyond a certain size, perhaps 50,000, but the fact remained that 70 per cent of the population of Britain lived in large towns, and of these half were resident in the great conurbations of Greater London, the West Midlands (Birmingham and the Black Country), Merseyside, the Selnec (Manchester) area, West Yorkshire, Tyneside and central Clydeside. C. B. Fawcett had drawn attention to the intense concentration of the British population in such areas by 1931 and twenty years later the 1951 Census gave special attention to the seven major conurbations mentioned above (p. 135). The initial task was to define them and this was done by the Inter-Departmental Committee on Economic and Social Research, which in fact used local experts (including geographers) to assist in its work (Fig. 14). One basic aid was described in the 1951 *General Report* of the Census: 'To enable useful statistical analyses to be made, arrangements were made to split up each area to a number of divisions and sub-divisions, which were designed to be as far as possible homogeneous in respect of age of housing and type of development' (Census 1951, 1956). But this was easier said than done, for there were few studies of the housing areas of towns available, even though on the ground the distinction between pre-1914 artisan housing and that of the inter-war local authority estates was generally clear. In fact it bore a strong resemblance to or even coincided with the distinction that had emerged between the areas of houses with gardens, coloured purple for towns on the Land Utilisation Survey's maps and

Northern

East and
West Ridings

North
Western
3

2

4

North Midland

Wales

West Midland

5

Eastern

South Western

Southern

London and South
Eastern

6

———— Boundaries of
Standard Regions

----- County Boundaries

▓▓▓ Major Conurbations

1 Tyneside
2 Merseyside
3 Selnec
4 W. Yorks
5 W. Midlands
6 Gt. London

0   50

Miles

those without gardens, coloured red. Nevertheless many of the lines drawn on the maps in the *Conurbations* volume of the 1951 Census were speculative, and the author remembers that as those for the Selnec (Manchester) conurbation were drawn he was earnestly hoping that they would not be accepted as authoritative by later writers (Census 1951, 1956). He need not have worried: they were not.

Nor was that all. While major town centres were well known to those who used them, their exact location and especially their limits had received little attention. Fortunately the work of R. E. Murphy and his associates in America on the central business district of large cities (Murphy, 1972) stimulated interest, and even some work, on the central areas of British towns and for the 1961 Census civil servants worked with local geographers and others to define the central business districts of the major conurbations (Census 1961). This was done as a basis for the statistical investigation of the number of people who came daily to work in such areas, which had few permanent residents. It was an enquiry of considerable social significance, and the Census of Retail Trade of 1961 included much interesting material on the shopping facilities of central areas, defined by local observation (Board of Trade, 1964). This progress in knowledge of British towns was encouraging, but more study was needed on the actual distribution of the population.

The statistical information in the Census showed the general distribution per acre and the actual occupation of houses so that an estimate of crowding of dwellings could be fairly easily acquired. It also showed the prevalence of necessary modern amenities such as hot and cold water or fixed baths and other toilet facilities, but only for wards that might include 20,000 or more people. And it did not reveal the intermingling of industrial premises, some of none too pleasant a character for the neighbours, with housing, or the distribution of open spaces available for rest and recreation. For this reason some local investigations such as a study of the areas of inner Birmingham, formerly of a favoured residential character, where guns and jewellery were made, aroused considerable interest. Comparable but more broadly based studies on the Potteries were obviously significant for the future planning of a famed but aesthetically repellent industrial areas (Wise, 1949; Beaver, 1964). On London, the greatest enigma of them all, progress was slow and the geographer's contribution scant until the

---

Fig. 14 Standard Regions and conurbations.
This map shows the Standard Regions as established, from their wartime origins, in 1946 and also shows the areas recognised as 'conurbations' in the 1951 Census when the term originally coined by Patrick Geddes in 1915 and used by C. B. Fawcett in his study of the urban population of 1931 appeared (Fawcett, 1931). Later, as shown in Fig. 17, p. 176, the provincial conurbations were more generously defined.
Reproduced from Freeman, T. W., *Geography and Planning* (London), 1974, p. 98.

1960s when two books by P. G. (Peter) Hall appeared (p. 161) and several more valued contributions were made on the welcome occasion of the meeting of the International Geographical Congress in London in 1964 (p. 169). And in time more detailed research was made possible by the provision of statistics for enumeration districts, having perhaps a few hundred people, in towns.

In the early 1950s writers made a sharp distinction between urban and rural areas, and rightly so as the aim of the time was to prevent the spread of housing along arterial and other roads which had been so marked a characteristic of the inter-war period. But there was also a widespread assumption that the decline of rural population was a matter of social concern, though in fact it was mainly due to mechanisation of farming with far higher standards of living for the increasingly skilled workers on the land. In the thirty-odd years since 1945 the rural areas, particularly villages, have received many urban workers as house-holders, both in new and old property. The papers written in early years after the war deal with circumstances preceding this social change but that has in no way detracted from their value (Stevens, 1946: Vince, 1953; Willatts and Newson, 1953). One main interest of the writers was to show the relative numerical strength of the primary population, that is those directly connected with the land in farming (and mining with quarrying in Stevens's paper but not with the others), those living in the countryside and directly serving the primary producers (the secondary population), and the third element, the 'adventitious' who had settled in the countryside from choice but worked elsewhere or had other resources such as pensions or private means. Vince's work showed that the average proportion of the primary population (agricultural) approached 50 per cent in East Anglia, Lincolnshire and the East Riding and over 60 per cent in the Fenlands, even in one rural district 75 per cent (in 1931). In Wales as a whole the proportion was 55 per cent, but higher figures were recorded away from the areas influenced by industrial and residential settlement. Vince also showed that there was a distinct correlation between the density of the primary population and the type of farming practised, with the highest densities in cash crop areas such as the Fens, south Lancashire, north Kent and the Isle of Axholme and the lowest in mountain and moorland areas such as central Wales.

Similar but earlier work by Catherine P. Snodgrass showed comparable and naturally not unexpected results for Scotland (Snodgrass, 1941). E. C. Willatts and Marion Newson were more concerned with the general population changes in England and Wales from 1921 to 1951 and showed that one feature of the widespread redistribution of the country's population during that time was the continued decline in certain 'hard core' areas, notably the remote and generally high-lying areas of rural Wales, north Devon, the north Pennines, parts of the North Yorkshire moors and the Vale of Pickering. Several of the older industrial areas had also lost population consistently, such as the South Wales coalfield, the northeast and the textile areas of Lancashire and Yorkshire. The movement from central urban areas was most notably seen in the county of London, which had lost over a million people since 1931. Expectations that any stability of population might be achieved proved vain for there was continued redistribution, as later studies showed (p. 175).

Local government areas in Britain were known to be archaic long before the Second World War and in the 1947 Report of the Local Government Boundary Commission (issued in 1948) a new arrangement of local government units was suggested (Gilbert, 1948). These were to consist of (new) counties having a population of not more than 1 million people or less than 200,000 within which there would be (new) county boroughs with between 60,000 and 200,000 people. A one-tier or single autonomous county would have a population of 200,000 to 500,000 people but in the two-tier counties two or more county boroughs would together have 200,000 to 1 million people as noted above. The county boroughs were to have wide powers of local government, including education, health, care of the old and disabled, and – partially – town and country planning and highways. Some counties were to be divided; for example, Lancashire into five, Yorkshire with the north bank of the Tees in Durham into eight. In fact the proposals were not implemented and the discussion or local government boundaries continued to its final solution in 1973 (implemented on 1 April 1974), twenty-five years later. But the 1948 proposals had two things in common with the eventual rearrangement, of which the first was the union of urban and rural areas within single administrative units and the second was the recognition that such units should have a considerable population, preferably at least 200,000 except in sparsely settled rural areas. Gilbert provided maps to show some of the projected new administrative areas, which ironically enough the initial Report failed to do, and he also discussed the new Standard Regions of 1946, which were based on the Civil Defence Regions used from 1939 to 1945 to meet the special needs of the time (p. 140).

Unfortunately the historic Town and Country Planning Act of 1947 made the counties and the county boroughs the sole local planning authorities and regional organisation, except for such purposes as gas and electricity supply, the activity of the National Coal Board and Hospital boards (the last based on university medical schools), proved to be a tender plant watered from time to time by friendly supporters. Gilbert concludes his article with the claim that 'the work of geographers is very relevant to the whole issue of local government' and that 'what is needed is more research on social geography'. As shown on p. 177 virtually the same comment was made by Derek Senior in his minority report as a member of the Redcliffe-Maud Commission over twenty years later.

Much of the concern with planning, whether of urban and rural land use or of new administrative units, was due to the recognition of pressing needs in the life of Britain. Fortunately, the recreational use of the countryside was appreciated and national parks were zealously advocated by the Council for the Preservation of Rural England from its foundation in 1926. The National Trust, founded in 1895, had opened woods and mountain peaks for walkers and even acquired legal powers to prevent undue exploitation of areas under its control. Neither body, however, had the resources to establish national parks, for which the case was excellently stated in two government reports (Freeman, 1958, 1974; Sheail 1975). The Hobhouse Report laid down four principles for land use and development in national parks: first, the characteristic landscape beauty should be strictly preserved; second, access and facilities for 'public open-air enjoyment' should be amply provided; third, wildlife and places of architectural and historic interest should be protected; and fourth, established farming must be effectively maintained.

It was never the intention to make a landscape museum, nor indeed was it possible as all the national parks were farmed areas with other features of economic significance, including (apart from tourism) water supply for towns and the electricity grid, forestry and quarrying. Their use for military purposes was controversial. The parks designated were ten in number (Fig. 15): in 1951 the Lake District (866 sq. miles), the plateau-dominated Peak District (542 sq. miles) Snowdonia (845 sq. miles) and Dartmoor (365 sq. miles); in 1962 the Pembrokeshire coast (mainly a coastal belt with some inland extensions 225 sq. miles); in 1954 the Yorkshire dales (680 sq. miles) and Exmoor (265 sq. miles); in 1956 Northumberland (398 sq. miles); and in 1957 the Brecon Beacons (519 sq. miles). Altogether these national parks covered 5,258 square miles, 9 per cent of the area of England and Wales and from 1956 other areas 'of outstanding natural beauty' were added. In all these areas there has been special control of new building and industrial enterprise, but the work of the National Parks Commission, through its local boards, has been positive in character: numerous parking spaces, picnic areas and other amenities have been provided and one highly successful enterprise has been the opening of long-distance footpaths of which the first was the Pennine Way (of 250 miles) in 1951, the Pembrokeshire coast path (167 miles) in 1953, the Offa's Dyke path (168 miles) in 1955, the South

---

Fig. 15 National parks in England and Wales.
In addition to the ten national parks there are also areas of outstanding beauty and long-distance footpaths. Much of the early propaganda for the opening up of mountain areas came from walkers, either as individuals or in organisations, and some of the first areas to be made available were quite small woods in the Lake District bought for the public by the National Trust, later instrumental in opening large areas. The Countryside Commission is still extending the work of its predecessor, the National Parks Commission, established under the National Parks Act of 1947. Originally published in Freeman, T. W., *Geography and Planning* (London) 1974, p. 160.

Coast of
Northumberland

Northumberland

Newcastle

Solway
Coast

Lake District

Middlesbrough
North York Moors
and Cleveland Way

Barrow

Dales

Forest of Bowland

Leeds

Hull

Anglesey

Prestatyn

Liverpool

Peak
District

Sheffield

Norfolk Coast

Lleyn

Snowdonia

S.H.

C.C.

Nottingham

Derby
Leicester

Suffolk
Coast
and
Heaths

Pembrokeshire

Brecon
Beacons

Birmingham

Malvern Hills

Cotswolds

Dedham Vale

Chilterns

Coast

Swansea

Gower

Cardiff

Chepstow

Surrey
Hills

N. Downs
Way

Exmoor

East
Hampshire

Kent
Downs

North
Devon

Quantocks

South Downs Way

Dartmoor

Exeter

Dorset

Sussex Downs

Plymouth

(Coast Path)

Chichester
Harbour

Cornwall

(Coast Path)

	National Parks
	Areas of Outstanding Beauty
—·—	Pennine Way
——	Offa's Dike Footpath
S.H.	Shropshire Hills
C.C.	Cannock Chase

0   50

Miles

Downs Way (80 miles) in 1963 and the Yorkshire coast and North Yorks Moors path (93 miles) in 1965. A path round the southwest coast from Studland to Minehead, 515 miles long, was opened in sections between 1952 and 1963. Frustrated by the lack of means the National Parks Commission may have been, but their achievement has been impressive and their work still continues, since 1968 as the Countryside Commission. Recently the term 'recreational geography' has become fashionable in Britain, and in the delineation of small countryside parks, as in its earlier work on national parks and areas of outstanding natural beauty, the Countryside Commission has a clear contribution to make.

The wider world

In the late 1940s several geographers, some of whom had acquired their interest during their war service, were able and eager to seize the opportunity of working overseas. This was apparent in the publication of O. H. K. Spate's *India and Pakistan* in 1954, fifty years after any major book on its subject had appeared. Happily this elegantly written and constantly informative work was republished with the co-operation of A. T. A. Learmonth in 1967: of the original edition Spate wrote that it 'contains many facts, most of them probably authentic, and some opinions'. It is in fact a classic. Residence abroad was a stimulus to various writers, such as R. J. Harrison Church who published *Modern Colonisation* in 1951 and *West Africa* in 1957 and also to Monica Cole whose large book *South Africa* appeared in 1961. There were also many smaller and more detailed studies in journals, and during the immediate post-1945 period there was an eager welcome for work on overseas territories, with a special interest in the underdeveloped world, including especially those territories still dependent on the major powers. In spite of the statement of Winston Churchill that it was not his intention to preside over the liquidation of the British Empire it was patently clear that the colonial period was almost ended and that the Statute of Westminster in 1922, which in effect laid the foundations of the British Commonwealth, had been a far-sighted piece of legislation.

One obvious need of the post-war period was to rebuild some kind of international organisation that would have a better chance of success than the League of Nations of the inter-war period. This must include not only the discussion and – hopefully – the settlement of international problems but also provision for assistance to countries torn by disasters such as famines and civil war and also to organisations dealing with world health problems, food and agriculture, naturally developed from those that had been set up after the First World War. To some extent they were research institutes and their concern with such matters as the feeding of the world's people attracted widespread interest: they were also a stimulus to many charitable enterprises that attracted – and still attract – devoted support. Of all the problems that arose after 1945 none was clearer than the continued rise in the world's population, mainly due to the fall in the death-rate rather than to any dramatic rise in the birth-rate. This was most apparent in the underdeveloped world, especially in India with Pakistan, in Africa and in Latin America.

Of the great world problems that engaged the attention of some geographers after 1945, the first was hunger and the second was peace. From his work on land use in Britain, L. D. Stamp turned to the world scene and wrote a number of papers and one book, *Our Undeveloped World* (1953), later reissued with significant modifications as *Our Developing World* (Stamp, 1960). The first book was marked by a certain pessimism of outlook and contained the argument that the underfarmed areas of the world were not, as many people supposed, in the tropics but rather in middle latitudes, especially in North America where the extensive form of farming gave low yields per acre. Within the next few years Stamp had reached the conclusion that 'world-wide shortage of food is not just round the corner; with existing techniques widely applied the world could support four or five times its present population . . . techniques are at present being vastly and rapidly improved under the new agricultural revolution' (Stamp, 1960, p. 181). Nevertheless it was clear that a substantial proportion of the world was underfed, probably half and perhaps even more. It was not a problem easy of solution, for in many areas the density of population on the land was high and the agricultural surplus available for sale negligible. Nor did it follow that countries needing more food would have the means to buy it, or even the wish to accept it on a charitable basis. Industrial development might reduce the proportion of people on the land by attracting workers to the towns, but unemployment or underemployment in towns was all too apparent in many countries.

Only to a limited extent could emigration solve problems of population pressure, for in the twentieth century few areas were still open to settlers. Obviously the need was to make local studies in various countries on problems of food production and density of population; and at the first post-war Congress of the International Geographical Union, held at Lisbon in 1948, a commission was appointed to study world land-use problems: these were excellently summarised by L. D. Stamp (East and Moodie, 1956). Four studies of land use were published: on the Transvaal lowveld by Monica M. Cole in 1956; on Hong Kong by T. R. Tregear in 1958; on Cyprus by D. Christodoulou in 1960; and on Tobago by D. L. Niddrie in 1961. But the main aim of the Commission, of which L. D. Stamp became chairman in 1956, was to encourage more investigation and mapping of land use throughout the world. Modern techniques of air photography, research on the agricultural replanning of various countries, continued work by Ordnance Surveys and national atlas organisations, as well as individual enterprises by researchers in universities or in government departments or institutes – all contributed to the study of land use.

Much was owed to L. D. Stamp who became a familiar figure at a wide variety of international conferences, some of them organised by the Food and Agriculture Organisation of the United Nations and others by the United Nations itself, among which was the Conference on Comparative Resources at New York in 1949. The association of land use with population problems was made abundantly clear at conference after conference, and notably at the World Population Conference at Rome in 1954 and at meetings of the Pacific Science Conference. It would perhaps be wrong to ascribe such world-wide interest in land use to the success of the Land Utilisation Survey of Britain because the problem of using the surface of the earth intelligently is obviously one that abides in the mind of all thoughtful people. Nevertheless the Land Utilisation Survey of Britain was much admired, and perhaps one tribute to its success was the contribution it had made to its own obsolescence, for its revelation that Britain was underfarmed had been crucial and after 1939–45 the general view was that in no circumstances should farming sink to the level of the inter-war period.

Beginning in 1959 with a pilot study in the Isle of Thanet, Alice Coleman and K. R. A. Maggs launched a new survey which conformed to the proposals set out by the International Commission and developed into a nation-wide enterprise (Coleman, 1961). The new maps were on the 1:25,000 scale and a far more detailed classification of land use was employed than that of the earlier Stamp survey: this in itself was a tribute to the advance in geography teaching in the schools through the years, for much of the actual surveying was carried out as part of educational fieldwork programmes. In all land-use survey there is an obvious concern with population study. And there is no need to emphasise that real or even imagined population pressure may be a fruitful cause of political strife, even of wars.

Much of the interest in political geography seen during the immediate post-war period developed from the new alignments of international politics, and especially from the emergence of Russia as a major world power, one of only two according to E. G. R. Taylor in 1947 (Taylor, 1947) or of five, including the United states, China, France and Great Britain, according to UNO. Always in British thinking on political geography the now venerable and by some venerated figure of H. J. Mackinder appeared, and his book on *Democratic Ideas and Reality*, originally published in 1919, was reprinted in 1942, only a few months after the United States became a belligerent in the Second World War. Mackinder had seen his study of German power in Europe used by geopoliticians, notably by Haushofer, and even by Hitler himself and had argued that 'there should be a tier of independent states between Germany and Russia'. Without the United States of America, in his view, the League of Nations could not be effective and on this, as on many other matters, he was right. But the main point in Mackinder's argument was that the Heartland possessed remarkable defensive strength and command of interior lines for overland communication. W. G. East summarised his view in these words:

Geographical position, physical remoteness from the world oceans, natural security from attack afforded by the frozen Arctic seas and by the mountain–desert–steppe expanses of central Asia and space – so much space as virtually to defy the logistics of an enemy approaching from without – all these considerations seem to have entered into Mackinder's evaluation of the Heartland as a citadel for defence and as a secure base for offensive warfare (East and Moodie, 1956, p. 116).

As originally defined the Heartland had only about 30 million people though by the end of the Second World War there were over three times as many, owing to the great expansion of settlement and industrial activity in Siberia, especially after the German invasion in 1941. Indeed Mackinder's Heartland did not even include the western part of the USSR. But whether the Heartland concept meant much in an age of air transport has been often debated. In 1956 W. G. East left this a somewhat open question, while recognising that air warfare, dependent on the great industrial resources of the areas marginal to the Heartland, notably in western and southern Europe, the oil-rich states of the Middle East and Japan ('its role now recast as a base from which to resist aggression') not to mention the vast potential military strength of the United States, could strike effectively at the interior of the continental mass known as the World-Island. Of more immediate interest are the relations between Russia and China, which have obviously changed considerably since the book edited by W. G. East and A. E. Moodie (1901–70) was published in 1956.

Isaiah Bowman's fascinating book on *The New World*, first published in 1920 and revised for later editions to 1928 had, said East and Moodie, become 'an historical text, a picture of a bygone time'. Their new book, *The Changing World*, 1956, written by twenty authors of whom five were resident in the United States and three in Canada, covered more than a 1,000 pages and dealt with the whole world. It is marked by a certain pessimism in places, and shows traces of contemporary fears, fortunately not realised during the succeeding twenty years. But some of their prognostications have been amply justified. A. E. Moodie shows (East and Moodie, 1956, p. 116) for example that the states between Germany and Russia, the *cordon sanitaire* so precious to designers of the new Europe after 1919, could only survive with the dominance of Germany or Russia. Between the wars these states (Poland, Czechoslovakia, Yugoslavia, Hungary, Romania and Bulgaria) were left to work out their own economic salvation with little or no external assistance, says Moodie, perhaps not remembering that those who might have assisted were themselves struggling with problems of massive unemployment.

Possibly it was the world economic crisis that set the stage for the Second World War, partly because it induced the Germans to look eastward for expansion and thereby to make the eventual clash with Russia inevitable. As it turned out Europe's eastern marchlands came within the Soviet orbit and the Germans in eastern Europe were expelled from areas that, in some cases, their ancestors had occupied for hundreds of years. H. G. Wanklyn was fortunately able to visit Czechoslovakia in 1947, and wrote of its changing circumstances in an article in 1948 and a book six years later (Wanklyn, 1948, 1954). Having lost its Jewish community during the German occupation, it lost its German community after 1945 so that whole villages were deserted. But this was only part of a wholesale displacement of people in central and eastern Europe which in all affected some 30 million people. To some geographers the Soviet Union and the countries of eastern Europe remained a source of lively interest, but it was some time before they could be visited and friendly contacts once more made with geographers in countries beyond the Iron Curtain.

The study of the homeland

Maybe it was unkind to quote C. A. Fisher's comment on the dangers of concentration on the parish (p. 149) as if it were itself the world. What any individual geographer does will depend partly on his tastes and circumstances and it may not be possible for some to travel extensively, to carry out investigations in remote areas, to spend long periods away from their own homes and universities. But the immediate homeland may offer interesting opportunities for research, as for example the present writer found during his stay of fourteen years in Ireland from 1936 to 1949. One example of devoted work on the homeland was the publication of *An Economic Geography of Great Britain* in 1949 by Wilfred Smith† (1903–55), who had obviously spent many years on its preparation. Any author of such a book faces the problem that economic circumstances may change rapidly and this was especially true at the time when Smith worked. The book deals thoroughly with the historical aspects and also with the distributional aspects of industries, though the treatment of agriculture is concerned more with economic aspects of grass and arable farming than with actual farms and their produce. Smith's work was a constrained exercise, heavily relying on the available sources that included the excellent work of several economic historians and applied economists: only rarely is there any direct association with any place so that the geographer turns with some relief to a short discussion of the transfer of cotton mills in Burnley to other manufacturing uses. But as it happened Smith and others were able to write a thorough survey of Merseyside for the 1953 meeting of the British Association (Smith, 1953). The volume on Merseyside has some interesting work on the industrial life, social problems and urban structure of Liverpool and also includes chapters on the neighbouring industrial areas, including the middle Mersey chemical belt, the west Lancashire coalfield and the industrial belt in Chester with North Wales. There is also a full treatment of the physical geography of the area and of its history.

Several of the volumes published on the occasion of British Association meetings were notable contributions to geography for they included essays by local workers who knew the area well. (Incidentally it was generally assumed that staffs of university geography departments would be knowledgeable on the local area.) Liverpool had a strong tradition of such work, partly because the *Town Planning Review* had been published there from its foundation in 1910. Wilfred Smith had himself written a *Physical Geography of Merseyside* in 1946 and his comments in the 1953 book still have relevance.

The internal structure it displays is not dissimilar in its general nature to that of many other cities of Britain of comparable size and many of its architectural features express the culture of their period. But the pattern on the ground is individual in accordance with the individual qualities of the site and it displays sharp areal definition owing to the simplicity of the structure of the economy and of the urban fabric arranged symmetrically around the river and fanwise around the focal central area of Liverpool (Smith, 1953, p. 199).

In short, there is some uniformity with other areas, but individuality at the same time. But in 1953 little was heard of models and local authors were deeply conscious, perhaps in some cases over-conscious, of the individuality of the areas on which they wrote. Conversely, some later writers seemed anxious to ignore individuality in their search for a paradigm, claiming that geographers have been excessively concerned with uniqueness.

London exercises a continuing fascination on its residents and its visitors, and it is therefore surprising that until recently so little had been written on it by its numerous geographers except for H. Ormsby's short book *London on the Thames* (London, 1924) and Ll. Rodwell Jones' *London River* (1931). Two books of unusual interest were *The Geography of the Port of London* (1957), by James Bird and *The Industries of London since 1861* (1962) by P. G. Hall. Of these Bird's book includes a historical geography of the port, considered in relation to the general growth of London including the industrial aspects, with the markets and general trade. Bird's book was followed later by his survey of British ports (Bird, 1963). Peter Hall describes his book as 'a study in economic geography, treated historically'. At the outset Hall criticises the assumption in the Greater London Plan of 1944 that '*now* London (was) the country's most important manufacturing centre' for in fact it had been so since 1861 and probably much longer. Older industries studied include clothing, furniture and printing, and newer industries general and electrical engineering with vehicle manufacture. The work includes a careful study of directories with mapping of the evidence they provide and some of the volumes in the admirable, but so often neglected, survey of Charles Booth, *Life and Labour of the People in London*, using the edition of 1892–7. By the time Peter Hall wrote his book a number of articles had been published on London's industry, notably in the *Town Planning Review* which welcomed local studies perhaps more eagerly than some of the geographical journals. The work on London was well timed, for an excellent opportunity of publishing the results was given when the International Geographical Congress came to England in 1964 (p. 169).

Geographers studying their home areas were turning the microscope on the towns and countrysides with which they could easily become familiar. In some cases they were following a long-established practice of contributing to the social and economic welfare of the areas in which they lived. This too was well established, even though their actual work at times appeared to be merely the revelation of a problem rather than a contribution to its solution. And geographers were not alone in such activities. When the problems of acute unemployment and high outward migration from certain industrial areas became apparent in the early 1920s the Government commissioned some studies by economists of problem areas such as South Wales and the textile area of Lancashire and Cheshire, and this work led to the development area policy that has continued, with appropriate modifications, to the present time (University of Manchester, 1932, 1936; University College of South Wales, 1932). Later, as shown on pp. 136 and 145 geographers gave valuable evidence to the Barlow and Scott enquiries which had great influence on the replanning of Britain after the Second World War. Geographers, economists and others made a study of the Swansea area, said by one of its workers to be the result of 'hectic and unplanned industrialization', and published some useful reports in 1939 and 1940 (University College of Swansea). The Department of Geography in Newcastle upon Tyne maintained a continued interest in its home area and had a particularly friendly association with the authorities developing the trading estates in the northeast: an interesting series of population studies was made in the 1950s by J. W. House in association with various *ad hoc* survey committees (North Tyne Survey Committee, 1952). Examples of such work could be multiplied for there were many other cases of mutually helpful association with planning authorities and local administrative bodies. Mention should also be made of the work on derelict land and its reclamation by S. H. Beaver of which the first example was a survey of the West Midlands conurbation carried out in the earliest years of the Ministry of Town and Country Planning in 1943, followed later by studies of the reclamation of areas from which sand, gravel, iron ore and other minerals had been extracted (Beaver, 1944, 1955).

Unfortunately, education has often failed to induce in people the power of seeing the interesting features of their own immediate environment, of recognising the fascination of the living stage on which their own lives are set. In the search for a wider understanding of the world which must be desired by anyone of education, many people were oblivious of their failure to discern the qualities of the area they knew best and, in the case of geographers, where they could most conveniently work. Therefore one could argue that while geographers should be concerned with the whole world, and while some of them may be rash or fortunate enough to work in remote places far from their own homeland, yet at the same time there is a constant need for local study, not only for its intrinsic interest and probable social value but also for the light it may shed on general principles and even those 'general laws' earnestly devised by some workers but surprisingly difficult to establish with sincerity and truth. Perhaps the reason for this is that geography, though firmly based in the physical environment, is concerned with people.

Chapter 9
The challenge of new opportunities

High hopes were entertained for geography in Britain in the years after the Second World War. In common with other countries, there was an expansion of the universities and the growth of specialisation. What before 1939 had been taught as human geography became subdivided under urban, social, settlement, population and numerous other headings, while economic geography re-emerged as agricultural or industrial geography, regional economic development or locational analysis. Historical geography, treated by Roxby and others as the great sweep of civilisation through the ages, now re-emerged as a close study of limited areas and limited periods. There were parallel developments in cognate subjects, particularly in history departments of universities where some courses covered only a few years instead of several centuries. The same trend was apparent in studying the physical environment, for geomorphology was split up into hydrology, glaciology and other aspects while the study of soils and vegetation was similarly divided. With such an emphasis on specialisation, there would appear to be little hope of satisfying a wish of F. K. Hare that a 'high priority' should be given to 'the unification of physical geography, involving the creation of a single discipline out of climatology, soil science, theoretical hydrology, and parts of plant ecology and geomorphology'. Hare's aspiration recalls the idea of the unity of the world that meant so much to earlier geographers and derived its inspiration from Charles Darwin and his contemporaries (Hare, 1967).

Regional geography sank from a position of veneration almost to one of vituperation at this time. No longer was the 'regional concept' fashionable: by some geographers it was arrogantly discarded. For this there were two main reasons. Firstly, much regional work appeared to be a hotchpotch of unrelated facts drawn from a wide range of systematic specialisms, with a little physical geography (perhaps a cursory summary of an area's physical history), a bit of climatology, agriculture, industries, towns, transport, population and much else besides even including – from some geographers – archaeology and historical geography. Boundaries were generally drawn on a physical basis, though as Stevens (in his teaching as supporter of regional geography) showed in 1939 (p. 140) this might be irrelevant. A second objection lay in the excessive generalisation of some regional work. Could one really believe that the North American lowland had the neatly defined agricultural belts labelled corn, winter wheat, hay and dairying? Or even that in Britain there really were the neat agricultural regions of the textbooks ranging from cash crop farming to hill pastures used only for sheep and in Scotland for deer? In fact the detailed investigations of the Land Use Survey showed that (perhaps by a happy chance) such generalisations were more valid than might have been expected, but the explanation of their existence might prove more complex than a simple correlation between crops, soils and climate, for farming is an enterprise developed through tradition, custom, capital resources, adjustment to economic circumstances, availability of markets, even government benefits and regulations.

Neither the over-zealous inclusiveness of the regional texts nor their inept generalisations gave an adequate reason for the thoughtless abandonment of regional teaching in British universities. If one thought little of E. W. Shanahan's book on South America, Preston James's *Latin America* was a book of a very different calibre. And many other regional works of quality have been produced. As it happened, regional geography, having been pushed out through the front door, returned by the back door in Britain, notably during the 1960s when regional economic development and devolution of government, not only to Scotland and Wales but also to various major regions of England, became live issues. The need for a more thorough regional geography was abundantly revealed when the Report of the Local Government Commission was published in 1969 (p. 177). And when interest in conservation developed, Hare's suggestion of the need for research of 'an interdisciplinary or cross-linked character' seemed more compelling and relevant than before.

Opportunities of the 1960s

Despite the denigration of regional geography, the meeting of the International Geographical Congress in 1964 was regarded as an appropriate occasion for publishing regional as well as systematic studies for the visitors from over sixty countries in addition to those from Britain; there were also some welcome supplements to the geographical literature on London and its environs. L. D. Stamp noted in 1964 that the 1928 volume issued for the earlier Congress remained 'the standard work on the regional geography of Britain' of its time. Like other regional texts of merit, it is now of some historical as well as geographical significance. Jean Mitchell, editor of the new volume, *Great Britain: geographical essays* (Mitchell, 1962), says in her preface that the book was 'not a new edition' of the 1928 volume for 'that collection stands enduring, a testimony to the Britain and to the geographers of its period'. However, the British National Committee for

Geography of the Royal Society (the body responsible for sponsoring the Congress) took the view that the occasion should be marked by a volume of a different character from that of 1928 or its successor of 1962. From this fortunate decision came *The British Isles: a systematic geography* edited by J. W. Watson and J. B. Sissons published in 1964. In the preface to this volume, L. D. Stamp wrote that as a 'stocktaking or inventory of the present state of British Geography' it was designedly specialist so that 'one topic after another is taken up and the present state of knowledge analysed, and assessed by one of the leaders in the particular aspect of geography concerned'. He also observes that Britain is a fortunate area in which to become a geographer for: 'It would be difficult, indeed impossible, to find any comparable area on the earth's surface exhibiting such a wide range of natural environments, and where such varying responses have been evoked from such a succession of human inhabitants' (Watson and Sissons, 1964, vi). Many of the visitors to the 1964 Congress would echo this statement, like those who accompanied the writer on a field-tour of the north of England and found it far more varied in its scene and character than they expected.

With full appreciation of the undoubted scholarship in the 1964 book, one still wonders if it was trying to achieve the impossible in attempting to give a satisfying picture of the British Isles, or, to be realistic, Great Britain and Ireland (for the British Isles is no longer a political unit) within a single volume. And the same question comes to mind when reading the 1962 book, with three general chapters, on relief: climate, vegetation and soils, and population, followed by twenty-seven regional chapters (Mitchell, 1962). As in the 1928 volume no general map of regional boundaries is given though several of the authors indicate clearly what they regard as the limits of the regions which they discuss. The traditional view that physical features gave appropriate limits is no longer acceptable to many people. Nevertheless there are cases where a clear line can be drawn, as in the English Fenlands (cf. pp. 131, 133), an area which has attracted several geographers and is excellently treated in this book by A. T. Grove. Unfortunately the Potteries were not discussed at all, an omission happily remedied by a fine study later (Beaver, 1964). In some areas a line of demarcation, or at least a marginal zone, may be discerned through the presence or absence of industry; Wales for example in this book, is discussed in two chapters, one on the industrialised South Wales coalfield with its margins and associated ports and the other on rural Wales, marred perhaps in its pristine qualities by the holiday and residential area of its northern coast which, says E. G. Bowen dismissively, is 'an overspill of industrial Lancashire rather than a part of rural Wales' (Mitchell, 1962, p. 253). Yorkshire is similarly divided between its industrial and rural areas, and a comparable distinction is made by K. C. Edwards between the 'East Midlands' and Lincolnshire: of these the former has its clear core in the three ancient but now industrialised towns of Nottingham, Derby and

Leicester, though its outer circumference is indeterminate, while Lincolnshire is dominantly rural and more akin to the Fenlands than to the coalfield which gave the East Midlands industrial strength. In this book one can see the search for an individuality, for a personality, of the areas the authors discuss: this is frankly stated by K. C. Edwards who says that: 'The East Midlands refers to an area, entirely indefinite as to boundaries, in which the term has an accepted currency among the people concerned. . . . To claim that the East Midlands have developed a regional consciousness would be an exaggeration, yet it is not unfair to suggest that human activities, economic and social, operating within this territory impart to it a measure of coherence' (Mitchell, 1962, p. 287). This was to become a subject of wide interest later, especially when the local government boundaries were revised, after many years of discussion, in 1973. In short, do regional boundaries exist, either as clearly recognisable lines or as zones?

To condemn efforts to write regional geography because much of the work of this character has been unsatisfying is an evasion of responsibility. The trouble appears to lie in the attempt of regional geographers to achieve the impossible, to give a complete synthesis based on such a wide range of rapidly developing systematic studies. In fact some regional geographies include a series of chapters on systematic geography as a basis for regional study. This was so in the work by nine members of the geography department staff at Aberystwyth on *Wales*, edited by E. G. Bowen (Bowen, 1957). Subtitled 'a physical, historical and regional geography' it divides half its space between physical and historical geography and gives the remaining half to the nine regions into which Wales is divided. Bowen (1957, pp. 267–9) in introducing the regional section, says that the regional geographer 'seeks to present for a given area a synthesis of its physical, historical and present-day human geography. Such, indeed, may be considered the goal of geographical studies', a view that many would regard as impossible of achievement. The nine regions are not defined on 'any precise physical, historical or human criteria' nor are they 'natural regions' but 'purely subjective', 'based on a long-established familiarity with the land of Wales, its people and their history'. Nevertheless, there is a recognisable principle in Bowen's choice of regions, for he begins with 'a centrally placed core or heartland', largely Welsh-speaking and mountainous, surrounded on all sides by a number of peripheral regions. The book on Wales owes much to Bowen's deep knowledge of the Welsh countryside and its people, and his concern for historical origins (shown for example in his book of 1954, *The Settlements of the Celtic Saints in Wales*). In 1959 Bowen suggested that Wales could be studied in terms of the 'heartland', meaning the area primarily rural in its population with a high proportion of Welsh speakers, and of the fringe areas (Bowen, 1959). Essentially this is a social approach, taking the most thoroughly Welsh area first and the areas of greater cultural intermingling later. It is selective, using 'those areal facts and phenomena which are relevant to our particular field of enquiry'. This is clearly at variance with the traditional view, expressed by Richard Hartshorne, that 'regional geography is the study of the totality of inter-related phenomena in a particular area'. Bowen also suggested a historical approach of a more direct nature (*v.i*).

Could it then be argued that the time for publishing regional texts was over? In the 1950s a 'Regions of the British Isles' series of fourteen volumes was planned under the editorship of W. G. East, of which the first three to appear were A. E. Smailes, *North England* (1960), A. C. O'Dell †(1909–66) and K. Walton (1923–79), *The Highlands and Islands of Scotland* (1962) and G. H. Dury, *The East Midlands*, (1963). Of these the first two show a strong development of the historical approach to current problems and this was followed to some extent by the authors of the fourth volume to appear, on northwest England (Freeman and Rodgers, 1966). Only two other volumes were published, A. H. Shorter, W. L. D. Ravenhill and K. J. Gregory, *South-west England* (1969) and F. Walker (1914–76), *The Bristol Region* (1972) and the publishers abandoned the series. The failure to cover Britain by regional studies during the 1960s may be indicative of diminishing faith in the value of such an enterprise (though perhaps also of the reluctance of designated authors to do the work).

Bowen suggested in 1959 that a new approach to regional geography might be to take some central theme, such as historical geography, and with that show the relevance of the physical landscape at different periods in time. Both farming and rural population density, at any period, can only be adequately studied in relation to the physical environment if a satisfying historical geography is to be achieved. Historical geography is only one of several possible themes. The writer has often reflected that a regional geography of Ireland could be written with population distribution, past and present, as a basis and (pp. 169–70) several recent texts are based on economic factors and, not less significant, social welfare. It might also be possible to write a regional geography of Ireland (or for that matter of Scotland) based on the marked disparities of natural resources from west to east, to begin with the remoter areas rather than with those nearest to England. But would one expect a work on Scotland to deal first with the Hebrides and to reach Edinburgh and Glasgow after several chapters or would this appear to be precious, perhaps archaic and unrealistic? In Wales, as elsewhere, an economic heartland and a cultural heartland may be two different areas but that comment raises many controversial issues. All that can be said with safety is that as the old 'traditonal' approach is no longer binding there is the possibility of finding new ways of presenting regional geography.

Books dealing with particular areas of Britain were widely appreciated. Not all of them were 'regional' in any normal sense, but the handbooks published by the local governmental authorities or the visit of the British Association for the Advancement of Science generally gave an excellent series of studies of the area's physical geography, climate, population and economic life, probably with other contributions on the botany, zoology, geology, history and educational facilities of the district. The International Geographical Union's Congress in London of 1964 was marked by the publication of several books, including J. T. Coppock and H. C. Prince (eds), *Greater London* (1964) and J. E. Martin, *Greater London: an industrial geography* (1966), though neither of these attracted the attention given to Peter Hall's *London 2000*, first published in 1963 and reprinted with supplementary comments later. Designedly controversial, this book showed the dangers as well as the opportunities of planning. Much interesting local material was included in R. Clayton, *The Geography of Greater London* (1964) designed as a source book for teachers and students, and there is also much material of permanent significance in the *Guide to London Excursions*, issued in 1964 and edited by K. M. Clayton. The move to a study of specific problems was seen in T. J. Chandler, *The Climate of London* (1965) and D. Thomas, *London's Green Belt* (1970). Geographers were in fact only doing what historians and others had done for London, and this work was continued in the publication, from 1968, of the *Atlas of London and the London Region*, edited by E. Jones and J. D. Sinclair.

Land use has become a widespread interest in Britain and some of the argument about any projected change has an emotional character, naturally enough as most developments affect someone's living conditions. In these circumstances, close study of the situation on the ground has been valuable, and the situation in the early 1960s was discussed in R. H. Best and J. T. Coppock, *The Changing Use of Land in Britain* (1962). Both authors enriched their work by a historical approach and the problems inevitable in change were shown in detailed studies of the Chilterns and of Teeside as examples of dominantly rural and urban areas. But the main problem lies in the social need to provide for inevitable town expansion and at the same time to preserve and develop the productivity of farming. Since 1962 both authors have written more on their chosen specialisms; Best has shown in an excellent series of papers that the recent loss of land annually from farming is less than during the inter-war period (Best, 1965) and Coppock has published numerous papers on agriculture, and in 1971 *An Agricultural Geography of Great Britain*.

Such works are partly regional in approach though they could equally well be regarded as social and economic. But to many who have worked on agriculture, especially those who have either some practical experience of farming through upbringing or even fieldwork with interviewing, it would seem that economic returns do not of necessity explain the attitudes of farmers to their work. Coppock explains that 'normative economic theory' rarely explains 'satisfactorily the spatial variations in the agriculture of a country'. He adds that geographers had begun to study 'satisfaction' as equally if not more decisive than the achievement of maximum profits: obviously here one is near or even on a margin with psychology and sociology. Equally the farmer may have his own conception – perhaps misconception – of the hazards of floods and droughts as well as of his own ability to combat their effects. Increasingly it is realised that in practical terms it is the perception of circumstances that determines attitudes and actions. Perception may induce a fine adjustment to scientific possibilities and economic realities but this is by no means universal.

Industrial geography also became a favoured study during the 1960s, and two works on London, P. G. Hall, *The Industries of London Since 1861* (1962) and J. E. Martin (ed.), *Greater London: an industrial geography* (1966) were a welcome addition to the earlier works on London noted on p. 161. For a very different area, G. Manners and others (ed.), *South Wales in the Sixties* (1964) gave a broad view of an area where the changes in population distribution and economic activity have been so great within a short time that they are of unusual interest. Similar changes, though of a less dramatic character, were the subject of D. M. Smith, *Industrial Britain: the North West* (1969): in this book the author is concerned partly with planning problems and suggests that certain areas in which growth is already apparent, notably the Merseyside–Manchester axis, should be developed. This, however, is controversial, for the rehabilitation of the older industrial areas, notably those in the Pennine valleys, is favoured by many people, and especially by some of their more vigorous representatives in Parliament.

Surveys such as those of the industrial geography of London, South Wales and the northwest have an obvious relevance to current planning problems for they are basically applied geography. Along with those noted above, mention must also be made of *Merseyside: social and economic studies*, edited by R. Lawton and C. M. Cunningham (1970). The tradition of co-operative survey was well established in Liverpool from the pioneer work of D. Caradog Jones, whose *Survey of Merseyside* was published in 1934. It had been a main concern of Wilfred Smith, and was reflected in the notable *Handbook* published for the British Association in 1953 (p. 160). But since then there had been many changes, not least in the development of the motor industry and in the clearance of a high proportion of Liverpool's obsolete housing. And there are many individual contributions elsewhere, in some cases written by geographers working as consultants for local authorities or government departments.

The concern for the future

Immediately after the Second World War the expectations of creating a new Britain were high, though many people were concerned about the financial possibility of implementing the excellent schemes for rebuilding cities, modernising transport and rehabilitating decayed industrial areas. A far simpler problem, it seemed, would be the reorganisation of local government, but as it turned out this led to almost thirty years of dreary and repetitive debate. Even so innocent an enterprise as the definition of the major conurbations for the 1951 Census (p. 149) was regarded as dangerous by many local councillors because it might lead to some governmental reorganisation of such areas for local administrative purposes as, with modifications, it did twenty years later. In time, however, much that is at first resisted by large numbers of people will be accepted as inevitable by most of them. To what extent a geographer as such should provide a direct answer to known social problems is a matter for personal decision: some people are by nature controversialists who enjoy the cut-and-thrust of debate and the statement of their case in the attractive journalistic prose of the *avant-garde* weeklies or the works of the Fabian Society, while others care more for academic detachment and are willing to brave the scorn of the 'committed'.

Even the Royal Geographical Society will on occasion welcome an argumentative article on a matter of public debate, such as the need for a third London airport, to be located at Foulness on the Thames estuary, after the Roskill Commission had begun its work by considering seventy-eight sites, reduced them to four, and finally recommended one (Cublington) which was rejected by the Government. The article of 1971 by J. G. U. Adams has an evocative title, 'London's third airport: from TLA (Third London Airport) to Airstrip One?' (*Geogr. J.* **137**, 1971, pp. 468–504). Adams admits that increased mobility has been of social and economic benefit to humanity but doubts if 'these trends, extrapolated toward infinity, will always continue to make for "progress"'. He shares the concern expressed by J. P. Misham 'about runaway growth rates of a great range of things from population through pollution, crime and drug addiction, to mobility and GNP. It seems not notably implausible to a growing number of people that such trends, which appear so similar, might in some complex way be causally related.' He finished his article by expressing the fear that in time these may be a 'completely polarized society', with the rich and powerful living in a mobile electronic world and the poor inhabiting a 'dismal, dirty, pedestrian world', similar to that of George Orwell's *1984* in which England had become 'Airstrip One'. Fortunately, Adams concedes that 'it can be argued that it is improbable' in many of its details. But to those in touch with the younger generation, it is immensely refreshing to read such an article, for it shows their increasing concern with what are known as 'environmental problems', a vague term that covers such matters as pollution, world food supply, the differences in opportunity available for various social and economic groups in the community, and even the dangers of a restless mobility that may be harmful socially. In fairness one must mention that the article includes a careful analysis of the statistical arguments in the Roskill Report: indeed though the article might seem polemic to a seasoned academic, to the first speaker in the discussion, Mr Peter Masefield of the British Airports Authority, it appeared to be 'rather an academic introduction to the subject'. But it is natural that geographers should be as interested in the possible effects of building a new airport on the Thames estuary, and therefore a vast town, or in the construction of a Channel tunnel, as they were in the cutting of the Suez Canal or the Panama Canal at an earlier time. As it has turned out, no third airport is planned for any near future.

Whatever the attitude of geographers to regional study by the 1960s it became part of the Labour Government's policy to promote regional development and for this purpose nine economic planning regions were defined (Ministry of Housing and Local Government, 1964: Department of Economic Affairs, 1964–6). Of these six conformed to the Standard Regions of 1946 but three others were new for the Southeast Region covered the three areas previously defined as the Eastern, Southern and London and Southeastern Region, as well as the Soke of Peterborough (united to Huntingdonshire in 1965), the new Yorkshire and Humberside Region included the Lindsey area of Lincolnshire as well as the East and West Ridings of Yorkshire, and the new East Midlands Region was the same as the former North Midland except for the loss of Lindsey and the Soke of Peterborough (Fig. 16). These 'regions' could be described as *ad hoc* in character for they were merely convenient divisions based on existing administrative county boundaries. Naturally they were heavily criticised by some geographers including B. E. Coates and A. J. Hunt who noted that 'a new pattern of control over economic development has been introduced' (this was in fact hardly so in realisation) and that the Sheffield Region had been split between two regions and Sheffield itself, 'the sixth largest city in England, on the margin of the Yorkshire and Humberside region, with which it has little in common in terms of interests and problems, but excluding its urban field on the east and south'. (Coates and Hunt, 1965). The two authors reach the gloomy conclusion with which it is impossible not to agree that traditional administrative boundaries were unrealistic for planning and research and that therefore 'the prospects

---

Fig. 16 Economic Planning Regions.
The Standard Regions were based on wartime emergency measures for the provision of services in the event of dislocation through invasion or air attack. Except in a few places they conformed to county boundaries and they were made the basis for the post-war replanning of Britain. By the 1960s a new drive towards economic regional planning made further changes desirable, such as the recognition of Humberside as at least a potential entity. The London Region was perhaps the hardest to define, for although by 1965 a Royal Commission's recommendation had given what has been regarded as a somewhat restricted definition of London itself, Mackinder's idea of 'metropolitan England' appeared to have more validity than ever before. By 1979 the future of the 'development areas' was under critical discussion.
Reproduced from Freeman, T. W., *Geography and Planning* (London) 1974.

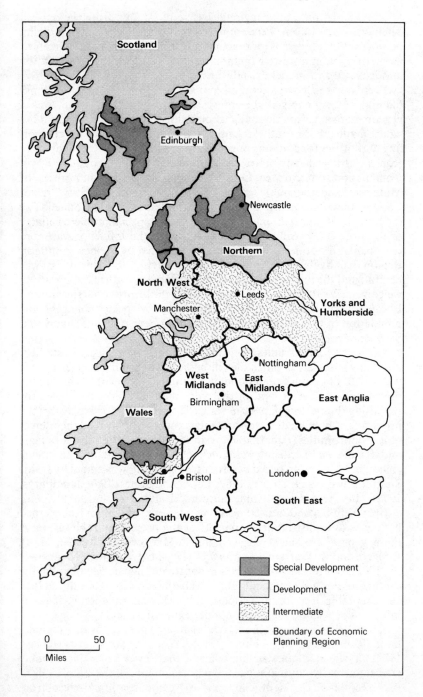

Scotland

Edinburgh

Newcastle

Northern

North West

Leeds

Manchester

Yorks and
Humberside

West
Midlands

East
Midlands

Nottingham

East Anglia

Birmingham

Wales

Cardiff • Bristol

London ●

South East

South West

Special Development

Development

Intermediate

Boundary of Economic
Planning Region

0   50

Miles

for future planning on a regional basis are vitiated from the outset'. Their views, however, were contested by Osborne (1965). In fact any new definition of regions for practical governmental purposes is likely to use existing administrative boundaries, however awkward they may be and irrelevant to modern conditions.

Even so, the recognition of a need for some form of regional planning, presumably to be integrated into a national plan, was a welcome advance for the basis of planning had been the Act of 1947 which made administrative counties and county boroughs the controlling authorities for planning purposes, which led to conflict perhaps best seen in the jealously patriotic attitudes discovered by the Royal Commission on Greater London among the local authorities of Middlesex and its county council (1961): by creating a new Greater London they managed to abolish the Middlesex County Council. The definition of Greater London, however, was a special problem capable of solution, but its sphere of actual and potential influence was more reasonably, if not necessarily accurately, defined by the new Southeast Region than by the three regions it superseded (Fig. 16). This at least was helpful, and the first of the regional reports on the southeast was warmly welcomed. Written by unnamed officials in the Ministry of Housing and Local Government, it dealt with the current and expected changes in the population of the southeast and the planned developments that would become necessary.

Other regional studies followed and all were eagerly studied, especially in the areas which they discussed. Attention was given to a far wider field of enquiry than population and employment, including the prevalence of derelict land in the older industrial areas, the need for rehousing the existing population as well as providing for expansion, the provision of higher education and the numbers who availed themselves of its opportunities (remarkably low in some areas), the balance of male and female employment and much else of a social and economic character. A series of books on 'Industrial Britain' was edited by D. M. Smith (Smith, 1969; House, 1969; Lewis and Jones, 1970; Humphrys, 1972). In these books some authors deal more thoroughly with environmental conditions than other authors, but all are concerned mainly with industrial developments of the present and the future. A more general treatment is given in G. Manners, O. Keeble, H. B. Rodgers and K. Warren in *Regional Development in Britain* (Manners *et al.*, 1972), but in this book Wales is not treated separately but with the southwest, the West Midlands and the northwest. This is hardly likely to be acceptable to certain sections of Welsh opinion though it raises interesting speculations on economic regionalisation.

Essentially such works are studies in applied geography on a regional basis. With them may be linked *The UK Space* by six authors (House, 1973) in which the statement is made that 'even in an increasingly environmentally-conscious age the physical nature of the UK is likely to take second place, in official eyes, to regionalisation derived from economic, social or political attributes, in so far as these may be adequately disentangled' (House, 1973, p. 9). This point is developed further by G. Humphrys, who observes that:

In the past when geography was confined to the study of man's relationship with his environment, especially with his physical environment, it was in the heavy industries that such relationships seemed most obvious . . . this emphasis by geographers on the heavy industries has outlasted the conditions which gave rise to it. Geography has expanded to become much more concerned with understanding the spatial structure of society, than just with man–land relationships (House, 1973, p. 252).

He goes on to explain that by 1970 in the UK there were over 12 million people employed in the service sector, compared with only 8 million in manufacturing and less than 2 million in primary production. The wish of many authors is to emphasise what is happening at the present time, to be fully aware of the inevitable dynamic of society. If in this they sometimes forget that in the past geography was broader than merely 'man's relationship with his environment' this may be regarded as easy acceptance of the 'bad old days' outlook.

Many writers regard regional planning as the great need of the time, for there is no *status quo* in a rapidly changing society and writers on regional economic planning are concerned not only to discern but also to guide changes in the use of land, realising that this is a matter of choice more complex in character than is generally appreciated. Hopes of making a better environment in towns do not always bear fruit. There is much to encourage and much to discourage. Slum clearance, for example, has made possible the extension of universities and other institutions in some cities, and despite the loss of office employment in many places the central areas of British cities remain economically powerful and attractive. But the outward movement of people and industries is making some inter-city areas social deserts, awaiting development for many years, and some of the earlier post-1945 housing schemes have proved to be socially disastrous. Deprivation is not merely a matter of defective homes with inadequate amenities but also of the creation of new slums in areas of new housing. This appears to have surprised some geographers, but it was a situation with which Victorian housing reformers were entirely familiar.

The modern geographer deals with the problem of regionalisation in a dynamic society. He will not be satisfied merely with a study of population distribution for he will also want to know something of the quality of life of the people. That it was possible to recognise differences of a social character even in the *ad hoc* regions defined in the 1960s (as in the 1946 Standard Regions of which they were a modification) was clearly shown in the reports then produced. Some of these social differences were easier to identify than to explain, such as the lower proportion of women taking paid employment in the mining areas or the smaller percentage of young people seeking higher education in some areas than others, for though there was some correlation with income level that was hardly the complete answer. Why should the number seeking such opportunities be far higher in Wales than in areas of equally high, or even higher, income level in many parts of England? Fascinating speculations arise here, and many of them have been thoughtfully investigated in B. E. Coates and R. M. Rawstron, *Regional Variations in Britain*, (London, 1971). Significantly, this book has the subtitle 'studies in economic and social geography'. Among the subjects they discuss are personal incomes, employment, the overseas-born, health services, mortality and education and there is an obvious and

welcome concern with human welfare. That more work along these lines could be fruitful is undoubted but meanwhile, said one reviewer, 'it is essential reading for readers in all walks of life who doubt that some of the people born equal need be quite as much more equal than others' (*Geogr. J.* **137**, 1971 pp. 562–4).

Administrative units have an involved history and in many cases also a long one. Once established, they become of significance to the residents and especially to those elected as councillors or appointed as officials to serve the public. As noted on p. 153 the administrative map of Britain was recognised as archaic after the Second World War, and also by some writers much earlier. Finally a new system was evolved by 1973, after approximately thirty years of discussion (Fig. 17). The story of the successive enquiries is far too complicated to be told here, but many geographers were deeply interested in the report of the Redcliffe-Maud Commission which appeared in 1969 with a minority report of almost equal length by Derek Senior (Royal Commission, 1969). That a minority report may be of great significance needs no emphasis to students of such commissions, but Senior pointed out that far too little was known of the social geography of England (and is more known of Wales or Scotland?). He based his demarcation of administrative units on a regional scheme, using great cities as the main centres and towns of lesser size as local centres. Fundamentally this was the concept of the 'city region' with local administration based on towns accessible to rural or semi-urban hinterlands. In the end, as always, a compromise solution was reached, with a reorganisation of counties and the recognition of some major built-up areas of considerable size as metropolitan counties, each divided into a number of districts (Fig. 17). What contribution geographers made to this administrative redefinition of Britain is only partially known, though various memoranda are known to have been sent to the Commission and it was discussed in various geographical journals.

A fascinating position now arises in the regional study of Britain.

Fig. 17 The county solution of 1974.
Loyalty to the idea of the county proved in the end to be stronger than many planners expected though substantial changes were made in the structure of local government, of which the most interesting was the recognition of six metropolitan counties: the West Midlands, Merseyside, Greater Manchester, South Yorkshire, West Yorkshire, Tyne–Wear. Greater London was defined earlier. The most interesting of the new counties are perhaps Cleveland, Humberside and Avon for these are based on modern industrial growth around ports. That there was considerable opposition to many of the new boundaries needs no emphasis, but nevertheless Rutland became part of Leicestershire and the people of a rural landscape near Oxford (with many commuters in the villages and towns) had to accept absorption into Oxfordshire, despite the fact that they had previously belonged to the Royal county of Berkshire.

Books and papers on regional development include distribution maps based on administrative divisions such as counties, county boroughs, urban districts and rural districts, that have now disappeared. Some statistical data for small areas, such as urban districts within conurbations, will no longer be available from 1981 and it will therefore be interesting to see if some of the broad generalisations, as well as those based on more detailed local material, will confirm those already in general circulation. That the administrative areas used for mapping closely influence the product achieved is well demonstrated in K. E. Rosing and P. A. Wood, *Character of a Conurbation*, (Rosing and Wood, 1971). For the whole of the West Midlands (Birmingham–Black country) conurbation they used statistical material for wards, of which there were 161, but for Birmingham they had data for 472 enumeration districts. The authors present their maps side by side and so demonstrate the greater accuracy of the finer mesh: for example the ward figures for the entire conurbation show a percentage of population over sixty-four years old ranging from 4 to 16 while the enumeration districts show a range from 1 to 25. This atlas uses computer techniques for its calculations and for its graphic presentation. Some geographers of modern times incline to, or in some cases emphatically support, the view of Lord Kelvin that truth lies in measurement and must be conveyed statistically. The work of Rosing and Wood shows that with modern resources such as computers a thorough statistical analysis can be made of an area having a population of almost 2.5 million and their work gains strength from their obvious local knowledge that is allowed to illuminate the distributions of a social and economic character with which they are concerned. Here, as in many modern works, the regional element has slipped into the story, perhaps rather timidly but nevertheless surely.

Analysis of towns has proved to be absorbing for many geographers, and several books as well as a multitude of articles have been published in recent years. As B. T. Robson has pointed out, urban studies are 'distinctly multi-disciplinary rather than inter-disciplinary' for they have attracted economists, historians, lawyers, political scientists and sociologists and one may add others including psychologists (Robson, 1969). The fascination of towns lies partly in the obvious fact that they are perpetually changing. Rosing and Wood (1971, pp. 98–9) noted that 25 per cent of the people of Birmingham and the Black Country had changed their address between 1961 and 1966, partly due to slum clearance. Moves are also related to changes in 'life-style', by which one may live for a time in a flat or hired rooms, move to a house for family reasons, perhaps later to another and larger house if sufficiently prosperous and eventually to a small house or flat when the family have dispersed (Johnston, 1971). Obviously there is no standard pattern for some people never move while others may do so frequently as their careers involve transfers to other towns. Models have been constructed to illuminate the patterns so frequently, but not invariably, observed.

Then, too, the character of a neighbourhood may change, probably by decay and decline in status though this is not inevitable, for in some cities, notably in London, there are signs that some neighbourhoods are rising in status as the houses are modernised and redecorated. The process of 'gentrification' is perhaps more widespread than is commonly realised for the expense of commuting gives many people a wish to live as near as possible to their work.

Several authors have written about the development of 'ghettos' in British towns: indeed the Booth survey of London in the 1890s had much interesting material on the Jewish ghettos then developing in the East End of London. In more recent times the interest has been in areas populated by Negroes, Indians and Pakistanis, but gradually they, like the Jews, Poles and other immigrants, are moving outwards from the original ghettos so that many areas are mixed in population. Belfast shows in its artisan area a division between Catholic and Protestant households that, though traditional, is more firmly entrenched than ever (Boal, 1969, 1970–71). When F. W. Boal and others began to study the artisan areas of the city they found that people showed their political and social convictions by flags or other embellishments, and even patronised different shops: the Catholic and Protestant ghettos became even more definite as tension mounted. All this, however, was only part of a complex social situation. At one time, in the immediate post-1945 era, it was frequently assumed that people would act in a predictable manner by patronising the nearest shops or other facilities, but this is only partially true. In urban study, as in so many aspects of geography, the search for a paradigm may be futile for every town has its individuality, acquired not only from its site and situation but also from its social, economic and perhaps also political history.

Underlying many of the enquiries of the present time there is the consciousness that in the densely settled lands of Western Europe the abiding problem is the right use of land, not only for the present generation but also for those whom come after. This is undoubtedly one reason for an increasing concern with outdoor recreational activities as well as those available under cover in sports halls, gymnasia and swimming-baths. As noted on p. 154 preservation of the countryside as well as its availability to all for recreational purposes is the continuing responsibility of the Countryside Commission. Students in all ages appear to love a word or a phrase and to charge either with emotional overtones: at present 'conservation' and 'environmental pollution' have become so charged, but this hardly matters for it is leading the more thoughtful to consider such problems in their climatic and biological aspects as well as in terms of economic resources and land use. In economically advanced countries, agricultural production per acre increases steadily and stock are reared by so-called factory methods, but in the minds of many people there are uneasy questions about the wisdom of such practices. And as if that were not enough, there are fears that man, having made the earth productive, may also destroy it by his very fecundity. From the local problem one turns again by an easy but not universal process of thought to world problems, and therefore at some time many geographers having some curiosity about the world, will look again to problems of the world beyond their immediate living space.

Curiosity about the world has been a fundamental driving force in the activities of geographers for thousands of years. Nevertheless, a geographer may often be discouraged by the smallness of the amount of the earth's surface which he can actually see and comprehend for himself. Inevitably much must be taken on trust, or at least it is, as P. Haggett showed in a description of a second visit to Brazil, where 'speculations on the persistence of forested zones based on localized field-work . . . were only partially sustained when the survey was extended' over a wider area with sampling methods (*Geogr. J.* **130**, 1964, p. 135). And how may one be sure that the samples are fortunately chosen? Only by detailed local study can the truth be sought, for just as individuals do not conform to mass economic behaviour or in various degrees from mild disapproval to revolutionary activity oppose a community's political ethos, so people evolve a way of living according to their perception of opportunities. Elsewhere Haggett refers to an article by James Bird in which he shows that while Brittany and Cornwall as a whole have much in common, small areas have not: two each of approximately 6 square miles, chosen to be as similar as possible, proved on investigation to be very different, notably in their agricultural life (Bird, 1956). This surely illustrates the danger of generalisation without an adequate basis of local investigation, for which both statistical sources and fieldwork are used as those who read Bird's article will observe. It also raises the question of why such differences should exist, and on this several answers are possible. In the case of Brittany, however, Camille Vallaux found that the pattern of fields and farming was closely influenced by the system of land tenure (Carré, 1978). Vidal de la Blache, as his thesis supervisor, queried the geographical relevance of this observation, but it shows that between man and the land there is always a middle dimension, circumstances of custom and tradition, perception of what is possible and what is not.

Clearly the relation between man and the land is a matter of complexity. A difference in landscape between the northeast of Ireland and the southwest of Scotland, so similar in physical features, that interested the writer appeared to be due to a difference in agricultural history, for southwest Scotland had been divided into farms of substantial size by the deliberate policy of the landlords while in northeast Ireland the smaller farms and smaller fields had evolved through vastly different social and economic historical circumstances. As a result, the density of rural population was far higher in northeast Ireland than in southwest Scotland (Freeman, 1959). In fact the story does not end there, for the agricultural landscape of northeast Ireland is being re-formed with fewer farms, larger fields and a lower density of population. All these considerations show that generalisation is only generalisation, useful perhaps but only partially true, essential no doubt in the process of learning but only as a stage in the search for greater light. There is the further consideration that statistics, however intelligently handled, are useful only as one of several lines of enquiry in any geographical study.

The forward view

Never at any time have the opportunities for research in Britain by geographers been more favourable than now. Their vast increase in numbers needs no emphasis and there are grants available for post-graduate workers, with possibilities of studying or even finding employment abroad for a few years. Specialism has been a natural development, giving workers a form of academic satisfaction denied to earlier scholars conscious of the hazards of the generalisations they were obliged to make. The nineteenth-century concepts of the relation between physical and human factors may now seem simplistic: that there is a relation cannot be questioned. The physical aspects of geography, including geomorphology, climatology and biography, all have their disciples and what was once called 'human' geography, derived from the German 'anthropogeography' and the French *géographie humaine*, has now been divided into a vast range of specialisms. In these, however, some unification of purpose may be seen, for there is the dominant motif of social concern. Land-use study is concerned with agriculture, forestry, mining and quarrying, the rural population, conservation and recreation; urban geography with much more than trade and industry, including the welfare of the entire population, not least the deprived, and with this the provision of recreation in its many forms. Along with this there has developed a growing interest in the aesthetic aspects of landscapes. Other specialisms survive in strength, including historical geography with an increasing interest in the history of geographical thought.

Books on various aspects of systematic geography proliferate and there have been many additions to the literature in regional geography, notably on Russia. Some show extreme, but laudable, concentration of interest, such as Marjorie Sweeting's *Karst Landforms* (London, 1972) while others, such as C. A. M. King's *Beaches and Coasts* (London, 1959, and later) take a somewhat broader view. But it is now hard to imagine that students of geomorphology in a university course could be satisfied with a single text, such as those used by a former generation. Many stimulating works have been produced by collaboration, notably *Frontiers in Geographical Teaching*, edited by R. J. Chorley and P. Haggett (London, 1965), followed by *Models in Geography* in 1967 and by other books on comparable themes since then. These books, by several authors, have shown the relevance of statistical and model-building techniques to a wide range of readers, and the writers show a wider degree of tolerance for varied points of view than some of their disciples. Undoubtedly the appeal of the model and the statistical equation is the certainty it appears to convey, but its real value lies in the stimulus it provides for further enquiry.

Apparently few geomorphologists would now accept the erosion cycle models of W. M. Davis as authoritative, possibly because they were not based on any quantitative methods of research but rather on observation enlivened by intuition. And perhaps by now the Christaller system of a hexagonal settlement pattern is seen to be a fascinating abstraction never realised in the actual landscape (as indeed Christaller himself showed in his text) but none the less worthy of careful thought. They are in fact generalisations, and at present that of Christaller probably receives more respect that that of Davis. J. H. Paterson in introducing his book *Land, Work and Resources*, (London, 1973) adroitly quotes the saying of William Bunge in 1966 that 'science . . . is willing to sacrifice the extreme accuracy obtainable under the uniqueness point of view in order to gain the efficiencies of generalisation'. Paterson argues that 'verbal generalisations are themselves based upon and summarize a rapidly increasing volume of case work' while 'the use of mathematical symbols may well create an entirely spurious impression of precision in situations where our knowledge is precise in only a few specific cases, on which the generalisation has been founded'. In fairness one must add that Paterson also states that 'by means of statistical methods, an areal generalisation can be formulated which is more precise and, at the same time, contains a larger number of elements, than one arrived at by the traditional, word-based method'. This does not appear to be in opposition to the view of R. J. Chorley, as of Bunge, that geographers had been excessively concerned with the unique and distrustful of generalisation, and that 'the attraction which geographers have felt towards the artistic aspects of natural and social science has militated against the quantification of geography in general and geomorphology in particular'.

Nevertheless, earlier geographers, consciously seeking a method, were prone to make generalisations – especially as correlations – that have not stood the test of time. The search for a key to the whole problem of man on the earth led to environmental determinism and conversely to a failure to recognise that there are limits to profitable settlement (as Griffith Taylor showed in Australia) and to the unfortunate use of such terms as 'man and his conquest of nature'. Theories of racial qualities, advocated by H. J. Fleure and others (pp. 95, 111) have also been tactfully forgotten while studies of rural settlement proved that no cause-and-effect approach could be valid for, as noted on p. 137, 1,000 papers appeared to suggest that every case was unique. Therefore, while it is reasonable to seek generalisation some earlier efforts appear to have produced a house of cards.

Concern with the future now appears to be more prevalent among many British geographers than concern with the past, but the publication of the series of volumes on Domesday geography has been completed with H. C. Darby as editor, and a volume of twenty essays, all of them previously published, appeared in 1970, A. R. H. Baker, J. D. Hamshere and J. Langton, (eds) *Geographical Interpretation of Historical Sources* (Newton Abbot): other compilative volumes have appeared. Some geographers have contributed volumes on industrial archaeology, which attracted considerable attention in Britain from the late 1950s as the rapid reconstruction of towns, and especially of the major cities, involved the demolition of numerous old factories, mills, railway buildings and even canal warehouses and bridges. Industrial archaeology has attracted a variety of specialists including many economic historians with an interest in history on the ground, and the fascination of canals and – even more – railways is experienced by a wide variety of people. The future of many railway lines is a cause of concern to many who wish to preserve such nineteenth-century structures as the original station in Manchester of the Liverpool and Manchester Railway, opened in 1830. Preservation of such relics is a forward-looking attitude, and many British people deplore the losses of fine buildings from the nineteenth and earlier centuries that modern reconstruction of the towns and cities has entailed. For the historical geographer of the future many pictorial records and scale drawings of demolished buildings have been collected in libraries concerned with local history.

Allowing that many old buildings cannot be preserved, it is perhaps surprising that comparatively little attention has been given by historical geographers to the Victorian period, though it is good to note that almost half of the *New Historical Geography of England* edited by H. C. Darby, (Cambridge, 1973), deals with the nineteenth and early twentieth century. (Darby's earlier work of 1936 covered only the story to the eighteenth century.) There have been other contributions to the geographical study of the Victorian town, such as E. W. Gilbert's study of Brighton (Gilbert, 1954) which, however, is in part a social history (and why not?) or the strikingly original work of Ewart Johns (Johns, 1965) on 'townscapes'. The abundance of suitable material on the nineteenth century such as the Census, statistics, government reports, Ordnance Survey maps, contemporary articles in journals such as those of statistical societies (then having wide social interests), reports of medical officers of health and of other municipal officials – all presumably survive for later workers. What may not survive is much of the residential town, or the central areas except in the case of some churches and magnificent civic monuments such as the great provincial town halls that expressed the sanguine outlook of the city fathers. While a number of historians work on the Victorian period the contribution made by geographers is not as considerable as it might be, though a search through the literature will show some interesting articles, for example, in the *East Midland Geographer* and in several of the British Association handbooks. Some articles are concerned with transport and others with industry, population and town growth. An expected development, much discussed at various meetings of historical geographers, is the use of modern statistical and model-building techniques in dealing with past periods.

In historical as in other aspects of geography, advance may come from new techniques, but much of the evidence survives on the ground. Archaeologists have been given embarrassingly rich opportunities of excavating Roman and other early settlements in many towns torn asunder pending reconstruction. An economic historian, M. Beresford, has made people aware of the existence of hundreds of abandoned villages (Beresford, 1954) and W. G. Hoskins in his more varied approach has shown the wealth of 'history on the ground' (Hoskins, 1959). All this confirms, if confirmation were needed, the traditional geographical view that successive generations of inhabitants have made and re-made the landscape. But the study of the landscape offers a far greater challenge than many geographers realise. Without discarding any new techniques, there is still a need to preserve those that have been honoured by generations of former workers. From the French and German schools of geography the idea of landscape study has been absorbed by British geographers though historical studies also involves the use of maps and other printed (or even in some cases manuscript) sources. The fact remains that changes may be so swift and considerable that dating of any particular feature in the landscape is difficult. No subject is more complex that rural settlement, on which one contribution was D. Sylvester's *The Rural Landscape of the Welsh Borderland*, (London, 1969), an area 'astride the highland–lowland line' that was itself 'a separate region' having its own 'hybrid settlement landscape'. This area has been settled by many people with varying traditions, but it is dominantly rural and therefore the land use and settlement is of dominant interest. Much from a remote past is encapsulated in the present landscape, though even for such obvious features as villages clustered round a church, a green with a pond, an inn, many theories of origin are possible. But the dispersion of population on farmsteads outside the villages offers problems such as the period when the first farmhouses were built, the influence of landowners, even the conditions of climate over a period of years. None of these difficulties need deter investigators. But they illustrate a statement made by many geographers that 'the landscape is an end-product' and also show that to discern how the landscape itself was made is no easy task.

It has been one of the misfortunes of geography in Britain that specialists in one branch of the subject have not uncommonly been unappreciative of colleagues having different interests. It is tempting to regard such attitudes as a reaction against the universal knowledge to which many earlier geographers appeared to aspire. Some of these were concerned with all the world over all periods of time, fortified by such concepts as the 'Holism' of General Smuts. And university teachers, however specialist in their researches and published works, were normally required to teach a wide range of courses. But there is a deeper reason for specialism than mere inclination: through the years, and especially since the Second World War, the number of practising geographers has so vastly increased that research has been multiplied with fortunate results in the publication of a vast number of books and articles. It will seem strange to students of the 1970s that fifty years earlier there was so little to read on many aspects of geography that one welcomed anything new with joy. A new article by P. M. Roxby on China, the 1928 volume of essays on Great Britain edited by A. G. Ogilvie, the 'Corridors of Time' volumes by H. J. E. Peake and H. J. Fleure, and other books of that epoch were eagerly read, as were the small number of American texts, not least Isaiah Bowman's fascinating *New World*. French texts by Jean Brunhes and Vidal de la Blache were also eagerly read, by many students in the original language. Now there is a far more adequate range of books, at a price. So much progress has been made already that some complacency might develop, but fortunately that is rare, so rare indeed that as one reads the Institute of British Geography's fascinating publication, *Area*, written mainly by the younger geographers, it seems that people are still as eager to ask where they (and especially others) are going and why.

Chapter 10

The past and the present

A new idea does not spring up in the mind with no foundations for it is foreshadowed by experience and observation. The term 'breakthrough' belongs more to the journalist than to the scholar, for research is a continuing process in which, at certain times, a new synthesis may appear to be valid. Charles Darwin's *Origin of Species* crystallised ideas that had been in the minds of naturalists for many years and its originality lay in its correlation of much scientific observation and experiment, including Darwin's own, to give a view of the ordered scientific unity of the world and particularly of all organic life in relation to the inorganic world. The emphasis was on environment and the adaptation of organic phenomena to the environment of which other organic phenomena were part. To geography this proved to be an inspiration but already, by the time of Darwin, geographers were concerned with the relation between vegetation and climate, with the world distribution of fauna in relation to climate and vegetation, as well as to soil, all of which was part of an effort to explain the diversity of man known to exist from the dawn of human history. And as the world was opened up by exploration its fascinating diversity became known to a wider public eager to know more of lands previously undiscovered or merely sketched in outline on atlas maps. That this exploration came at a time when means of transport, industrial activity and political imperialism were developing with strength gave new hopes of human power and achievement. Along with this the population of the world was increasing and the prospects of world peace and prosperity appeared to be unlimited. The pioneer through pathless African forests was venerated, for he was opening new ways for commerce and civilisation, to be administered by advanced European nations. Just as the voyage of the *Beagle* in 1831–6 gave inspiration to Darwin and others so in 1872–6 the *Challenger* voyage solved many of the world's climatic mysteries, though the achievement went far beyond this for it laid the foundations of modern oceanography and marine zoology. It is not remarkable that two of Britain's 'modern' geographers, H. J. Mackinder and – still more – H. R. Mill, were concerned with oceanography for it was a favoured scientific study of their time.

By the 1880s many observers, including some of the wiser supporters of the Royal Geographical Society, were conscious of the need to analyse and systematise the abundant raw material that was being provided by explorers, missionaries, colonial administrators and others. This led to continued and finally successful appeals for university recognition as well as the development and improvement of geography teaching in all other educational institutions. Much of this enterprise was directed to encouraging explorers to observe and map the areas they visited with greater efficiency, but there was also the wish to study the world's natural resources with a view to commercial expansion and to equip teachers for their work. Geography was drawing inspiration from some new textbooks, especially on the physical side, T. H. Huxley's *Physiography* (1877) and H. R. Mill's *Realm of Nature* (1892), but beyond this lay a wish to study the whole landscape, human as well as physical and this led to an enthusiasm for regional study, both on a local and a world scale. Both Mackinder and Mill clearly understood that nobody could be a good geographer if he failed to see and understand the geography of his own immediate environment and in this they were following the views of French and German workers, at one and the same time conscious of the immediate and the remote, knowing that though the world was their parish, their parish was itself an expression of the world.

All through this time the mapping of the world continued, and much of the raw material on various countries was eagerly incorporated in maps by the cartographical firms and in works of an encyclopaedic character. By the end of Queen Victoria's reign progress had been remarkable, but there were still many gaps in the exploration of the world and of these the greatest was Antarctica. Whether the many brave explorers who went from several countries (not all of whom managed to arrive) appreciated the scientific enlightenment that would follow is doubtful and certainly the general public appeared to be mainly concerned with the question of who would reach the South Pole first. The heroic element naturally had a consuming appeal, but meanwhile the idea of world and local regionalisation was growing even though A. J. Herbertson's view of natural regions was coolly received by the experts of the time (p. 79) and H. R. Mill's idea of detailed home regional interpretation (p. 59) remained a dream. But there were advances, notably in vegetation mapping under the inspiration of Patrick Geddes in Scotland and by others in England: this led to the foundation of plant ecology, but biogeography has remained a specialism, perhaps undervalued and too little studied at times. Geddes had a wide influence over at least some of the young geographers of his time, for out of his plethora of ideas there came an inspiration to look at human problems with a broad vision and hope for the creation of a better human environment. His views were not accepted as a guide to research and policy but rather as an approach to such work, for in him there was a prophetic zeal difficult to ignore. Although the newer approaches to regional geography had removed the servitude of geography to political boundaries, realists such as H. J. Mackinder knew that they still mattered even though his essay on the Heartland of the Old World of 1904 and his broader study of 1919, *Democratic Ideals and Reality*, received limited attention on their publication. At the beginning of the First World War the Royal Geographical Society published some papers on boundaries (p. 94), but the contribution of British geographers on the new political units of the post-war period was limited.

The post-war period covered only twenty years but it was a time of marked advance in geography, in which French and – to a lesser extent – German works were closely studied and American work, notably the political geography of Isaiah Bowman, was favoured. Many geographers in Britain studied the human geography of French writers, especially Vidal de la Blache as well as the work of Ellen Churchill Semple and Ellsworth Huntington. Although the number of professional geographers was small, there were several anxious to deal with human problems, covering a wide conspectus and including political, social, economic and other aspects. Much of this work seemed to be of dubious value to the Royal Geographical Society, which maintained its interest in cartography and exploration with a helpful acceptance of pioneer work on geomorphology. A wider range of papers appeared in the *Scottish Geographical Magazine* and several British geographers looked to the American *Geographical Review* as a possible outlet for their work while the Geographical Association gave space to writers on human aspects of geography. One motive for the foundation of the Institute of British Geographers was to publish research monographs rather than papers and also to provide a form for the presentation and discussion of new work. Geography in Britain was marked by increasing vitality at this time. L. D. Stamp's Land Utilisation Survey proved to be an academic exercise with great planning implications and the publication of a volume of essays edited by H. C. Darby on the historical geography of England to 1800 (Darby 1936), with many detailed studies in journals and in time the Domesday Survey, opened new doors to workers on historical geography. Probably the widespread interest in an historical approach owed much to the French school, though another influence was that several leading geographers of the time had taken their initial degrees in history. There was no orthodoxy and some geographers, notably H. J. Fleure and his disciples, spread their work over a wide range of problems in archaeology and anthropology. It was certainly a time of fruitful academic experiment and by the time war was declared Eva G. R. Taylor was advocating a national atlas and presenting material on the location of industry, on the invitation of the Royal Geographical Society, to the Barlow Commission.

War brought new and in some cases unexpected opportunities of government service to geographers, of which the most obvious result in publication were the geographical *Handbooks* prepared for the Admiralty at Cambridge and Oxford. Early in the war, indeed at a time when the prospects of an Allied victory seemed remote, attention was given to the future planning of Britain and in time geographers were to become numerous among professional planners, following appropriate post-graduate study. The relevance of geographical study became a live issue, for though some were content to follow the peaceful paths of Academe and engage in researches for which no practical application could be expected, many more wished in some way to become 'involved', for changes in the economic and social life of Britain came swiftly and of these one that gave new opportunities was the rapid expansion of universities and other colleges of higher education. Professional geographers became far more numerous and geographical education became firmly established in schools, despite fears that it might be merged into some vague miasma of social or environmental studies. Advance was not achieved without some difficult interludes, of which perhaps the least fortunate was an absurd controversy between 'regional' and 'systematic' geographers: in fact the regional approach remained, though without the veneration for presenting all possible aspects of the environment which was traditional.

As one academic fashion succeeds another, much remains from the past despite the eagerness of innovators to make all this new and even to claim discovery of the one pearl of great price. On p. 156 for example, it is suggested that the wish to know the whole world, especially the distant world, is as strong as ever and the wish to understand the home environment does not decline. Some themes acquire new researchers, such as medical geography and yet A. Haviland was writing on this over a century ago, even if his views now seem somewhat eccentric (pp. 62–4), and the value of mapping the incidence of diseases was shown in the cholera epidemics of the nineteenth century. There are times when opportunities appear to have been missed or at least to be appreciated too late: after the Second World War there was a surge of interest in colonial geography, but much written then would have been valuable to administrators of African territories thirty or forty years earlier. Regrettably the efforts of A. G. Ogilvie and a few others to add geographical study to the records of African exploration from 1926 met with only a limited response. Early explorers painted a glowing picture of boundless fertility as a basis for a happy and prosperous future, but this would be tested only by close investigation of rainfall, temperature, soil characteristics and other environmental qualities: lack of such knowledge led to many disasters and some experience in agricultural expansion was dearly bought. Still, there remains the problem of the vagaries of climate in many parts of the world, of disasters and hazards, and one great service given by H. R. Mill in his years at the British Rainfall Organization from 1901 was to establish many more recording stations.

Nothing is easier than demonstration of missed opportunities and past mistakes. When the economic and social aspects of geography found a place in the *Geographical Journal* of the inter-war period, the theme chosen was the 'habitable world', for the centenary celebrations of 1930. Obviously this was of supreme human importance for it was then appreciated that the world's population was increasing and would continue to increase. Concern about the world food supply was growing and the malnutrition of a high proportion of the world's population was well known. Despite the advances of knowledge, this still remains a challenging question, never fully investigated. Who could say that the solution is in sight? Some governments are more concerned to maintain power than to solve such problems, even to debase some sections of the population by keeping them in a subordinate economic position. As some modern writers clearly understand, the acquisition of wealth through exploitation of natural resources may benefit only a limited section of the population who may be insulated from knowledge of poverty and degradation. All this is common knowledge, but at least it illustrates the point that the hope of some geographers that a simple revelation of man and environment could never be adequate for people's lives are conditioned by many customs, traditions, practices, taboos, political, social and economic circumstances.

Inevitably the geographer thinks of people, in the mass and as individuals, in relation to place. The inspiration of nineteenth-century geography lay in its study of the earth as the home of man, and the attraction of much that was published lay in its revelation of the way people lived in various little-known or unknown parts of the world, with special emphasis on those who were living close to nature, dependent on local resources with few trading relations to others. That some glorified the noble savage, or at least romanticised the primitive subsistence way of life, with its home crafts, sometimes transformed into peasant industries if the opportunity was available, is hardly surprising for many Victorians were fully aware of the industrial horror of their own time, and the concentration of people into what Lewis Mumford called the 'insensate town' at a later time naturally repelled many sympathetic and sensitive observers. Geography, and this was especially so of regional geography, provided escapist reading. Industrial expansion, though contributing to national greatness, had its perils in the inevitable town growth with the fears of disease and crime. Although by the 1840s there were more people in towns than in rural areas in Britain, the appeal of geography was primarily rural, away from the towns which covered only a small part of the total area of the country, indeed only 5 per cent as late as 1900 when four-fifths of the total population lived in towns.

There has been a great change in British geography for now the concern in regional study is industrial, commercial, urban, with the frequent use of such phrases as 'spatial structure' and an emphasis on transport, on linkages between one industrial area and another, on a commuter population moving from home to workplace and, as the private car becomes ever more prevalent, to recreational and other areas. Although some four-fifths of the British population still lives in towns, much the same proportion as in 1900, in fact most rural residents work in towns apart from the small percentage of the national population, now only 3 per cent, who work in farming. If, therefore, the approach to regional study in Britain is through occupations and support of the population, the stress is on towns, but if it is through land use the character of the rural areas remains a prime consideration. That both approaches have been seen is perhaps not remarkable: of these the rural-based approach will be considered first.

Many geographers look back to the work of H. R. Mill (pp. 59–61) on Sussex as an example of a regional treatment that could with advantage have been followed for the whole country. It earned the admiration of numerous geographers for Mill appreciated the qualities of the physical environment when he divided the South Downs into its five segments and four valleys separating these: he chose an area with well-defined physical units having a distinct type of agriculture. The South Downs are of interest for themselves, as well as because they form a scenic background for Brighton and other towns on the costa geriatrica. Unfortunately nothing came of Mill's enterprise, though in it there was one of the forerunners of the Land Utilisation Survey. Some thirty-odd years later, J. F. Unstead produced comparable ideas, with the hope of building up a network of regional units from those of small size like those of Mill, to large units such as the English lowland which in turn could be thought of as part of a western European lowland, rich in agriculture but also – and this is how it would now be considered by some contemporary geographers – the nuclear area of the EEC countries, with their great urban concentrations, their vast industrial wealth, dependent on sophisticated transport systems and commercial organisation, as well as on political and managerial power (Unstead, 1933).

Criticism of much of the work done in regional study is easily made. It may be true that Vidal de la Blache's *pays* are no longer as definable as they once were for French agriculture has been rationalised and industrialised, yet certain areas with their particular qualities of soil, microclimatology and location still remain suited to certain crops. The vines still grow on certain long-chosen and dedicated sites, while other areas are favoured for grain, cattle and sheep. Contrary to what has often been said, Vidal de la Blache never claimed a homogeneity in any *pays* unless it clearly existed, for in some of them local glacial or other superficial deposits gave a different soil and land use. Undoubtedly, Vidal de la Blache's treatment of France was the inspiration of much thought on regional entities in Britain and his *Tableau de la géographie de la France* of 1903 was widely read: a smaller number of people read the various regional monographs published by French graduate students as higher degree theses. There was the real regional geography, it seemed: the geography of Demangeon who in writing his thesis was said to have walked along almost every lane in Picardy and knew and loved his land. In several universities of Britain it was normal for students to write a regional study as part of their degree work and mapping of crops and grassland on 6 in. to 1 mile maps were sometimes included, though this enterprise over the whole country was the work of the Land Utilisation Survey.

Herbertson's natural regions were primarily climatic, though he also used major physical divisions for his world map. His aim was to lead geographers beyond their devotion to political units, tiresomely followed in many texts of the time. At a later stage, however, many thought that though no educational purpose was served by emphasising counties with their 'leading towns', some administrative boundaries, even those between England and Scotland or Wales, were of considerable interest and indeed so too were some county boundaries, such as those no longer appropriate to modern conditions including those along major rivers, including the Thames, Tyne and Tees. This did not preclude the making of 'regions' on varied criteria, and Mackinder in 1902 in *Britain and the British Seas* gave both a division of Britain into its lowland and upland and also, for England and Wales – metropolitan and industrial areas, with the boundary between them approximating to a line drawn from the Severn to the Wash. In the following seventy years the whole distribution of industry has changed and the emphasis Mackinder places on 'the northwest' (including Birmingham and the Black Country) with its 'wide uplands, the Cambrian and the Pennines . . . whose . . . lower slopes, together with the plains around, contain the coal, and bear the chief industrial life of England', reads nostalgically now to those conscious of the economic problems of many of its famous mining and manufacturing areas. Herbertson was anxious to achieve a physical regionalisation that was permanent, but Mackinder looked to the human landscape and had much of interest to say on the history and economic development of the two areas as well as on its physical features. Herbertson emphatically stated that geography was not concerned with one or a few elements of distribution but with all, but he died before his views on the human aspects of geography, on which he lectured, were adequately published.

Discarding boundaries thought to be irrelevant was part of the enthusiastic search for the regional totality of the environment. C. B. Fawcett, however, was convinced that some new arrangement of England was needed for administrative purposes and looked to the creation of provinces based on major regional capitals as a reasonable rearrangement of the country. Through all the long discussion on administrative units this idea persisted, crystallised as the 'city region', for the large provincial centres had major commercial, cultural, medical and social facilities used, at least on occasion, by people drawn from a wide radius. This was a regionalisation based on the urban life of Britain, with the great cities as the core areas having a far wider range of services than any smaller towns, having developed a metropolitan status of some strength, surpassed only by London, and deriving benefit from their distance from the capital. Fawcett looked at the metropolitan areas around some of these regional capitals in his work on conurbations, in

1974 to be distinguished as the metropolitan counties of Greater London, the West Midlands, Merseyside, Greater Manchester, West Yorkshire and Tyne–Wear.

Just as Unstead, when he came to London in his analysis of the English lowland, recognised that it must be considered as in itself a regional unit, or indeed Patrick Geddes saw in south Lancashire from Liverpool to Manchester and beyond into the Pennine valleys a man-made region (a 'conurbation') so Fawcett recognised the supremacy of urban life as an experience of the people, with its influence radiating into the remotest and most rural of districts (of which incidentally he also had direct experience). The idea was widely canvassed. When the Report of the (Hancock) Commission on Local Government was published in 1969, Derek Senior wrote a minority report advocating the regionalisation of the whole country's administration on a basis of major provincial capitals, with lesser towns as subsidiary centres. Had geographers been uncertain about the value of their detailed work they had done earlier, they might have meditated on Senior's remark that so little was known on the detailed social and economic geography of England.

Even so, much of the old regional work was regarded as inadequate and irrelevant and the term 'systematic' became academically fashionable. In fact the region came back to favour, for it was a fact of experience. People belong to some region – the West Midlands, Tyneside, rural Wales, the Highlands of Scotland, the Orkneys and Shetlands. They were not concerned with the boundaries of their regions, but with the economic opportunities and quality of life around their homes. The ebb and flow of economic circumstances meant constant change in the landscape, notably seen in areas where industry and mining were abandoned but also actuated by developments such as rehousing, industrial expansion and the provision of modern roads. The emphasis of this modern regionalisation is on economic development as crucial to the support of the population, and therefore the main concern is with towns and their outlying areas, with modern planning problems such as the relocation of industry, the balance of workers and employment, the removal of dereliction, the preservation of amenity and – to an increasing extent – the provision of recreational facilities. Basically it is a regionalisation of a social and economic character. That some areas of a country, of a continent, are richer than others in agricultural possibilities and industrial resources needs no emphasis; that new technologies may bring unforeseen wealth to certain areas poor in agriculture or even, as in some oil states which are climatic and vegetational deserts, bring untold if temporary wealth, is equally well known. Somewhat timidly geographers used to speak of 'changing geographical values', meaning that in any area new economic possibilities might be found and used, such as coal in South Wales or even tourism in mountain and coastal areas whose traditional resources had been peasant farming and fishing. Given an assured water supply, cities with several hundred thousand inhabitants have arisen in Phoenix and Tucson in the Arizona desert and modern technology offers apparently unlimited possibilities of expansion, though the conservation lobby may fear such advances as destructive of the supposedly 'natural' environment.

Much of the disillusion with regional geography has arisen through the idea that by a correlation between physical and human features of the landscape it was possible to discern 'natural' regions. In their laudable effort to make the whole world known, our Victorian forefathers – including the compilers of atlases – made structural, climatic, vegetational, zoological, agricultural and other regions which, however generalised, at least provided a basis of understanding of the world's fascinating variety. From this it was an easy, and perhaps inevitable, step to look towards a regionalism that would cover all aspects of the physical and human environment on the global scale, or any other scale to the most local and detailed. That Herbertson found a main key in climate with physical structure is not surprising (p. 79): later Fleure offered the 'human regions' approach as a complement to that of Herbertson, suffused with the idea of constant change according to the enterprise and technology of the residents. Neither seems satisfying today for both involved heavy generalisation and Fleure's work appears to be vague and imprecise and also contains many comments on racial qualities that few critics would now accept. But there are differences in physical character between one area and another and these have fascinated people ever since the earliest geographers speculated on what lay beyond the Mediterranean Sea. That mankind can destroy the earth as well as remake it is accepted, and yet the warnings of conservationists are still useful.

Despite the emphasis of many modern geographers on the 'here and now' of experience, it is still true that in Britain there is still a wide interest in areas overseas, with a fruitful concentration on certain areas in particular universities, the Middle East at Durham, South Asia at Cambridge, Latin America at Liverpool, West Africa at Birmingham, Africa at Cambridge and Edinburgh, South-East Asia at Hull, the Near and Middle East at Oxford, Japan at Sheffield. There is also the strong Department of Geography at the School of Oriental and African Studies in London University and some university departments, notably Liverpool, have several members of staff with African experience. In addition, some universities have strong links with departments of American studies. Any suggestion, therefore, that British geography has lost its concern with the world in general would be fallacious for a plentiful supply of books, papers and monographs deals with the areas named, and indeed with others written by individuals whose interests lie in various parts of the world. And under modern conditions of air travel, areas remote in distance are no longer remote in time: assuming that there are no financial constraints it is possible for researchers to pay frequent visits to the areas they study. What may well distinguish one geographer from another is power of observation, now as in the past varied as the Royal Geographical Society abundantly realised in its work of encouraging exploration since its foundation in 1830.

A world view has been retained and with that a concern to provide specialist studies dealing with various parts of the world as an extension of the generalised regional work available earlier. In the past the world view was associated with imperialism and economic expansion but that is no longer so: many geographers would like to think that it is now associated more with concern over world food supplies, the standard of living of various peoples and with such problems as hunger and famine. The news may bring some area of the world to sudden prominence: in the summer of 1979 for example, the problems of the movement of refugees from Vietnam suddenly became of compelling interest at a time when the war in the same unhappy country was finished. But the wish to know something of parts of the world other than the home ground is permanent, even though economic, political and humanitarian aspects may become prominent at particular times.

Some fears of geographers have proved to be unnecessary. Among these the apprehension of S. W. Wooldridge and others after the Second World War that geomorphology would cease to be a respected and favoured specialism within geography now seems unnecessary for it has many devoted workers. The emphasis placed by Wooldridge on the complete regional synthesis as the outstanding if potential achievement of geography no longer commands wide acceptance, for after a time when it was fashionable to discard regional geography altogether, many geographers have worked on regions, though with a variety of approaches, including several derived from a quantitative approach. Fears that British geography might lose its social, indeed humanitarian, approach have hardly been justified by events, for any tendency to concentrate solely on the material expression of life, the 'cultural landscape' in a materialistic sense, have met with little approval though some people may think that 'social commitment' has led workers into dangerous political paths. This is a risk that in a democracy nobody would fear to take and danger arises only when conviction leads to intolerance of other views.

The continuing challenge

Given that by the end of the 1970s geographers were more numerous in British universities than ever before, with a large representation in polytechnics and colleges of education, and that in schools geography was the third most popular subject, outdistanced in public examinations only by English and mathematics, it would seem that the subject had been successful beyond the wildest dreams of its friends who struggled for recognition in the 1870s and 1880s. But as always it is easier to win a war than to win the peace that follows: the unease of the 1970s comes out in two surveys written on the occasion of international congresses in

1972 (Montreal) and 1976 (Moscow). There is, however, a difference between these two surveys for the first, by R. W. Steel and J. W. Watson (1972) takes a more optimistic view than the second by R. U. Cooke and B. T. Robson (1976). In 1972 the quantitative revolution had spread its influence far and wide: the crucial period of revolt in the universities of the late 1960s appeared to have spent its force, but this was hardly so for no longer could authoritarian geographers of riper years expect younger people to follow their lead in the methodology and practice of the subject. To some this seemed a welcome relief from the sycophantism of former years, though in fact some of the younger people who, generally in groups, set themselves up as arbiters of progress in scholarship found that others were no more ready to accept authoritative judgements than they themselves had been at an earlier time. The young Turk of today may find that tomorrow he becomes the relegated conservative. Nevertheless much is owed to innovators, even to would-be innovators, and one encouraging sign was that people were asking fundamental questions, and still are. Of these perhaps the most significant is whether geographical data can be systematised into natural laws, connoting that geography belongs to the natural sciences, fortified by research on a quantitative basis, or does it rather share the uncertainties of the social sciences, having in its very essence the unpredictability of human action and reasoning.

By 1972, despite the increased use of quantitative methods, Steel and Watson note that 'there is still an emphasis on the quality of description for the portrayal of regions and landscapes': but by then description had become 'mere'. They also observe, however, that many geographers appear to be more concerned with process than with places and sometimes more with statistical manipulation than with environmental reality. Allowing that there was a need to experiment, the testing of hypotheses became favoured: in this geographers were following tracks familiar to others, especially sociologists and, like them, were hoping to discern new and valid generalisations. To be afraid of making a generalisation, either by caution due to inadequate evidence or by emphasis on the unique character of all phenomena in space, now appeared to be wrong. Naturally some were eager to point out the dangers, not only of using mathematical techniques as 'evidence' but still more of making models to which processes, both physical and human, might conform. Then there was also the problem of relationship, the impossibility of isolating phenomena except for clarity in one stage of an argument, for as Steel and Watson point out 'the central concerns of geographers remain the same – the analysis of man/land relationships and of spatial patterns'. This carries one back to the great inspiration of nineteenth-century geographers, the unity of the world and of all phenomena within it. And, as will shortly appear, this idea, even if forgotten for a time by geographers immersed – quite properly – in their own specialist research, was to remain valid, even compelling, in the late 1970s.

In 1976 Cooke and Robson found a wider range of problems than their predecessors recognised four years earlier. It seemed that a new generation of quantifiers had arisen, whose work was of so esoteric a character that it would be incomprehensible to earlier workers. This might perhaps be regarded as a modern variant of an earlier phase (p. 149) then castigated as introducing esoteric jargon, much of it borrowed perhaps without a full understanding of its meaning. Certainly Cooke and Robson thought that 'the years since 1972 may well be seen as an inevitable, if frustrating, anticlimax after the heady enthusiasm and elevated hopes of the earlier period'. But there were signs of enlightenment, remarkably so in the expectation of solving mysteries such as the problems of long-term landform evolution based on existing knowledge of processes through mathematical modelling, for example, based on mass balance of water and sediment, there are now theoretical solutions to problems of long-term landform evolution based on existing knowledge of processes, discussed in *Hillslope Form and Planning* by R. A. Carson and M. J. Kirkby (1972) and later works. This means that hypotheses such as those of W. M. Davis and others involving landform development over millions of years may now be mathematically tested, which is exactly what many of us who (a long time ago) used W. M. Davis's work as a convenient teaching device had long wanted to see. In general, Cooke and Robson recognise an emphasis on process in all work on physical geography and a helpful tendency for combination between specialists in various branches of geomorphology, climatology and biogeography. Perhaps contrary to earlier experience, Cooke and Robson also note that 'the relatively unruffled course of physical geography can be argued to have diverged from that of the more turbulent human geography'. And another hopeful sign is that man–environment relationships have attracted an increasing number of physical geographers, notably in environmental problems such as the study of hazards, resource management and cultural ecology. The emphasis on conservation of the environment developed strongly and fears that man was destroying the earth were widespread.

Turbulence in human geography could be charitably interpreted as a sign of progress. At least it represents a move forward from the phase of repetitive debate on possibilism and determinism, for much of the current argument has developed from study of the man-made social environment and from the application of quantitative methods to human distributions. Probably Cooke and Robson are hitters of nails on heads in commenting that 'the mere use of quantitative techniques is no longer sufficient in itself to elicit admiration since they need to be justified by the problem in hand'. There is for some workers the attraction of positivism, in the sense of finding the paradigm of human knowledge in natural science rather than in history, especially if reinforced by quantitative analysis and statistical expertise. This involves the view that workers in human geography should seek efficient causes and invariate laws and the belief that human actions can be characterised with regard purely to an external reality without consideration of the actor's own viewpoint. Here once more is the search for a general law, over and above the reaction and judgement of individual workers.

In fact there cannot be a value-free approach to the analysis of human phenomena since even a concept of efficiency is underlain by a set of values. Individuals have different responses to common stimuli: efficiency, maximum profit, advance in living standard, educational progress, material and spiritual welfare of a community, recreation – all seem desirable but in varying degrees to different people. And what one wants for oneself is unlikely to be exactly what others wish to have. There is therefore a natural recoil among many people against any integration of people into defined groups whose response to circumstances and opportunities is predictable and easily classifiable. Politicians have an obvious concern with the wishes of majorities of an electorate as without such support they cannot achieve power. Educationalists have intellectual and social standards that they wish to disseminate among those under their care. However austere and detached a scholar may wish to be he still has his outlook on the world and if, as in human geography, he is directly concerned with people, this will inevitably affect his work. Here then is the science of behaviourism and perception, concerned with the reactions of people to circumstances and their assessment of them. Between mankind and environment there is always the idea. However objective a writer may wish to be, he faces the impossibility of losing subjectivity of judgement as a human geographer and this imperative of human experience has been cheerfully accepted by many modern workers.

In this there is an element of disillusion with quantification. Hopes that it could provide all the answers to human problems have proved to be vain, though this does not mean that it was a futile exercise but rather that man's life is so infinitely complex that geographers must be aware of all human study, including psychology. Sessions of the section on behaviourism and perception at the Montreal I.G.U. Congress in 1972 carried the writer back to the teaching on general and educational psychology of his student days forty years earlier, for many of the ideas on psychology were not new. The problem of perception has been excellently stated by the theologian, Austin Ferrer, in *Reflective Faith* (S.P.C.K., 1972, pp. 48–9): 'Human knowledge is a very imperfect instance of knowledge in general: it apprehends the realities through a thick veil of sensation – signs and abstract mental impressions. From these interpretations and signs it can never perfectly separate that which it grasps through them. Therefore the character of the object comes to "exist in the mind" only in a very qualified manner, when that mind is human.' And the same author sounds a warning note on models that some readers might like to ponder:

We cannot do without models but we examine the models and recall the crudity of their provenance; not with the object of casting direct light on the field in which we apply them, but with the negative purpose of escaping the misleading suggestions they offer. In sum: everything that is objectively valuable in casual thinking is contributed by the evidence of the experimental data. Experiment not only supplies the matter of the answer, it corrects the form of the question too (Ferrer, p. 211).

Just as in psychology, there is a natural interest in people with special difficulties so it would appear that many geographers have found deprivation a fruitful study. The charm of the simple life, the nostalgic admiration of peasant ways, the romance of transhumant farmers on Alpine hillsides no longer appeals. The era of romantic geography is over: instead there is a move to the towns where – in developed countries – the vast majority of the people actually reside. There is an active concern with immigrants, ethnic minorities, housing, health, mental disorders, as well as with such expressions of the corporate will as electoral behaviour and even civil strife. All this can be listed as social welfare, social well-being both in its detailed concern and in its preoccupation with world hunger and economic strategy. Geographers who take a Marxist view regard the present distribution of resources as the product of a capitalist society designed to perpetuate an existing class structure. All workers in social geography face a dynamic situation, for cities are torn apart – at least in Britain – and rebuilt quickly, their shopping centres are remodelled, their industrial life transformed and their communications by road and rail drastically altered by modernisation. Nineteenth-century social workers were concerned with the appalling congestion of cities, with their smoke-laden atmosphere, but though much has been done to alleviate such conditions there are now fears that some of the central and inner residential areas will become human deserts, avoided by all who can avoid them even though the replacement dwellings are far healthier and more convenient than the slums they superseded. Generalisation is difficult for in some places, conspicuously parts of London, areas that once had a comparatively humble social status have become favoured by a new type of resident, far more affluent than those of an earlier time and able to transform houses into modern homes: so far little appears to have been written on this process of 'gentrification'. Nor has much attention been given to the absorption of immigrants, though observation suggests that white immigrants are absorbed comparatively rapidly.

Is the ghetto temporary or permanent? Only time can show whether Britain will successfully achieve a multiracial society and whether the capacity to absorb minorities with tolerance will extend to people differing in colour. On this, geography in itself has no moral judgement to offer: judgement is given by the geographer as an individual and much as the present writer agreed with the views of P. M. Roxby on race relations, he could not agree that it is the purpose of geographical study as such to inculcate a tolerant view. But to what degree can anyone be detached? Just as, for example, some geographers were led by their studies to advocate imperialism or at least the strengthening of the British Commonwealth in earlier times, so many now find that their more detailed work leads them to make judgements on matters of current social concern, whether it be environmental pollution, social justice in the city, better recreational facilities and much more that contributes to the making of a finer world. Assuming that the geographer is a person of good will towards others (so far as is humanly possible) he may become an 'applied' geographer, using his study for some practical purpose, helping to solve some discernible and perhaps urgent problem. This does not mean that there is no place for historical geography or for any other specialism that may appear to be remote from current experience. In fact some studies in historical geography, especially but by no means exclusively of the nineteenth century, shed light on current problems such as housing and industrial location while the preservation of amenity in the landscape, both in town and countryside, is fostered by an appreciation of history. We cannot understand the present without knowing something of the past for it lives on as a feature of human experience.

Many current problems of planning attract geographers and in this, as in so much else, the hopes of past geographers have been met. There may in fact be dangers in the success of geography as Cooke and Robson suggest, for although work with an obvious application brings financial support and prestige and has undoubtedly given friendly association with people in other disciplines, there is the fear that 'the energies of some of the most productive researchers could well become dispersed on highly empirical routine, time-consuming exercises which have little theoretical, methodological or substantive interest and which are without innovative significance . . . the important quality of independent judgement could be sacrificed at the shrine of relevance' (Cooke and Robson, 1976, p. 89). On the other hand, geographers have given valuable service to many bodies, including the Department of the Environment, the Sports Council, the Location of Offices Bureau, various select committees of the House of Commons as well as to commissions such as those on Environmental Pollution and Local Government Boundaries. In some cases the work for such bodies has been specially commissioned and, in particular cases, produced rapidly without long-considered research, while in others the work begun out of interest or even curiosity proved to be relevant to current problems and welcomed for that reason. Of this the Stamp Land Utilisation Survey is an obvious example (p. 144), and it is no accident that some geomorphological work proved to be of unexpected human relevance (p. 123). And while local regional studies no longer have the kudos they once possessed, it is regrettable that, as Derek Senior pointed out in his excellent minority report to the Local Government Boundary Commission, 1969, they were so few

(p. 177): on many areas of England little had been written for many years at a time of sharp change.

Since the Second World War a major advance in British geography has been the work on towns. This has not been confined to geography, for there has been a comparable development in other subjects, notably sociology. Much that was studied earlier, such as the size, functions and linkages of towns, has been pursued with energy and increasing sophistication and this applies also to the detailed land use within towns. Urban study has been international, with many of the pioneer papers and books emanating from France, Germany and the USA, but in Britain a particular stimulus came from the town and country planning legislation of the post-war years which required that a study of existing and potential land use should be made for all towns. Naturally, in a country having four-fifths of its people living in areas defined as towns and a substantial proportion of those being in areas defined as rural working in towns, interest developed in the commuter belts of suburban growth beyond towns and in the villages housing urban workers. Efforts to avoid past errors, such as the spread of houses in ribbon development along roads between towns, led to the designation of green belts, of which an interesting study is D. Thomas, *London's Green Belt* (1970), which shows that the main legislative effect has been to 'fossilize the land-use pattern which was in existence at the time its boundaries were designated', though with minor changes.

Control over land use in Britain is now accepted and does not preclude new housing developments, road construction and industrial relocation, and geographers dealing with economic and social aspects are dealing with a dynamic situation, discussed in J. W. House (ed.), *The UK Space*, 1973 or G. Manners (ed.), *Regional Development in Britain*, 1972. Regional in this context means the government's 'standard economic regions' which have 'received a good deal of official study and interpretation in recent years, and for which a widening range of socio-economic statistics is readily available', though some modifications are made, notably that North, Central and South Wales are taken with the northwest of England, the West Midlands and the southwest respectively. The emphasis of this modern regionalisation is on the distribution of population, and the socio-economic approach has obvious planning implications.

Although traditional regional geography was based primarily on agricultural and rural life, this is now generally studied in terms of land use except in specialised studies such as J. T. Coppock's *Agricultural Geography of Great Britain* (1971) with the continuing work of the Second Land Use Survey organised by Alice Coleman (p. 158). That more attention could be profitably given to agriculture few would doubt, but here again the interest of townspeople is seen in the concern with recreation, on which a pioneer work in Britain was J. A. Patmore's *Land and Leisure* (1970). Through the work of the Countryside Commission, the Sports Council and other bodies, much data has been gathered on the use of leisure facilities of every description, ranging from local sports to the use of second homes as retreats for weekend and longer visits. Inevitably – and rightly – much of the work on recreation has been concerned with people's choices and habits, for although there is a considerable demand for physical activities, for example in national parks, the vast majority of the visitors appear to have other ideas. Some sports are gaining popularity while others remain stable in demand or are declining. A logical development of such study would be a closer investigation of the tourist trade, increasingly significant in Britain as in many other countries. Maybe the present work on recreation shows the townsman's approach, seeking active sport or visits to the countryside as a relief from the constricted life of the office, factory or study: the type of recreation chosen will depend largely on opportunity, education and physical aptitudes. Although much has been done by various workers, it might be possible to extend the view of recreation to include such activities as music and art, even to look at the wide range of clubs and societies that exist in most British towns as a broad study of social geography.

Aesthetic interests have been studied by various workers and it is common knowledge that areas now regarded as of scenic beauty, especially mountains, were regarded as repellent in the eighteenth century. Whether this was due in part to the fear that men from the mountains might be dangerous is not clear, though in Scotland and Ireland such a view might be justified. It was largely university and public school men who were pioneers of mountaineering (as of many other physical activities): D. Lowenthal and H. C. Prince have written fascinating accounts of landscape tastes (Lowenthal and Price, 1964, 1965). The beauty of coasts was a favourite theme of Vaughan Cornish (p. 123) and through the work of the National Parks (now Countryside) Commission, it is now possible to walk along public footpaths for hundreds of miles in England and Wales.

Many will find it difficult to accept a classification of grades of scenic beauty, such as that given by D. L. Linton for Scotland. Points are given for 'landform landscapes' of six types: mountains 8, bold hills 6, hill country 5, plateau uplands 3, low uplands 2 and lowlands 0. Then follows a map of 'land-use landscapes': wild landscapes +6, richly varied farming landscapes +4, moorland +3, treeless farmland +1 and – adverse ratings – continuous forest –2, urbanised and industrialised landscapes –5. Adding the two ratings together the highest scores for 'scenic resources' are given by the Western Highlands and mountainous parts of the islands, the Cairngorms and the Grampians, with the Merrick area in the Southern Uplands: the lowest scores occur in central Scotland with the Ayrshire coast. As an exercise in perception it could be argued that this assessment was the work of a geographer with a discriminating eye for scenery and a particular liking for mountains, mindful of the effects of long-continued planting of woods in farmed valleys such as Deeside and Speyside and disliking continuous forest plantations. Although the final result is an assessment very similar to that made by tourist bodies, with maps such as those of Michelin marking particular roads as scenic, and the main emphasis on the western part of the Highlands, there is an individual element in any such work. And there must be (Linton, 1968). Inevitably this will bring criticism, for example from Jay Appleton in his *Experience of Landscape* (1975) who, having commented on the fashion for quantifying everything ('geographers, planners and others ... believe that they could measure anything quantitatively and if they could not it was not worth considering') adds that nobody was better qualified than Linton to divide a landscape into landform regions, it is 'questionable' whether 'individual components of landscape, such as 'low uplands' can be said to have intrinsic aesthetic values at all' (*ibid.*, p. 245).

Appleton asks the fundamental question, 'What is it that we like about landscape and why do we like it?' and his approach is concerned with hazards, prospects and refuges. No two people are likely to react in the same way and Appleton uses landscape paintings as expressions of his theory. As David Lowenthal has commented (Lowenthal and Bowden, 1976, p. 3): 'The lineaments of the world we live in are both seen and shaped in accordance, or by contrast, with images we hold of other worlds – better worlds, past worlds, future worlds. We constantly compare the reality with the fancy. Indeed, without the one we could neither visualize nor conceptualize the other.'

Probably the concern of some geographers, in fact just a few, with landscape is a reminder that the ultimate concern is with people and land, with man making and remaking the earth, providing an environment for mankind on which the continuing drama of human existence takes place. What has been done in the past affects what can be done now and what is done now affects the future. A geographer teaching students of planning may find that they look forward to a career of power in which all environments can be changed, even totally redeveloped, for the general benefit of the whole community. That much can be altered with excellent results is beyond doubt, but there are still the realities of the physical environment, the processes of its moulding by climate and weather, the hazards of vulcanicity, earth movement and climatic fluctuations, the fears that now as in the past human activity may initiate phases of natural destruction such as soil erosion by clearing forests or even by removing hedgerows, the problems of fuel supply or of the possible exhaustion of mineral and other raw materials in a world of constantly increasing population everywhere having the hope of an improved standard of living. Mankind to the geographer can never be conceived merely as an abstraction, though for a time any research worker may usefully concentrate his attention on one facet of the human story. Where he may fail is in claiming more for his research than it can give for in any human study, especially one concerned with the environment, the solution of one problem has a way of raising many more problems than were previously foreseen. In this lies his hope for the future of geography in a constantly changing world, and many workers of the past would wish their researches to be regarded not as the law of the prophets but as a basis for further study and enlightenment on man and his world.

Geographical biographies

A wide variety of men and women are included in these short biographical sketches. Inclusion does not mean that the subject was a professional geographer leading a life of austere and dedicated scholarship. Even within the limits of extreme brevity this biographical section will show how varied in character, education, activity, professional and social circumstances geographers have been. Some of those included have been primarily historians, civil servants, educationalists, planners, natural scientists, classical scholars, theologians, but all of them have been led into geographical study from their varied backgrounds and in their own varied ways have made some contributions to the development of the subject.

Aberdare (Bruce), Henry Austin (1815–1895)

Lord Aberdare had a distinguished political career and was Liberal Member of Parliament for Merthyr Tydfil from 1852 to 1868. From 1862 to 1868 he was an Under-Secretary of State at the Home Office. Having lost his seat in 1868, he successfully contested Renfrewshire and became Home Secretary until 1873, when he was raised to the peerage. He was President of the Royal Geographical Society from 1880 to 1885 and 1886 to 1887 and became chairman of the Niger Company. Among his interests was the possible foundation of a university for Wales. *Geogr. J.* **5**, 1895, pp. 386–90.

Arden-Close, Sir Charles Frederick (1865–1952)

Born into a military family, Charles Close (the name was changed in 1938) spent his early Army years attached to the Survey of India and in 1895 was sent to Africa to define, with a German Commission, the Nigerian–Cameroon frontier. In 1905 he became chief of the Geographical Section of the General Staff and from 1911 to 1922 was Director-General of the Ordnance Survey. He was an enthusiastic supporter of the 1:1,000,000 map. While President of the Royal

Geographical Society from 1927 to 1930, he saw the new extensions to its building completed. The final honour was his presidency of the International Geographical Union from 1934 to 1938. He was a man of pragmatic mind not entirely sympathetic to imaginative colleagues eager to extend geographical horizons.

The Times 22.12.1952: *Geogr. J.* **119**, 1952, pp. 251–2: *Geography* **38**, 1953, p. 109.

Baker, John Norman Leonard (1893–1971)

Entering Jesus College, Oxford, in 1913 from Liverpool College as a history exhibitioner, Baker spent all his life there except for war service in France and India and a year lecturing at Bedford College, University of London, from 1922 to 1923. He was awarded the diploma in geography in 1921 and the B.Litt degree in 1922. Returning to Oxford in 1923 as assistant to the Reader in Geography (H. O. Beckit) he became Lecturer of Jesus College in 1932, Reader in Historical Geography in 1933 and Fellow of Jesus College in 1939. His book on the *History of Geographical Discovery and Exploration* appeared in 1931 and from 1926 he published papers on the history of geography, fifteen of which were collected into a presentation volume by his pupils and friends in 1963. Baker was an entirely unselfish citizen who gave devoted service to the British Association, the Hakluyt Society and the Institute of British Geographers. But he was particularly devoted to Jesus College and to the city of Oxford of which, having served on its city council from 1945, he became Lord Mayor in 1964.

Geogr. J. **138**, 1972, pp. 276–7; *The Times* 10.12.1971; *The History of Geography: papers by J. N. L. Baker,* (Oxford) 1963 (bibliography from 1923 to 1963).

Bartholomew, family map firm

The famous Edinburgh map firm has been in the same family for over 150 years. In 1856 John (1831–1893) took over the management of his father's firm, having studied with August Petermann, the German cartographer, at Gotha. Next in line came John George (1860–1920), who entered the draughtsman's office at sixteen and began the work of replacing hill shading by contours combined with layer colouring. Though Carl Ritter had advocated this method of showing relief, it was not used until the firm provided maps for Baddeley in *Guide to the Lake District* in 1880. In 1888 the reduced scale Ordnance Survey maps (1:126,720) first appeared and in 1895 the *Atlas of Scotland*. John George Bartholomew worked with Sir John Murray on the *Challenger Reports* and with many geographers and others, including A. Buchan and A. J. Herbertson (*q.v.*) in the *Meteorology* volume (1899) of the

Physical Atlas. Five volumes were planned but the only other one to appear was on *Zoogeography* in 1911. Bartholomew gazetteers and maps came in a solid stream, notably in geographical journals, and John George's final achievement was the splendid map showing the growth of Edinburgh in *Scott. Geogr. Mag.* **35**, 1919, pp. 281–329, an issue entirely devoted to the city. Always troubled by indifferent health, Bartholomew died at Cintra, Portugal, while on one of his recuperative holidays. His son John (1890–1962) completed the work on the *Times Survey Atlas* in 1922. This was a fine cartographical presentation of the world after the First World War, followed in 1955–8 by the *Times Atlas of the World*. Meanwhile the maps and atlases of the firm have continued to appear. *Scott. Geogr. Mag.* **36**, 1920, pp. 183–5; **78**, 1962, pp. 114–16; *Geogr. J.* **128**, 1962, p. 254; *Geogr. Rev.* **53**, 1963, pp. 145–6; Gardiner, L., *Bartholomew 150 years*, (Edinburgh) 1976.

Beazley, Sir Charles Raymond (1868–1955)

London-born, Beazley went to St Paul's School and King's College, London and in 1886–9 was at Balliol, Oxford, where he had a first in history followed by a fellowship in history at Merton College. In 1894 he was awarded the Oxford Geographical Studentship and in the same year he travelled round the coasts of Africa, following the routes of Portuguese and other explorers. He also went to Russia, including Siberia. From 1892 he was engaged on his famous *Dawn of Modern Geography* and he also wrote books on various explorers including Prince Henry the Navigator (1895) and the Cabot brothers (1898). He found a natural outlet for his interests in the Hakluyt Society and edited one of their volumes. From 1909 to 1932 he was at the University of Birmingham as Professor of Modern History, where his later publications, notably on the First World War, were of a controversial character.
Who Was Who; Biographical Press Agency, February 1903 (in British Museum).

Brown, Robert Neal Rudmose (1879–1957)

Born in Dulwich, Rudmose Brown was educated at Dulwich College and at the universities of Aberdeen and Montpellier. From 1900 to 1902 he taught botany at Dundee University College, and he spent the next two years as botanist and marine zoologist with the Scottish National Antarctic Expedition. From 1904 to 1907 he worked at the Scottish Oceanographical Laboratory in Edinburgh, and in 1907 he went to lower Burma to investigate the pearl fisheries of the Mergui archipelago at the invitation of the Government of India. A year later he became the first lecturer at the young University of Sheffield. His only formal instruction in geography was received at one of A. J. Herbertson's Oxford summer schools in 1908, but he was strongly influenced by Patrick Geddes and other lively minds, especially in Edinburgh. He went to Spitsbergen in 1908, 1914 and 1919 and during the First World War worked for the Admiralty on Siberia, Finland, Norway and Sweden. His book on *Spitsbergen* appeared in 1919 and was followed by *A Naturalist at the Poles* in 1923 (a biography of his friend, W. S. Bruce) and also by *The Polar Regions* in 1927. He wrote a large number of papers and, like many geographers of his time, encouraged school education by providing suitable material for teachers, including *The Principles of Economic Geography*, in 1920, which went into several editions. After sixteen years at Sheffield, he was joined by Dr Alice Garnett in 1924 and together they developed the honours course successfully by his retirement in 1945. He became the first Professor of Geography at Sheffield in 1931.

Geogr. J. **123**, 1957, pp. 576–7; *The Times* 29.1.1957; *Trans. Inst. Br. Geogr.* **23**, 1957, viii–x.

Buchan, Alexander (1829–1907)

An Edinburgh graduate, Buchan worked for a time as a schoolmaster and found his way to a meteorological career through botany. In 1861 he became secretary and editor to the Scottish Meteorological Society and he worked both with maps and statistics throughout his career. The meteorological data from the *Challenger* voyages was handed to him and in 1889 he produced his famous *Report on Atmospheric Circulation*. He was a supporter of the Ben Nevis Observatory and, with A. J. Herbertson, worked on the meteorology volume of Bartholomew's *Physical Atlas*.

Scott. Geogr. Mag. **23**, 1907, pp. 427–31; Mill, H. R., *An Autobiography*, (London) 1951, pp. 111–13.

Buchanan, John Young (1844–1925)

Glasgow-born, Buchanan studied chemistry in the city's university and also abroad. In 1872 he became chemist to the *Challenger* and his investigations on salinity, marine deposits amd minerals were basic contributions to the growth of oceanography. He had his own yacht for research but also travelled on the splendidly equipped yacht of the Prince of Monaco, as well as on the cable-laying ships of the Silvertown Company. From 1889 to 1893 he taught geography at Cambridge University. His interests extended to glaciers and deserts, many of which he visited on his widespread travels. Though he wrote over 100 papers, he accumulated a vast store of material which regrettably was never published.

Geogr. J. **66**, 1925, p. 575.

Bunbury, Edward Herbert (1811–1895)

Educated at home with his elder brother Charles (1809–1866), well known as a botanist, E. H. Bunbury was a successful classicist at Cambridge and in 1841 called to the Bar: from 1847 to 1852 he sat in Parliament as a Liberal. His initial fame in academic circles was made by his initials at the end of valued contributions to Smith's *Dictionary of Greek and Roman Geography*, and his classic *History of Ancient Geography* appeared in 1879. He spent much of his time in the Athenaeum and never married. On his brother's death he became the ninth baronet.

Geogr. J. **5**, 1895, pp. 498–500.

Cadell, Henry Mowbray (1860–1934)

A man of wealth, he was the grandson of William Cadell (1737–1819), one of the founders of the Carron Iron Company in 1759 and a pioneer in the industrial development of the Bo'ness district. From his father Henry acquired an interest in geology and mining and in 1882 he graduated in science at Edinburgh University. After a year at the Clausthal Royal Mining Academy in Germany he joined the staff of the Geological Survey and worked on the northwest Highlands and on the oil shales of the Lothians. His father died in 1888 and henceforth he was mainly concerned with the family estates, including a colliery, and with public work. An original member of the Royal Scottish Geographical Society, he contributed to its journal on a number of occasions including (vol. 45, 1929, pp. 7–22 and 81–100) a study of 'Land reclamation in the Forth valley', with which he had been connected from 1889. He was a physiographer of wide interests, and his books on *The Story of the Forth* (1913) and *The Rocks of West Lothian* (1925) deal with geological history and industrial development.

Proceedings of the Royal Society of Edinburgh, **54**, 1933–4, pp. 194–5; *Scott. Geogr. Mag.* **50**, 1934, pp. 169–70.

Cameron, Verney Lovett (1844–1894)

Son of the Vicar of Shoreham, Cameron served in the Royal Navy from 1857 in the Mediterranean, the West Indies, the Red Sea and the east coast of Africa. In 1872 he volunteered to serve on an expedition to find Livingstone but H. M. Stanley arrived at Zanzibar having done so. Cameron left for the interior of Africa in March 1873 and reached Ujiji in February 1874 where he found some of Livingstone's papers. Later he explored the southern half of Lake Tanganyika and was the first Englishman to cross Africa from east to west. He arrived at Catumbela, near Benguela, in November 1875, having endured great hardships and

frustrations with exemplary patience. His death was due to a riding accident. He has been described as a 'practical humanitarian and a realistic assessor of African potentialities'.
Geogr. J. **3**, 1894, pp. 429–31; Casada, J. A., 'Verney Lovett Cameron: a centenary appreciation', *Geogr. J.* 141, 1975, pp. 203–16.

Chisholm, George Goudie (1850–1930)

Chisholm was born in Edinburgh and educated at the city's famous High School and University. He was a man of encyclopaedic scholarship, especially happy with statistical data and the discriminating collection of facts. His much admired *Handbook of Commercial Geography* first appeared in 1889 and went through numerous later and much revised editions until 1927 when, to his relief, he persuaded L. D. Stamp to continue the work of modernisation. Much of Chisholm's time was spent on editing works for publishing firms, including Longman's *Gazetteer of the World* (1895). He worked in London from 1895 to 1908, writing and lecturing, partly at Birkbeck College and also in university extension courses. In 1908 he became the first Lecturer in Geography at Edinburgh University and in 1921 he was promoted to Reader. He attracted many students to geography courses and established a diploma in 1919 to be taken only by graduates. This provided an excellent basis for the full honours degree established in 1928. In his later years, Chisholm was greatly interested in population problems. He was a man of great learning and an excellent German scholar, with a good knowledge of French and Italian.
Geogr. J. **75**, 1930, p. 567; *Scott. Geogr. Mag.* **46**, 1930, pp. 101–4.

Cornish, Vaughan (1862–1948)

Born at a vicarage in Suffolk, Cornish had long family connections with Sidmouth in Devon, where he eventually laid out a coast path so that everyone could enjoy the scene. After graduating in chemistry at Manchester in 1888, he was Director of Technical Education for Hampshire to 1895. Private means enabled him to travel and write. His early work was on waves, in water and sand, but from 1910 to 1920 he was concerned largely with strategical and historical geography. The final period made him widely known for his aesthetic studies of landscape, both in town and country. Many of his views have commanded wide respect and acceptance.
Geogr. J. **111**, 1948, p. 294; *Geography*, **33**, 1948, pp. 149–50; *D.N.B.* 1941–50, pp. 179–80; Gilbert, E. W., in *British Pioneers in Geography*, Newton Abbot, 1972, pp. 227–56; Goudie, A., 'Vaughan Cornish: geographer,' *Trans. Inst. Br. Geogr.* **55**, 1972, pp. 1–16.

Debenham, Frank (1883–1965)

Debenham's father was a vicar in New South Wales who also ran a private school in which his son was educated until he went to the King's School, Parramatta and then to the University of Sydney where he graduated first in arts and then in science. He was attached as a geologist to Scott's Antarctic expedition in 1910 and in 1913 went to Cambridge to write up the fieldwork. After serving in the First World War he returned to Cambridge to work on the survey done by the expedition and in 1919 he became Lecturer in Surveying (an appointment made by the Royal Geographical Society). When Philip Lake retired in 1928, Debenham became Reader in Geography and Professor from 1931 to 1949. Polar exploration remained a consuming interest and he was a founder-member and the first director of the Scott Polar Institute (1926), from 1934 housed in a splendid building in Lensfield Road. Debenham with others founded the *Polar Record* in 1931, which became a respected journal. He was pragmatic in his work and his textbooks on mapping and survey were admirably clear and helpful. Though his interest in polar problems remained to the end, in later years he was fascinated by African studies which resulted in reports and papers on water supply and also on David Livingstone. He built up a friendly Department of Geography in Cambridge, excellently housed in the former Forestry School with well-planned extensions. During the Second World War numerous courses were given to cadets in the armed forces and afterwards Debenham was particularly helpful in advising the men who returned from war service to take their degrees.
Geogr. J. **132**, 1966, pp. 173–5; *Geogr. Rev.* **56**, 1966, pp. 596–8; *Geography* **51**, 1966, pp. 150–1; *Trans. Inst. Br. Geogr.* **40**, 1966, pp. 195–8.

Dickson, Henry Newton (1866–1922)

Born in Edinburgh and a graduate of its university, Dickson worked in the *Challenger* office and at the Ben Nevis Observatory. In 1891 he went to the Plymouth Marine Biological Station to study the salinity and temperatures of the English Channel, later of the entire North Atlantic. From 1899 he lectured in physical geography in Oxford and in 1906 became Professor of Geography at the University College of Reading, and head of the Commerce Department. He stressed the need for study of world distributions of wheat, fuel, power and transport in his British Association, Section E (Geography) address, 1913. In the First World War he edited the Naval Intelligence *Handbooks* and from 1920 he was an editor for *Encyclopaedia Britannica*.
Scott. Geogr. Mag. **38**, 1922, p. 183.

Fawcett, Charles Bungay (1883–1952)

County Durham was Fawcett's home area and he was educated at Gainford Grammar School and at University College, Nottingham, where he obtained the external B.Sc. degree of London University in 1908. After teaching for two years he went to Oxford to study under A. J. Herbertson for the diploma, which he gained in 1912, followed by the B.Litt. degree in 1913. Six years at Southampton followed, during which he lectured in the University College and worked for the Ordnance Survey and in 1919 he moved to Leeds as Lecturer in 1919 and Reader from 1920. There he built up a department with an honours course and in 1928 he was invited to succeed Professor L. W. Lyde at University College, London, where he stayed until his retirement in 1949. Two periods as Visiting Professor at Clark University before his retirement were followed by a stay of two years from 1949. His teaching and writing was influenced by Herbertson and Mackinder, and his first book, published in 1918, was on *Frontiers*, followed in 1919 by the *Provinces of England*, a work later republished and frequently discussed since as it dealt with possible local government units based on major provincial cities. His article on the urban population of Great Britain in 1931, in effect on conurbations (*Geogr. J.* **79**, 1932, pp. 100–16) was also closely studied for many years. Later he turned to major world political problems in *A Political Geography of the British Empire* (1934), and *The Bases of a World Commonwealth* (1943). He was always markedly conscious of population problems. Fawcett was a devoted worker for many learned bodies, including the Institute of British Geographers, the Geographical Association and the Royal Geographical Society.
Geogr. J. **118**, 1953, pp. 514–16; *Trans. Inst. Br. Geogr.* **18**, 1952, xi–xii.

Fleure, Herbert John (1877–1969)

A native of Guernsey, Fleure was so delicate in his youth that he had little formal education, but in 1897 he won an open scholarship at the University College of Aberystwyth, where he graduated with first-class honours in zoology in 1901. He was a research student in Zurich and returned to Aberystwyth in 1904 to lecture in zoology, botany and geology and to become Professor of Zoology in 1910. From 1908 he also lectured in geography, primarily to help young teachers in the new grammar schools of Wales to whom in later years he gave lectures in summer schools, especially those of the Geographical Association. In 1917 he became honorary secretary and in 1918 honorary editor of the Geographical Association, which he served devotedly for thirty years. He became Professor of Geography and Anthropology in 1917 and from 1918 a flourishing honours school developed. His earlier studies in natural science had led naturally to human geography, prehistory and physical anthropology and some of his research papers were on racial types: this was further developed in his books, *The Peoples of Europe* (1922) and *The Races of England and Wales* (1923). Already he had become fascinated by the idea of the region and his paper of 1919 on 'Human regions' (*Scott. Geogr. Mag.* **35**, pp. 94–105) was a plea for a new approach in which the people as well as the environment were considered. Perhaps his greatest achievement was the publication from 1927 to 1936 of nine volumes in his 'Corridors of Time' series with H. J. E. Peake (*q.v.*) and a final volume in 1956. Having moved to Manchester University in 1930 as its first Professor of Geography, Fleure became even more closely involved in a wide range of learned societies, and this continued after his retirement in 1944. He spent most of his remaining years in London and contributed a number of papers to a variety of journals, and to the end of his life retained his interest in a vast circle of friends as well as in research, including blood groups. In this last, one might recognise the continuing love of anthropology that developed from his initial work in the natural sciences.

Geogr. J. **135**, 1969, pp. 484–5; *Geogr. Rev.* **60**, 1970, pp. 443–5; *Geography,* **54**, 1969, pp. 464–9; *Trans. Inst. Br. Geogr.* **49**, 1970, pp. 201–10; Garnett, A., 'Herbert John Fleure 1877–1969', *Biographical Memoirs of Fellows of the Royal Society*, vol. 16, Royal Society, 1970, pp. 253–78.

Freeman, Edward Augustus (1823–1892)

Deeply conscious of the physical setting of historical events, Freeman's first major work was a five-volume *History of the Norman Conquest* (1867–76), followed later by his book on the reign of William Rufus. The *Historical Geography of Europe*, with an atlas volume, appeared in 1881. The books have many geographical descriptions based on his own observations. A Fellow of Trinity College, Oxford from 1845, he became Regius Professor of History in 1884.

Scott. Geogr. Mag. **9**, 1893, pp. 36–7.

Freshfield, Douglas William (1845–1934)

Possessing ample means, Freshfield was described as 'a cultivated Victorian . . . a great gentleman'. He was educated at Eton and University College, Oxford, where he graduated in history and law in 1868. Called to the Chancery Bar, he never practised. He ascended Mont Blanc in 1863 while still at Eton and later made many pioneer ascents in the Alps, also in the Caucasus from 1868 and from 1899 in India. In 1875 he published a book on the Italian Alps, followed in 1898 by *The Exploration of the Caucasus* and in 1903 by *Round Kanchenjunga*. From 1883 he helped to edit the Royal Geographical Society's *Hints to Travellers* and from 1872 to 1880 he edited the *Alpine Journal*: later, from

1893 to 1895 he was President of the Alpine Club. Geographical education was a main interest for many years, and he was instrumental in persuading the Royal Geographical Society to sponsor the enquiries of John Scott Keltie (*q.v.*) and to persuade Oxford and Cambridge universities to appoint geographers. In 1894 he ceased to be honorary secretary of the R.G.S. after thirteen years' devoted service for he was grieved by their refusal to admit women as Fellows. Fortunately, from 1897 to 1910 he was free to act as President of the Geographical Association and in time all was forgiven at the R.G.S., of which he was President from 1914 to 1917. He maintained his interests in mountains and in 1920 published his *Life of de Saussure*.

Geogr. J. **83**, 1934, pp. 257–62 (memoir by T. G. Longstaff); Mill, H. R., *An Autobiography*, (London) 1951.

Galton, Sir Francis (1822–1911)

A man of great wealth, Galton had an unhappy time at school and as an undergraduate in London and Birmingham. He acquired a taste for travel early in life and from 1850 to 1852 went on an expedition to Africa which brought him considerable fame. From 1852 to 1863 he wrote on exploration, including his *Art of Travel* in 1855 and a long essay on geography in 1855 which for its time showed considerable breadth of interest. In 1863 his atlas of European weather, *Meteorographica*, was published and in 1875 he produced the first weather maps to appear in *The Times*. Though he remained interested in the welfare of geography and gave voluntary service to the Royal Geographical Society, the British Association and the Royal Meteorological Society, the research of his later years was connected mainly with the study of eugenics, then regarded as *avant garde* and likely to explain many facets of human character.

Freeman, T. W., *The Geographer's Craft*, (Manchester) 1967, pp. 22–43; Forrest, D. W., *Francis Galton: the life and work of a Victorian genius*, (London) 1974.

Geddes, Sir Patrick (1854–1932)

Born at Ballater, Aberdeenshire, Geddes became a student of biology devoted to the new evolutionary thought of the time and was greatly influenced by the Huxleys at South Kensington. Later he went to Jena and met Haeckel and to Paris where he was attracted by the modern thought of Le Play, Demolins and Reclus on town planning and social study. He taught biology at Dundee University College and collaborated with his distinguished pupil, (Sir) J. Arthur Thomson in writing the *Evolution of Sex* and *Sex, Evolution and Biology* in the Home University Library, then a much-used series of short but authoritative works. His book, *Cities in Evolution* (1915) with its comments on 'conurbations' (his newly coined word) is still widely read. He was always forward-looking and in 1892 established the Outlook Tower in Edinburgh with its splendid slogan, 'Survey before action'. From 1914 to 1922 he surveyed and planned towns with some practical results, notably in Edinburgh, and in some fifty cities of India and Palestine. In 1920 he went to Bombay to a Chair of Civics and Sociology. The appeal of Geddes to geographers was considerable, for he was devoted to the idea of the relationship of all aspects of learning and to the essential human applications of all study. Many who were stimulated by his breadth of vision were sceptical of his Utopian tendencies and some were dazzled by the proliferation of ideas, for he was – as he himself said – 'the little boy who pulls the bell and runs away'. But he caused doors to open in people's minds and, as a contemporary said 'words poured from him as from Lloyd George or General Smuts . . . and it was all good stuff'. His son Alistair was killed in the First World War, but Arthur (1895–1968) carried on much of his father's work, notably in his researches on India and in work on Scotland, and from 1929 he was a colourful personality in the Department of Geography at Edinburgh University.

Mairet, P., *Pioneer of Sociology: the life and letters of Patrick Geddes*, (London) 1957; Kitchen, P., *A Most Unsettling Person: an introduction to the life of Sir Patrick Geddes*, (London) 1975; W. I. Stevenson, 'Patrick Geddes', *Geographers* 2, 1978, pp. 53–65; Learmouth, A. T. A., 'Arthur Geddes', *ibid.* pp. 45–51.

Geikie, James (1839–1915)

Geikie joined the Geological Survey in 1861 and was concerned largely with mapping drift. This led to the publication of *The Great Ice Age* in 1874 and *Prehistoric Europe* in 1881. He succeeded his brother Archibald as Murchison Professor of Geology and Mineralogy in Edinburgh in 1882 and retired in 1914. At the close of his life his books on *Mountains, Their Origin, Growth and Decay* in 1913 and on the *Antiquity of Man in Europe* in 1914 summarised his researches, which led him to believe that the interglacial periods could be correlated with the spread of Palaeolithic and Neolithic cultures. He deplored the wretched teaching of geography in Britain and worked assiduously for the Scottish Geographical Society with the Bartholomew family. He was, however, somewhat cautious on the need to establish geography in the University of Edinburgh.

Geogr. J. **45**, 1915, pp. 343–4; *Scott. Geogr. Mag.* **31**, 1915, pp. 202–5; Marsden, W. E., 'James Gikie', *Geographers* 3, 1979, pp. 53–62.

George, Hereford Brook (1838-1910)

Educated at Winchester and New College in classics and mathematics, he was called to the Bar in 1864 but returned to New College in 1867 as a Fellow and was ordained in 1868. He worked assiduously for the Oxford local examinations and saw the compelling need to give adequate education to the many teachers joining staffs of secondary schools. Military history and historical geography were his favourite studies, as perusal of his book of 1901, *The Relations of Geography and History*, shows. He was a dedicated Alpine climber, and in 1866 wrote *The Oberland and its Glaciers*.
Geogr. J. **37**, 1911, pp. 325-6.

Gilbert, Edmund William (1900-1973)

Of Yorkshire origin, Gilbert was the only child of the Vicar of Hemsworth and educated at St Peter's School, York and Hertford College, Oxford. He graduated in history in 1922 and stayed to read for the diploma in geography, in which he had a distinction in 1924. Meanwhile, in 1923 he became a junior lecturer at Bedford College for Women (London University) and in 1926 he went to Reading as Lecturer in Historical Geography. He returned to Oxford in 1936 as Research Lecturer in Human Geography, became a Reader in 1943 and Professor from 1953 to 1967. As a writer he contributed a number of published papers on urban geography, regionalism and the history of geography. His book, *British Pioneers in Geography* (1972) included his papers on geographers from Richard Hakluyt to Vaughan Cornish and Halford John Mackinder. He also wrote *Brighton: old ocean's bauble* (1954) which was a delightful mixture of geography and social history. His writings were marked by elegance and wit and his lectures were distinguished in content, expression and delivery.
The Times, 5.10.1973 and 18.10.1973; *Geography*, **59**, 1974, p. 68; *Geogr. J.* **140**, 1974, pp. 176-7; *Geographers: biobibliographical studies* **3**, 1979, pp. 63-71.

Green, John Richard (1837-1883)

Appropriately Green was born at Oxford and showed early signs of a scholarly temperament, though he was immensely disappointed by his years in Jesus College where he was regarded as a difficult undergraduate. In 1860 he entered the ministry of the Church of England and from 1863 to 1869 he was vicar of churches in the East End of London with considerable success. He devoted his leisure to archaeological excursions to various parts of England, and had become known to some eminent historians of the time, including E. A. Freeman (*q.v.*), James

Bryce and Bishop Stubbs. Green took a wide view of history and was fully aware of the relation with geography. This was seen in the *Short History of the English People*, ultimately issued in 1874 after being twice rewritten. In 1877 he married Alice, daughter of the Archdeacon of Meath who gave him immense help, especially when his health declined. Five years later *The Making of England* was published and much of the work on *The Conquest of England* was done, though Mrs Green (1847–1929) brought out this book after her husband's death at Mentone in 1883. They also prepared a geography text.

D.N.B.; McDowell, R. B., *Alice Stopford Green: a passionate historian* (Dublin) 1967.

Gregory, John Walter (1864–1932)

One of the most intrepid and courageous of explorers, Gregory was the son of a Bermondsey wool merchant and was educated at Stepney Grammar School in the East End of London, after which from 1879 to 1897 he worked in the wool business. For the next three years to 1890 he was an assistant in the Geology Department of the British Museum. Then began a long series of expeditions including East Africa in 1892–3 and Spitsbergen with Sir William Martin Conway in 1896. He became Professor of Geology and Mineralogy at Melbourne University in 1900, but in 1924 moved to Glasgow where he remained until his retirement in 1929. His impact on geology and physical geography came through his explorations and several books, including two (1896 and 1921) on the rift valleys of East Africa, *The Dead Heart of Australia* (1906), largely on artesian water supply, and *Geography, Structural and Physical* (1908). The human interest of his travels was shown in three books, partly concerned with white labour in the tropics, on *The Foundation of British East Africa* (1901), *The Menace of Colour* (1925) and *Human Migrations and the Future* (1928). He died in Peru on an expedition through a drowning accident.

Proceedings of the Royal Society of Edinburgh **52**, 1931–2, pp. 460–2; *Scott. Geogr. Mag.* **48**, 1932, pp. 226–8.

Grundy, George Beardoe (1861–1948)

Having entered the university at the age of twenty-seven, Grundy stayed in Oxford for all his remaining life. After graduating in classics he used a geographical studentship awarded in 1892 to study the sites of battles in Greece and Italy, on which his work was published by the Royal Geographical Society. In 1899 he became a part-time Lecturer in Ancient Geography but his main work, from 1903, was to be Fellow and Tutor in Ancient History at Corpus Christi College. From 1900 he edited a new edition of the large classical atlas published by John

Murray, enlivened – at his insistence – by the use of layer colouring. *Geogr. J.* **112**, 1948, p. 259; Grundy, G. B., *Fifty-five Years at Oxford* (London) 1945.

Guillemard, Francis Henry Hill (1852–1933)

Guillemard followed his father in taking a medical degree, but never practised except for a time during his second African visit in 1881 during the First Boer War. From 1882 to 1885 he was a naturalist on the *Marchesa* sailing in Borneo, New Guinea and Kamchatka and his two-volume *The Cruise of the Marchesa* appeared in 1886. Two years later he became the first Reader in Geography at Cambridge, but he resigned after one year (owing to ill health!) and devoted the remaining forty-four years of his life to art collection and literary activity, including the writing of a life of Magellan and editorial work, notably of the 'Cambridge County Geographies' and travel works. His ample means made a cultivated existence possible.
Geogr. J. **83**, 1934, pp. 350–2.

Hale, Rev. Edward (1828–1894)

Described as 'Senior Master of Eton College' in an obituary notice, Mr Hale went to Eton in 1850, shortly after taking his degree at Cambridge, as 'Assistant Mathematical Master' and never left it. Ordained in 1853 in the Church of England, he was greatly interested in army training and in sport, especially for the boys in his own house. When he went to Eton, even mathematics was regarded as a form of learning inferior to the classics but Mr Hale argued the case for greater breadth in education. He gave practical expression to his enlightened views by teaching not only geography but also various branches of natural science during the last twenty years of his life.
Material has kindly been provided by Patrick Strong, Keeper of the College Library and Collections, Eton College, and an obituary appeared in the *Eton College Chronicle* No. 660, 31 July 1894.

Haviland, Alfred (1825–1903)

Though born at Bridgwater, he was educated in London at the Hackney Church of England School and University College Hospital. Having qualified in 1845 he returned to practise medicine with his father. During the cholera epidemic of 1849 he took daily meteorological readings and formed the view that in calm weather many new cases appeared but in periods of strong winds there were few. From climate and weather his interest spread to geology in time. In 1855 he published a paper on 'Climate, weather and disease' and in 1864 the first edition of his *Geographical Distribution of Disease* appeared; of this the second much enlarged edition followed in 1892. In 1882 and 1883 he wrote on Brighton and Scarborough as health resorts and in 1883 on phthisis in the Isle of Man where in 1888 he founded the Manx Geological Society and became its first president. His numerous works included *Medical Geography as an Aid to Clinical Medicine* (1897). His view was that cancer was more fatal among women in clayey, flooded areas than on elevated areas with calcareous soils, that valleys were harmful situations for sufferers from heart disease and rheumatism and that phthisis patients would succumb to full blasts of strong prevailing winds. Always interested in such correlations, he became Honorary Lecturer on the Geographical Distribution of Diseases to the medical students at St Thomas's Hospital.

British Medical Journal 1903, **1**, p. 1522; *Lancet* **1**, 1903, p. 1844; *Medico-Chirugical Transactions* **87**, 1904, cxvii–cxxii.

Heawood, Edward (1864–1949)

Originally a classicist, he was fascinated by exploration and after graduating in Cambridge spent some years in India as part of his apprenticeship to geography. In 1884 he joined the librarian's staff at the Royal Geographical Society, where he retained his interest in discovery, especially of Africa. He wrote a textbook on Africa in 1896, a useful history of discovery in the seventeenth and eighteenth centuries in 1912 and a chapter on African exploration from 1783 to 1870 in the *Cambridge History of the British Empire* (1940). He became an internationally recognised authority on the history of cartography, and especially on watermarks and various kinds of paper employed.

Geogr. J. **113**, 1949, pp. 143–4; *Geogr. Rev.* **39**, 1949, pp. 677–8.

Herbertson, Andrew John (1865–1915)

Educated first at Galashiels Academy, Herbertson entered Edinburgh University when nearly twenty-one and followed courses in physics and mathematics, astronomy and agriculture with distinction, but never graduated as he omitted chemistry. From September 1892 he spent four months at the Ben Nevis Observatory and in the following summer he worked at the Fort William Low-level Observatory. He taught at Dundee University College in the summer of 1892, in Manchester University from 1894 to 1896 and at the Heriot-Watt College from 1896 to 1899. During these years he wrote his Ph.D. thesis on 'The monthly distribution of rainfall over the world', presented at Freiburg in 1898, and with Dr A. Buchan and others prepared the *Bartholomew Atlas of Meteorology*. From 1899 his life was spent in Oxford, where he became head of the department when Mackinder left in 1905 and gave Oxford its distinctive interest in human and regional geography. He was given a personal chair in 1910. His many activities included membership of the Royal Commission on Canals from 1906 to 1910, constant work for the Geographical Association and the editing, with O. J. R. Howarth, of the *Oxford Survey of the British Empire* in six volumes published in 1914. *Geogr. J.* **46**, 1915, pp. 319–20; *Geogr. Teach.* **8**, 1915–16, pp. 143–6; *Geography* **21**, 1936, pp. 18–27; *Scott. Geogr. Mag.* **31**, 1915, pp. 486–90; Gilbert, E. W., *British Pioneers in Geography* (Newton Abbot) 1972, pp. 180–210; a series of papers on Herbertson in *Geography* **50**, 1965, pp. 313–72 included 'an appreciation of his life and work' by E. W. Gilbert, shorter essays by J. F. Unstead and H. J. Fleure, a significant but remote paper on 'the Higher Units' originally published in 1913 and a study of his services to school geography with a full bibliography by L. J. Jay; Jay, L. J., 'Andrew John Herbertson', *Geographers: biobibliographical studies* **3**, 1979, pp. 85–92.

Hinks, Arthur Robert (1873–1945)

London born, Hinks went to Trinity College, Cambridge, from Whitgift Grammar School, Croydon, and from 1895 worked at the University Observatory. In 1908 he joined the staff of the Cambridge School of Geography as Lecturer in Surveying and Cartography, but in 1912 he accepted an administrative post at the Royal Geographical Society, of which three years later he became secretary and editor. Meanwhile in 1912 he published *Map Projections* and in 1913 *Maps and Survey*, both of which went into later editions and were known to many generations of students. In 1913 he became a Fellow of the Royal Society for his distinguished work in astronomy. Hinks devoted much of his time and talent to the advance of cartography and geodesy, and especially to the 1:1,000,000 map of the world. He also served as secretary of the Permanent Commission on Geographical Names founded in 1919. He prepared a new edition of the Royal Geographical Society's *Hints to Travellers* and his advice on equipment and methods was eagerly sought by explorers.
Geogr. J. **105**, 1945, pp. 146–51.

Hooker, Sir Joseph Dalton (1817–1911)

His father, William Jackson Hooker (1775–1865), became Professor of Botany at Glasgow University in 1820 and developed the Glasgow Botanic Gardens. His famous *British Flora* was first issued in 1830 and from 1841 he was director of Kew Gardens. Joseph Dalton Hooker had

his father's physical stamina, capacity for hard work and artistic ability. Initially he graduated in medicine in 1839 and from then to 1843 he was assistant surveyor and naturalist to the expedition of Captain James Clark Ross to the south polar seas, visiting Tasmania, New Zealand, South America and the Falkland Islands. He shared Charles Darwin's views on the struggle of plant and animal life for existence. He was also a devoted admirer of Alexander von Humboldt, whom he regarded as the founder of modern geography. In 1865, after ten years as assistant director at Kew, he succeeded his father as director until his retirement in 1885. A long and active life included many expeditions abroad, written up with devoted care. Both Hookers were good friends to geographers concerned with plant and animal distributions, the recognition of their evolution and their environmental association.
Geogr. J. **39**, 1912, pp. 165–8; Turrill, W. B., *Joseph Dalton Hooker* (London) 1963; Allen, M., *The Hookers of Kew* (London) 1967.

Howarth, Osbert John Radcliffe (1877–1954)

Educated at Westminster and Christ Church, Oxford, Howarth was attracted to geography by H. J. Mackinder, and in 1902 was awarded the diploma in geography at Oxford. From 1904 to 1911 he was geographical assistant to the editor of the *Encyclopaedia Britannica* and from 1909 to 1946 was secretary to the British Association. With A. J. Herbertson he edited the six volumes of the *Oxford Survey of the British Empire* published in 1914. After the death of both Herbertson and his wife in 1915, Howarth edited and himself wrote numerous volumes in the 'Oxford Geographies'. He was interested in the historical growth of geographical ideas and, with John Scott Keltie, wrote *The History of Geography* in 1913 and, with R. E. Dickinson, *The Making of Geography* in 1933. A notable contribution to this same subject was his presidential address to Section E at the British Association meeting in Edinburgh, 1951, to mark the centenary of the Geography Section: a valuable appendix consisted of short lives of nearly eighty geographers. He also wrote a book on the British Association in 1922, reissued in 1931, and his love of landscape was seen in his *Scenic Heritage of England and Wales* (1937) as well as in his photographs, some of which appeared in the *Oxford Survey.*
Geogr. J. **120**, 1954, p. 393; *Geography* **39**, 1954, pp. 291–2.

Johnston, Alexander Keith (1804–1871)

His first maps were published in a guide-book of 1830 and with his brother William he ran the family Edinburgh map firm from 1825. They published the *National Atlas* in 1843, after five years' work and the *Physical Atlas of Natural Phenomena* in 1848. This included some

material from the atlas of Heinrich Berghaus, but was an original production. Then followed, in 1850, the first edition of the *Dictionary of Geography, Descriptive, Physical, Statistical and Historical* and a physical globe 30 in. in diameter in 1851. Five atlases, labelled general, classical, physical, astronomical and military, appeared from 1851 to 1855, and in 1852 a large-scale drawing of a chart of the geographical distribution of health and diseases, also given on a reduced scale in the 1856 edition of the *Physical Atlas*. Every sheet of the *Royal Atlas*, which eventually appeared in 1861, was shown to the Prince Consort before publication. A. K. Johnston's son, also called Alexander Keith (1844–79) went to the Stanford firm in 1866, where he helped to produce the *Globe Atlas of Europe* of 1867 and the maps in Murray's *Handbook for Scotland*. In 1870 he published *Lake Regions of Central Africa* and later he worked on the Africa volume in Stanford's *Compendium*. He died on an expedition to the head of Lake Nyasa.
J. R. Geogr. Soc. **42**, 1872, c/xi–c/xiii; *Proc. R. Geogr. Soc.* **1**, 1879, pp. 598–600.

Jones, Llewellyn Rodwell (1881–1947)

From Kingswood, Bath (1892–9) a school for the sons of Methodist ministers, Rodwell Jones went to London University and became a schoolmaster teaching science until, in 1913, he went to Leeds University as Lecturer in Railway Geography. At that time, and for almost forty years afterwards, geography was taught to administrative workers on the railways and Rodwell Jones's first book, *North England: an economic geography* (1921) was designed for them. After serving with distinction in the First World War he returned to London and was largely instrumental in building up the Joint School of Geography in King's College and the London School of Economics, where he succeeded Sir Halford Mackinder as Professor of Geography in 1925. In 1924 the widely known text, which went into ten editions, on *North America*, written with P. W. Bryan first appeared. His love of ports was seen in *The Geography of London River* (1931). In 1945 he retired, hoping to write up material patiently collected, but his arduous administrative duties, made the more difficult by a nervous temperament, left him with only a short time before he died.
Geogr. J. **110**, 1947, p. 258; *Geography* **32**, 1947, p. 138: information from his sister Dr Hilda Ormsby and from Mr J. B. Field, Kingswood School, Bath.

Keltie, Sir John Scott (1840–1927)

Born at Dundee, Keltie studied at the universities of St Andrews and Edinburgh and from 1861 to 1871 was on the editorial staff of W. and R.

Chambers in Edinburgh, moving to Macmillan's in London from 1871 to 1884. He wrote for *The Times* from 1875 onwards and in 1880 began to work on the *Statesman's Yearbook*, which he edited from 1883 to the end of his life. From 1873 to 1885 he was subeditor of *Nature*. Chosen by the Royal Geographical Society as Inspector of Geographical Education, he produced the famous report of 1885 which showed the unfavourable position of Britain compared with France and Germany. He joined the staff of the Society and was its secretary and editor from 1892 to 1915. His book on the *Partition of Africa*, which appeared in 1893, was foreshadowed by articles on 'the Scramble for Africa' in *The Times*: he also wrote *Applied Geography* (1890 and 1898) and, in collaboration with O. J. R. Howarth, *The History of Geography*, in 1913. Keltie edited a series of volumes on the history of exploration and organised the geographical and statistical sections of the tenth edition of the *Encyclopaedia Britannica*.
Geogr. J. **69**, 1927, pp. 281–7; *Scott. Geogr. Mag.* **43**, 1927, pp. 102–5.

Lake, Philip (1865–1949)

Lake's father was headmaster of Morpeth Grammar School and Philip went from there to the Durham College of Science at Newcastle upon Tyne, and in 1883 to St John's College, Cambridge, where he had a first in both parts of the Natural Science Tripos in 1886 and 1887. After three years with the Geological Survey of India he returned home impaired in health and lived for several years as a private tutor, examiner and lecturer. In 1896 he became Principal of Colchester University Extension College and for several years he divided each week between this work and his normal routine in Cambridge. In 1908 he became Lecturer in Regional and Physical Geography in Cambridge University. Two years later his *Textbook on Geology*, written with R. H. Rastall, appeared and in 1915 his well-known *Physical Geography*. His interests were centred in both geology and geography and his papers included studies of the river systems of Wales, of hill slopes and of Wegener's theory of continental drift. He was unmarried and spent his retirement of more than twenty years in Cambridge, where he died.
Geogr. J. **114**, 1949, pp. 115–16; *Q. J. Geol. Soc. Lond.* **105**, 1949, lxxxv–vi.

Lewis, William Vaughan (1907–1961)

Born at Pontypridd, Glamorgan, Lewis spent his whole university life as student and teacher in the University of Cambridge from 1926. Having studied mathematics for one year, he transferred to geography and chose geomorphology and trigonometrical and geodetic surveying as his special subjects. In 1931 his first paper on shingle beaches appeared and this remained a lifelong interest. He was at work on Chesil beach, using a long series of observations, at the time of his tragic death in a motor accident. From 1936 he published numerous papers on glaciers and corries, based on observations in Iceland, Norway and Switzerland. Lewis was a devoted fieldworker and a man of charming personality who gave younger workers an inspiration that induced several of them to continue and develop his work.

Trans. Inst. Br. Geogr. **29**, 1961, ix–x; *Geogr. J.* **127**, 1961, pp. 286–7.

Linton, David Leslie (1906–1971)

Linton had first-class honours degrees in both geology and geography at King's College, London, where he became a demonstrator in 1927. His first publications, from 1930, were on the geomorphology of southeast England but in 1933 the first of several papers on Scotland appeared, for he lectured in Edinburgh from 1929 to the Second World War, when he worked on air-photo investigations. Having moved to Sheffield in 1945, he continued to publish papers on Scotland with some controversial material on glaciation, based on detailed fieldwork both in Scotland and England and in areas still under active glaciation, including Antarctica. He was an acute observer of the physical landscape and his field classes were greatly appreciated by students and others. World social problems, such as those of underdeveloped areas, were to him a constant concern reflected in several articles revealing a sympathetic but apprehensive mind. Linton wrote with distinction and illustrated his work with maps and sketches showing artistic talent. As editor of *Geography* he gave the journal a high standard of content and presentation.

Geography **56**, 1971, pp. 341–3; *Trans. Inst. Br. Geogr.* **55**, 1972, pp. 171–8.

Lyde, Lionel William (1863–1947)

Lyde was drawn to geography through his study of history and the classics at Sedbergh School and Queen's College, Oxford and published his first work, *An Introduction to Ancient History*, in 1890, when he was English master at Merchiston School, Edinburgh. From 1895, he published *Man on the Earth* and other 'Man and . . .' textbooks of which millions of copies were sold: like other geographers of his day he regarded textbook writing as essential for geographical progress. From 1899 to 1903 he was headmaster of Bolton School, but he accepted an invitation from University College, London to become Professor of Geography at a salary of £50 a year. He remained there until 1928 as an interesting and slightly eccentric character, amassing material for his books on Europe and Asia largely from press cuttings, searching for a philosophy of geography, considering problems of physical and social

anthropology and of comparative religion. His teaching, said one of his students, was enlivened by his fine voice, the flash of his brilliant eyes and unfailing dignity. On retirement he returned to the study of the classics.
Geography **32**, 1947, pp. 34–6; *Geogr. J.* **109**, 1947, pp. 154–5.

McFarlane, John (1873–1953)

Having graduated with first-class honours in history at Edinburgh University in 1897, McFarlane studied history and economics at Cambridge with success and lectured in history at St David's College, Lampeter, until 1903, when he became Lecturer in Political and Economic Geography at Manchester University. In the first seven years he also lectured on economics, but from 1906 he held the title of Lecturer in Geography. The first edition of his substantial text, *Economic Geography*, appeared in 1914. From 1916 he worked with H. N. Dickson (*q.v.*) at the Admiralty and in 1919 he went to Aberdeen University as Lecturer in Geography, and Reader from 1923 to his retirement in 1945. He was closely concerned with school education, including work for examining boards. McFarlane, a generous man of unusual charm, acknowledged his gratitude to G. G. Chisholm (*q.v.*) and also to A. J. Herbertson (*q.v.*), with whom he spent one term at Oxford when he began his geographical work in Manchester.
Geogr. J. **119**, 1953, p. 250 and **120**, 1954, pp. 118–19; *Trans. Inst. Br. Geogr.* **19**, 1953, ix.

Mackinder, Sir Halford John (1861–1947)

Mackinder's father was a medical doctor at Gainsborough, Lincolnshire, and from the town's grammar school he went to Epsom College and Christ Church, Oxford, where he read both natural sciences and history. His oratorical gifts brought him the presidency of the Union. He became a lecturer for the University Extension movement and in 1887 spoke at the Royal Geographical Society on the 'New geography'. This notable lecture helped him to become Reader in Geography at Oxford University, where he worked till 1905, though from 1892 to 1903 he was also Principal of the new college at Reading (ultimately to become a university) and from 1895, the year of its foundation, he also taught at the London School of Economics, of which he was director from 1903 to 1908. He remained as Reader in Geography at the London School of Economics to 1923 and as Professor until 1925. From 1910 to 1922 he was a Member of Parliament and he served on many government commissions. His writings included *Britain and the British Seas* (1902) and *Democratic Ideals and Reality* (1919). The first was widely respected for many years as a careful study of Britain's geography, and the second was a fascinating view of world strategical problems, developed from a series of papers on political geography from 1904 onwards. Mackinder cared very much for the educational aspects of geography, on which he wrote several papers and, in 1914, a book on *The Teaching of Geography and History*. From 1906 he issued six school texts most carefully written and revised. On a far more advanced level, he developed the School of Geography at Oxford and acquired premises for it in 1900 – the first in any British university. He also gave the subject a position of consequence in the new college at Reading and in the London School of Economics.

Geogr. J. **110**, 1947, pp. 94–9; *Geography* **32**, 1947, pp. 136–7; Unstead, J. F., 'H. J. Mackinder and the new geography', *Geogr. J.* **113**, 1949, pp. 47–57; Gilbert, E. W. and Parker, W. H., 'Mackinder's *Democratic Ideals and Reality* after fifty years', *Geogr. J.* **135**, 1969, pp. 228–31; Gilbert, E. W., *British Pioneers in Geography* (Newton Abbot) 1972, pp. 139–79, 257–9; Blouet, B. W., 'Sir Halford Mackinder as British High Commissioner to South Russia', *Geogr. J.* **142**, 1976, pp. 228–36.

Markham, Sir Clements Robert (1830–1916)

From Westminster School Markham joined the Navy at the age of fourteen and within the next eight years he hunted pirates in the Mediterranean and travelled to the Arctic as a member of the Franklin search expedition. Soon after leaving the Navy in 1852 he spent two years in Peru, partly inspired by von Humboldt, nominally to study the Inca civilisation though his initial fame rested on the successful collection of the cinchona plant and its cultivation in India for supplying quinine. From 1853 to 1888 he was honorary secretary of the Royal Geographical Society, closely associated with Livingstone, Stanley and the numerous other renowned explorers of the time. Later, as Vice-President or President he worked for school and university education in geography and for the Society's own scheme of training intending explorers. He was a constant supporter of polar exploration and especially of the ill-fated Scott expedition of 1911. The devotion of Markham to the Royal Geographical Society was vital in raising its membership from 1,000 to 5,000, and he also gave fifty years' service to the Hakluyt Society, during which he edited many of its volumes. His professional career began in 1854 with the East India Office, from 1858 the India Office, where he used every opportunity of developing geographical surveys. A ready author, he wrote a large number of books and articles. Honours received were numerous. Like many very active and able people he was somewhat impatient and autocratic in dealings with others, though singularly gracious to young people of enterprise, especially explorers and naval officers and men. A son of the Vicar of Stillingfleet, Yorkshire, he found a fascinating hobby in genealogy and heraldry, notably of the two aristocratic families from which he was descended. In modern terms he was an establishment figure.

Geogr. J. **47**, 1916, pp. 161–76 (by J. S. Keltie and others); Mill, H. R., *The Record of the Royal Geographical Society, 1830–1930* (London) 1930 (many refs); Mill, H. R., *An Autobiography* (London) 1951, pp. 95–8, 141–5.

Mill, Hugh Robert (1861–1950)

Chiefly known for his work on rainfall, Mill was a geographer with a wide range of interests. Initially trained in Edinburgh as a chemist and physicist, he worked on oceanography at the Scottish Marine Station from 1884 to 1887 on the *Challenger* material. From 1887 to 1891, he lectured at the Heriot-Watt College in Edinburgh and also gave extra-mural courses for the universities of Edinburgh and St Andrews. He then moved to London as librarian of the Royal Geographical Society, where his fascination for polar exploration became even more marked. On the first day of the new century he moved to the British Rainfall Organisation, which he served devotedly until eye trouble compelled him to retire in 1919. This retirement, however, was only partial, for he continued to be active in writing, with assistance, and his contribution on the rainfall of Britain to A. G. Ogilvie, *Great Britain: essays in regional geography* (1928), was notable. He wrote numerous papers, books on polar exploration, *The Siege of the South Pole* (1905), and a biography of Sir Ernest Shackleton published in 1923. He also edited the *International Geography* volumes. Born at Thurso, he was so delicate as a child that he had little formal education. A man of genial temperament, he was devoted to the Royal Scottish Geographical Society, the Royal Geographical Society and the Royal Meteorological Society.

Mill, H. R., *An Autobiography* (London 1951; *The Times* 6.4.1950, 12.4.1950, and 18.4.1950; *Scott. Geogr. Mag.* **66**, 1950, pp. 1–2; *Geogr. J.* **115**, 1950, pp. 266–7; *Geographers:* biobibliographical studies **1**, 1977, pp. 73–8.

Miller, Arthur Austin (1900–1968)

A native of Lincolnshire, Austin Miller had his school education in Oxford and graduated at University College, London, with first-class honours in geology in 1922. Initially a demonstrator in geology, he went to Reading University to teach geography in 1926 and remained there for forty years, specialising in climatology and geomorphology. His book, *Climatology* was first published in 1932 and his text on geomorphology, *The Skin of the Earth*, in 1953. From 1935 to 1939 Miller published a series of papers on erosion surfaces around the Irish Sea, including a reassessment of the geomorphological problems raised

by J. B. Jukes in southern Ireland in 1862. After the Second World War most of his papers were on climatology. Blessed by an extravert and happy nature, Miller was remarkably successful in his work for professional organisations and societies, including the British Association, the Institute of British Geographers, the Geographical Association and the Royal Geographical Society.
Trans. Inst. Br. Geogr. **46**, 1969, xix–xxi.

Murray, Sir John (1841–1914)

Canadian-born, Murray moved to Scotland in 1858 and, after a short period at Stirling High School, went to Edinburgh University. As a post-graduate student he worked in Professor P. G. Tait's famous laboratory, and from 1872 to 1876 he was on the *Challenger* as a naturalist. Murray returned to the Scottish Marine Station to work on the organisms collected and in 1882 succeeded Sir Charles Wyville Thomson as director of the Scottish Marine Station and editor of the *Challenger* publications, of which the last appeared in 1895. Murray, a powerful personality devoted to oceanography and to Antarctic exploration, established marine laboratories on the Firth of Forth and the Firth of Clyde and argued that there was only one continental land area round the South Pole of which he drew a map with the name 'Antarctica'. In 1901, with Frederick Pullar he began to work on the bathymetric survey of Scottish lochs, following the enterprise of H. R. Mill, Edward Heawood and A. J. Herbertson in the Lake District but with better equipment. He was also one of the founders of the Ben Nevis Observatory, which provided daily climatic readings from 1884 to 1903. Murray was a man of iron will and great devotion to scientific research, with a nautical air of brusque and colourful speech. He was killed in a motor accident on 16 March 1914.
Geogr. J. **43**, 1914, pp. 585–7; *Scott. Geogr. Mag.* **30**, 1914, pp. 197–200; Mill, H. R., *An Autobiography* (London) 1951.

Newbigin, Marion Isabel (1869–1934)

Born in Alnwick, Northumberland, Marion Newbigin became a botanist and zoologist and lectured in the extra-mural School of Medicine for Women at Edinburgh until 1916, when women were first admitted to the medical classes at Edinburgh University with the men. Her first book was on *Colour in Nature* (1899), but she was interested in a wide range of natural sciences and gradually turned to geography, in which she wrote about plant and animal distributions and also on its political aspects. Her general world survey was greatly valued as a textbook. In 1902 she became editor of the *Scottish Geographical Magazine* and for the rest of her life the magazine gained increasing

respect far beyond its homeland. By a tragic coincidence she died on 20 July 1934, the day when the Royal Scottish Geographical Society began its jubilee celebrations.
Scott. Geogr. Mag. **50**, 1934, pp. 331–3.

O'Dell, Andrew Charles (1909–1966)

Aberdeen University was O'Dell's main concern from 1945, when he became head of its Geography Department, first as Lecturer and from 1951 as Professor. In those years he built up a flourishing School of Geography and continued his researches on Scotland, and in 1962, with K. Walton, he published *The Highlands and Islands of Scotland* as part of the (regrettably never completed) series of regional geographies of the Nelson firm. This was a natural development from his first book, *The Historical Geography of the Shetland Islands* (1939) based on his M.Sc. thesis of London University. He also wrote the Land Utilisation Survey memoirs on Shetland, Orkney and other Scottish counties. Two other main interests were Scandinavia, on which he wrote *The Scandinavian World* (1959), and railways, on which his best work appeared in various articles and in sections of the Admiralty *Handbooks* written during the war years. Born in the Transvaal, O'Dell was educated at Westminster City School and King's College, University of London. Before the war he lectured in Birkbeck College and the London School of Economics and his first published work was on population distribution. Curiosity about the far north of Britain and its links with Scandinavia resulted in a career of devoted service of great benefit both to the University of Aberdeen and to Scotland.
Geogr. J. **132**, 1966, p. 596; *Geography* **51**, 1966, pp. 391–2; *Scott. Mag.* **82**, 1966, pp. 198–201; *Trans. Inst. Br. Geogr.* **42**, 1967, pp. 189–92.

Ogilvie, Alan Grant (1887–1954)

Ogilvie's father was Principal of Heriot-Watt College in Edinburgh, but moved later to work in London museums. Alan was educated at Westminster School and Magdalen College, Oxford, where he graduated in history, though his interest was turning to geography which he studied in Berlin and Paris. In 1912 he was a member of the famous transcontinental excursion across America and before the war he became an assistant in the Geography School at Oxford. His war service in the Balkans led to an appointment on the Geographical Section of the General Staff and to his presence at the Versailles Peace Conference in 1919. After teaching for one year in Manchester University he worked at the American Geographical Society until his return to Edinburgh in 1923. He was primarily a physical and regional geographer, deeply involved in fostering research on Scotland. As editor of the 1928 volume *Great*

Britain: essays in regional geography he was a fortunate choice. His main work was to build up a strong department in Edinburgh, where he also gave devoted service to the Royal Scottish Geographical Society, the National Trust for Scotland and other bodies. On Europe his book, *Europe and its Borderlands*, was published posthumously in 1957 with the help of his literary executor, Dr C. J. Robertson. By nature sincere, unselfish and rather shy, he had a gift for friendship which resulted in fruitful links with geographers all over the world.

Geogr. J. **120**, 1954, pp. 258–9; *Geogr. Rev.* **44**, 1954, pp. 442–4; *Scott. Geogr. Mag.* **70**, 1954, pp. 1–5; Miller, R. and Watson, J. W. (eds), *Geographical Essays in Memory of Alan Grant Ogilvie* (London) 1956, pp. xi–xvi, 1–6; Freeman, T. W., *The Geographer's Craft* (Manchester) 1967, pp. 168–86.

Oldham, Henry Yule (1862–1951)

Educated at Rugby and Jesus College, Oxford, Oldham spent one year, from 1886 to 1887, as tutor to the Duc d'Orléans and studied in Paris during 1888. He returned to England and taught for two years at a grammar school in Manchester. Then followed a year's teaching at Harrow School and another as a student at Berlin University, after which in 1892 he returned to become the first Lecturer in Geography in Owens College, Manchester University. In 1893 he was appointed to lecture at Cambridge. Oldham wrote a few articles and reviews but spent most of his life as a college don, as comfortably as many before and since his time.

Who Was Who.

Peake, Harold John Edward (1867–1946)

By training Peake, son of the Vicar of Ellesmere, became an estate manager. As a young man he travelled widely in Japan, China and Mediterranean countries and lived for a time in British Columbia. Eventually he settled in Newbury, where he gave long service to the Berkshire Education Committee and was honorary curator of the museum. He wrote numerous papers, many of them in the *Antiquaries Journal* on the Bronze Age. He is best known among geographers for his collaboration with H. J. Fleure in the 'Corridors of Time' volumes (pp. 113–14) but he wrote several other books in his later years, including *The English Village* (1922), *The Bronze Age and the Celtic World* (1922), *The Origins of Agriculture* (1928), *The Archaeology of Berkshire* (1931) and *Early Steps in Human Progress* (1933). These are generally regarded as somewhat speculative.

Antiquaries Journal **27**, 1947, p. 213; *Geogr. Rev.* **37**, 1947, p. 507.

Ravenstein, Ernst Georg (1834–1913)

Of German birth, Ravenstein came to England in 1852 and became a cartography pupil of August Petermann. From 1855 to 1872 he worked in the Topographic Section of the War Office, after which he developed his geographical interests with immense industry and a fine critical faculty. His papers on migration appeared at intervals from 1876 but the most famous of them, in the *Journal of the Royal Statistical Society* for 1885 and 1889, were based on the censuses of 1871 and 1881. He wrote – or revised – several school texts for the Johnston firm, some originally written by A. K. Johnston the younger (*q.v.*) and, with J. S. Keltie and H. J. Mackinder, edited a series of volumes on 'The World's Great Explorers' from 1889. He also edited the European section of the *Universal Geography* of J. E. Reclus from 1878. Cartographical work included a twenty-five-sheet map of Eastern Equatorial Africa, on the 1:1,000,000 scale, published by the Royal Geographical Society from 1881 to 1883 and, in 1889, a nine-sheet map of British East Africa, and various other maps of Africa. His last book, *Martin Behaim: his life and his globe* (1908) was a critical examination of the materials used by the fifteenth-century Nuremberg geographer, and in 1898 he edited a volume on the first voyage of Vasco da Gama for the Hakluyt Society which also published, in 1901, his book, *The Strange Adventures of Andrew Battell of Leigh in Angola*. A man of immense energy and cheerful disposition, he was an expert gymnast and President of the London Swimming Club. He died at Hofheim in Taurus on 13 March 1913.
Who Was Who; *Geogr. J.* **41**, 1913, pp. 497–8; Grigg, D., in *Geogr. Mag.* **46**, 1974, pp. 246–7 and in *Geographers: biobibliographical studies* **1**, 1977, pp. 79–82.

Rawlinson, Sir Henry Creswicke (1810–1895)

In 1827 Rawlinson went to Bombay as a cadet in the Indian Army and from 1833 to 1838 he helped to organise the Persian Army until the British Government broke off relations with the Shah. His first paper, on a previously unexplored part of Persia, appeared in 1839 and, with others, was used by Ritter in *Erdkunde*. He served in Afghanistan from 1839 to 1842 and then, from 1843, as political agent and later, 1851–5, as consul-general in Baghdad. He had already developed his interest in cuneiform inscription, on which he wrote numerous papers in the *Proceedings of the Royal Geographical Society*, the *Journal of the Royal Asiatic Society* and other publications. He returned to Persia in 1859 as ambassador but stayed only for a few months and on his return home devoted much of his time to research, though he was a director of the East India Company and from 1865 to 1868 M.P. for Frome. He served on the India Council from 1868 to 1870 and was President of the Royal

Geographical Society from 1871 to 1873 and 1874 to 1876. In 1876 he attended the notable Brussels Conference on Africa and in 1880 he protested sharply at the British withdrawal from Afghanistan. A man of wide learning, notably on Arab geographers, he was also much concerned with matters such as the overland telegraph from Constantinople to Karachi, trade routes from Turkestan to India and military operations at the mouth of the Euphrates. He was definitely a 'character', described on his death as a man combining 'military ardour and scientific enthusiasm'.

Geogr. J. **5**, 1895, pp. 490–7; G. Rawlinson, *A Memoir of Major-General Sir Henry Creswicke Rawlinson* (London) 1898. George Rawlinson, Professor of Ancient History in Oxford University and a canon of Canterbury, was his brother.

Roxby, Percy Maude (1880–1947)

One of five sons of the Rector of Buckden, near Huntingdon, Roxby always loved the countryside of East Anglia. Educated at Bromsgrove School, he went to Christ Church, Oxford, where he graduated in 1903 with first-class honours in history. Already he was drawn to geography and from 1903 to 1904 he attended courses for the diploma in geography by H. J. Mackinder and A. J. Herbertson. In 1904, before he could take the examination, Roxby became an assistant lecturer at Liverpool where he remained, as Lecturer in Regional Geography, from 1906 and as Professor from 1917, when the first full honours course was established, to his retirement in 1944. In 1912–13 he toured the world as an Albert Kahn Fellow and was enthralled by China on which he wrote various articles and part of the *Geographical Handbook of China* (three volumes), which he edited, during the Second World War. He also wrote essays on natural regions and on varied aspects of human geography. In 1944 he went as chief representative of the British Council to China, where he died. Roxby was a fascinating speaker (especially on China) and a devoted supporter of numerous good causes connected with world peace, race relations and the Church of England.

Geogr. J. **109**, 1947, pp. 155–6; Gilbert, E. W., *British Pioneers in Geography* (Newton Abbot) 1972, pp. 211–26; Freeman, T. W., *The Geographer's Craft* (Manchester) 1967, pp. 156–68.

Russell, Sir Edward John (1872–1965)

Born at Frampton-on-Severn, Russell was the son of a Unitarian minister. Initially interested in the classics, he later studied chemistry at Manchester and went to Wye Agricultural College in 1901 as a soil chemist. With Daniel Hall he prepared a monograph on *The Agriculture and Soils of Kent, Surrey and Sussex* (1911): this work gave Russell a firm reputation and confirmed his life vocation of using science for the advancement of agriculture. It also convinced him that scientific work was of greater social significance than emotionally charged schemes such as one he evolved in Manchester for transporting people from the city's slums to an agricultural colony. In 1907 he followed Daniel Hall to Rothamsted as the first 'Goldsmith's Company's Soil Chemist' and from 1912 to 1943 he was the director. Rothamsted, founded in 1852 as an agricultural research centre, had been moribund before it was revived by Daniel Hall from 1902. Russell was deeply interested in geography and in the 1920s became chairman of the Standing Committee on Regional Surveys of the Geographical Association, which led to the Land Utilisation Survey, to which he gave devoted support. From 1938 to 1960, he was President of the Le Play Society. He was a frequent visitor to Russia and various other countries. In 1949 he was President of the British Association and when over eighty he published *World Population and World Food Supplies* (1954) and the *World of the Soil* (1957) as well as the delightful autobiography which reveals both his interesting life and his charming personality.

Geogr. J. **131**, 1965, p. 581; *Geography* **50**, 1965, pp. 380–1; Russell, E. J., *The Land Called Me* (1956), (an autobiographical volume).

Sclater, Sir Philip Lutley (1829–1913)

Few men were more productive of written papers, for Sclater is said to have written over 1,200 between 1844 and 1913, when he lost his life in a carriage accident. From Winchester he won a scholarship at Corpus Christi College, Oxford, in 1845, but as he was under age he went in 1846 and graduated with first-class honours in mathematics in 1849. He then travelled for two years and learnt French, German and Italian. Called to the Bar and made a Fellow of Corpus in 1855, he spent 1856 in the United States, and from 1859 to 1902 was secretary to the Zoological Society. He edited *Ibis*, the journal of the British Ornithologists' Union from 1859 to 1862 and again, alone or with a partner, from 1877 to 1912. In 1875, as President of Section D (Zoology) of the British Association, he spoke on 'The state of our knowledge of zoological geography'. His papers in the publications of the Royal Geographical Society and the book of collected essays published in 1899 show his enthusiasm for this theme and that of his son, William Lutley Sclater (1863–1943) who travelled even more extensively than his father and worked in India, at Cape Town, and in the United States. He was also secretary of the Zoological Society for a time.

Geogr. J. **42**, 1913, pp. 204–5; *Proceedings of the Royal Society*, Series B **87**, 1913–14, iii–v.

Smith, Sir George Adam (1856–1942)

Though Sir George Adam Smith's fame rests mainly on his contribution to biblical studies, his *Historical Geography of the Holy Land*, first published in 1894, reached its twenty-fifth edition by 1931 and was reissued as a Fontana paperback in 1966. Born in Calcutta, Smith was at Edinburgh University and New College, and also at the universities of Tübingen and Leipzig. He studied Arabic in Cairo, and made several visits to Palestine on foot. While a Presbyterian minister in Aberdeen, he wrote an exposition of the *Book of Isaiah*, in two volumes (1888–90). In 1892 he became Professor of Hebrew and Old Testament Exegesis in the Free Church College, Glasgow. He visited Palestine to collect material for his historical geography in 1891, with later visits in 1901 and 1904. From 1909 to 1935 he was Principal and Vice-Chancellor of Aberdeen University. In 1914, the *Atlas of the Historical Geography of the Holy Land* was published in collaboration with Dr J. G. Bartholomew (*q.v.*). Smith, G. A., *Historical Geography of the Holy Land*, 1966 edn, introduction by H. H. Rowley; *Who Was Who; D.N.B.; Geographers: Biobibliographical Studies* **1**, 1977, pp. 105–6.

Smith, Wilfred (1903–1955)

From Blackpool Grammar School Smith went to Liverpool University in 1921 and spent all his remaining years in the Geography Department. Having graduated with first-class honours in 1924, he became a Tutor, an Assistant Lecturer in 1928, a Lecturer in 1931, Senior Lecturer in 1945 and Professor in 1950. He was deeply involved in administrative work but made significant contributions to geography through his publications. His first work was on coal and iron in China, on which he wrote his Master's dissertation in 1926. Then followed work in Merseyside, culminating in two publications in 1942 and 1945 which were of value in the post-war planning of the area. The third concern was with economic geography on which his large book, *An Economic Geography of Great Britain*, first appeared in 1949. In his few remaining years Smith was still fascinated by problems of industrial location and in 1953 he edited, and partly wrote, the survey of Merseyside prepared for the British Association meeting in Liverpool. An infirmity made travelling difficult, but he found endless interest around the Mersey estuary.
Geogr. J. **122**, 1956, pp. 139–40; *Trans. Inst. Br. Geogr.* **21**, 1955, viii–ix.

Smith, William Gardner (1866–1928) and Robert (1873–1900)

The elder Smith was born in Dundee and studied at the University College, where he was taught botany by Patrick Geddes (*q.v.*) and zoology by d'Arcy Thompson. After a period of school-teaching, he

became an assistant at Edinburgh University and spent part of 1893 and 1894 as a Ph.D. student at Munich. He spent three years lecturing in Edinburgh and then moved to Leeds University where he inspired C. E. Moss, W. M. Rankin and T. W. Woodhead to work on the vegetation of the Pennines. His younger brother, Robert, was also inspired by Geddes and by Charles Flahault of Montpellier. From 1908 W. G. Smith lectured in biology at the Edinburgh and East of Scotland College of Agriculture. His devoted work in the Pennines, continuing that in Scotland of his younger brother (pp. 61–2, 85), and his encouragement of younger people led to the formation of the British Vegetation Committee which developed into the British Ecological Society.
Scott. Geogr. Mag. **16**, 1900, pp. 597–9; *Journal of Ecology* **17**, 1929, pp. 170–3.

Stamp, Sir Laurence Dudley (1898–1966)

London-born, Stamp was debarred from much normal schooling by poor health and early learned a technique of self-education. After graduating at King's College, London with first-class honours in geology and botany in 1917, he served in the Army and on demobilisation became a Demonstrator in Geology at King's College. He also became an external student in geography at London University and one of its first honours geography graduates in 1921. He then left for Burma as an oil geologist and in 1923 returned to England to marry his fellow-student, Elsa. Together they worked in Burma, at Rangoon University, until he became Reader in Economic Geography in the London School of Economics in 1926, and Professor in 1945. Already many of the widely known textbooks and a large number of geological papers had appeared, but the transition to geography became clear when his text on Asia was published in 1929. By 1931 the Land Utilisation Survey became familiar to geographers and many of the wider public, and this was to mark all Stamp's remaining years, for its significance in the replanning of Britain, as of other countries, was greater than people, including probably Stamp at first, realised. Not only was there the problem of feeding the world's population but also the allocation of land for housing, town growth, industry and recreation if people were to enjoy reasonable amenities or even good health. The making of the future was Stamp's real concern and he worked assiduously for human welfare to the end, which came suddenly in Mexico City during a conference. Few men were more generous, both with money and with time, for he served all kinds of organisations devotedly. He loved life and enjoyed it fully.
Geogr. J. **132**, 1966, pp. 591–4; *Geography* **51**, 1966, pp. 388–91; *Geogr. Rev.* **57**, 1967, pp. 246–9; Institute of British Geographers, Special Publication No. 1, Nov. 1968, *Land Use and Resources: a memorial volume to Sir Dudley Stamp*, esp. pp. 3–11, 71–81, 261–9.

Stanley, Sir Henry Morton (1840–1904)

Born John Rowlands in Denbigh, Wales, he was a workhouse boy and went to America as a youth where, in New Orleans, he met a benefactor whose name he assumed. Having served on both sides in the American Civil War, he became a journalist liberally supplied with funds by the *New York Herald*. The paper sent him to Abyssinia in 1867 and after extensive travels in India, Persia and Turkey he was told to 'find Livingstone', not seen since he left Zanzibar in March 1866. Stanley found him in November 1871 and returned to England in 1872. Now famous, he organised several more expeditions in Africa, notably in what became the Belgian Congo. Firmly convinced that European control was needed to give peace to Africa and to destroy the slave trade, he hoped to see material prosperity and Christianity established in time. Undoubtedly some of his belligerent statements in his papers and books aroused opposition from prominent politicians and especially from the Aborigines' Protection Society. But he was a famous figure of the day and in 1890 married a member of the wealthy Tennant family in Westminster Abbey. After lengthy lecturing tours in Australia and America he sat in Parliament for North Lambeth from 1895 to 1900. On his death the Dean of Westminster refused burial in the Abbey. He is still a controversial figure in the history of African exploration.
Geogr. J. **24**, 1904, pp. 103–6 (by E. G. Ravenstein); Halladay, E., 'Henry Morton Stanley', in Rotberg, R. I. (ed.), *Africa and its Explorers* (London) 1971, pp. 223–54 (with excellent bibliography).

Stevens, Alexander (1886–1965)

After a somewhat tentative period in geography teaching at Glasgow University Stevens arrived in 1919 as head of the department and for the remaining years to his retirement in 1953 poured all the resources of his fascinating but mercurial mind into his work. He had been employed by the Ordnance Survey and was a member of the Antarctic expedition under Scott from 1914. His essay on the Highlands and Islands of Scotland in the 1928 volume edited by A. G. Ogilvie, *Great Britain: essays in regional geography*, was largely geological, but later he became concerned with varying concepts of regional geography, on which he wrote his 1939 presidential address to the British Association. The course at Glasgow for honours students became entirely regional for final year students, though in his later years Stevens became greatly concerned with population distribution. Always alive to the possibilities of geographical research, Stevens spread his interest over many themes with somewhat bewildering rapidity. In consequence he failed to write much that would have been welcomed, for he wrote with zest and was never dull. From 1925 he represented geography on the senate of Glasgow University and in 1947 he became its first Professor of Geography.

Robertson, C. J., 'Scottish geography: the first hundred years', *Scott. Geogr. Mag.* **89**, 1973, pp. 14–15; obituary by H. Fairhurst in *Scott. Geogr. Mag.* **82**, 1966, p. 58.

Taylor, Eva Germaine Rimington (1879–1966)

Educated at the North London Collegiate School, Eva Taylor graduated in London University with first-class honours in chemistry in 1903. After teaching in a school she went to Oxford where in 1908 she was awarded the diploma in geography and the certificate in regional geography with distinction. For two years, to 1910, she was a private research assistant to A. J. Herbertson engaged on the preparation of wall maps and from 1910 to 1916 she worked on a well-known series of school texts with J. F. Unstead. A few years of writing and part-time lecturing followed, but in 1921 she went to Birkbeck College (London University). Then began her remarkable studies of Tudor and early Stuart geography, on which she published books in 1930 and 1934. This proved to be the beginning of a lifelong interest in navigation, which included a study of instruments and maps. She was at all times devoted to the advance of geography, and strongly advocated the preparation of a national atlas. During the Second World War she became an adviser to the new Ministry of Town and Country Planning and her views, always practical, were widely respected. From 1930 to 1944 she was Professor of Geography at Birkbeck College, and on her retirement her mental vitality triumphed over indifferent health for she continued her fascinating and unusual researches on navigation, and remained a devoted supporter of the Hakluyt Society.
Trans. Inst. Br. Geogr. **45**, 1968, pp. 181–6; *The Times* 7.7.1966; *Geogr. J.* **132**, 1966, pp. 594–6.

Unstead, John Frederick (1876–1965)

Geographical education was Unstead's main concern, and he began his working life as a pupil teacher in a London school. He won a Board of Education scholarship to the Day Training College in Cambridge, where he acquired his first degree in 1898. H. J. Mackinder advised him to turn from economics to geography, and in 1912–13 he published his D.Sc. research on wheat in Canada in the *Geographical Journal*. He also worked with A. J. Herbertson on the advance of geographical education and on the idea of the region, though his view was that it was better to proceed from the smallest discernible region to the larger units rather than to define the major world regions as Herbertson did. From 1905 to 1919, Unstead taught geography at Goldsmith's College for teachers, though from 1908 he also worked at Birkbeck College, where he became a Professor of Geography in London University in 1921. He wrote a number of textbooks and compiled wall maps, several in collaboration with his distinguished successor at Birkbeck, Eva G. R. Taylor. He retired in 1930 and continued to revise his textbooks and produce new ones, as well as a few articles, in one of which (*Geography* **18**, 1933, pp. 175–87) he crystallised his views on regional geography. The school texts were widely used and appreciated, but the work on regional method was valued more in Germany than in Britain.

Geogr. J. **132**, 1966, pp. 334–5; *Geography* **51**, 1966, pp. 151–3; *Trans. Inst. Br. Geogr.* **38**, 1966, pp. 199–200: *The Times* 30.11.1965.

White, Arthur Silva (1859–1932)

Throughout a life marred by poor health White was a devoted student of international affairs, and notably of Africa. When the Scottish Geographical Society was founded in 1884 he became its secretary and editor of the monthly journal. Forced to resign in 1892 for health reasons, he spent in all about fifteen years in travelling and residence abroad. In 1890, his book *The Development of Africa* appeared, to be reissued in 1892 and translated into French two years later. Later works included the *Expansion of Egypt* in 1899, and a large number of articles and reviews in a wide range of journals. From 1904–1909 he was the permanent secretary (with the title of 'assistant secretary') to the British Association and from 1912 to 1914 he was a special assistant at the Imperial Institute. Then followed, from 1915 to 1919, service for the War Trade Intelligence Division and two years, to 1921, as deputy director of the Reconstruction Branch of the Civil Service Commission.

Geogr. J. **80**, 1932, p. 560; *Scott. Geogr. Mag.* **48**, 1932, p. 357; *Who Was Who.*

Wooldridge, Sidney William (1900–1963)

At King's College, London, Wooldridge graduated with first-class honours in geology in 1921 and became an assistant in the joint Department of Geology and Geography in 1922, and Lecturer in Geography in 1927. From 1921 he published numerous papers, at first entirely in geological journals but from 1931 also in geographical journals. Clearly he enjoyed working on geological and geomorphological problems for their intrinsic interest, but he also wished to show the relation of physical features, as explained by detailed research, to human activities, notably in the Anglo-Saxon period. In later years he had much of interest to say on the post-war development of Greater London, including the sites chosen for the New Towns. He was an obvious and helpful choice for a government committee on the use of sands and gravels in the 1950s. Most of his work was done in collaboration with others and nobody did more to encourage field study among his students, including those taking the London degree externally and visitors to the centres established by the Field Studies Council.

Geogr. J. **129**, 1963, pp. 382–3; *Geography* **48**, 1963, pp. 329–30; *Trans. Inst. Br. Geogr.* **34**, 1964, xi–xiv.

Younghusband, Sir Francis Edward (1863–1942)

Belonging to a military family, Younghusband was educated at Clifton and Sandhurst and sent to India shortly after he was commissioned in 1882. He acquired a passion for travel which he was able to gratify by his flair for obtaining extended leave. Much of his travelling was in areas of interior Asia of which little was known, including Manchuria, but it was his remarkable success in Tibet, eventually leading to his appointment as British Commissioner in 1902–4, that made him famous. Another notable achievement was a survey in 1896–7 of the Transvaal and Rhodesia on which his book, *South Africa of Today*, was published in 1898. His name is chiefly associated with Asia and his book of 1910 on *India and Tibet* was welcomed as a fine contribution to historical and political geography. After his retirement in 1909 he gave devoted service to the Royal Geographical Society, and did much to encourage and assist the various expeditions to Mount Everest. One abiding interest was comparative religion and he gave most of his time in his last ten years to the presidency of the World Congress of Faiths.

Geogr. J. **100**, 1942, pp. 131–7.

References

ALCOCK *see* British Association.

ARDEN-CLOSE *see* Close.

BAKER, J. N. L., 1951, *A History of Geographical Discovery and Exploration*, Harrap (London).

BEAVER, S. H., 1944, 'Minerals and planning', *Geogr. J.* **104**, pp. 166–98.

BEAVER, S. H., 1955, 'Land reclamation after surface mineral working', *J. Tn. Plann. Inst.* **41**, pp. 146–54.

BEAVER, S. H., 1964, 'The Potteries: a study in the evolution of a cultural landscape', *Trans. Inst. Br. Geogr.* **34**, pp. 1–31.

BECKINSALE, R. P., 1972, 'The IGU and the development of physical geography', *Geography Through a Century of Congresses*, International Geographical Union (Montreal).

BERESFORD, M., 1954, *The Lost Villages of England*, Lutterworth Press (London).

BEST, R. H., 1965, 'Recent changes and future prospects in land use in England and Wales', *Geogr. J.* **131**, pp. 1–12.

BIRD, J., 1956, 'Scale in regional study: illustrated by brief comparisons between the western peninsulas of England and France', *Geography* **41**, pp. 25–38.

BIRD, J., 1963, *The Major Seaports of the United Kingdom*, Hutchinson (London).

BOAL, F. W., 1969, 'Territoriality on the Shankhill–Falls divide, Belfast', *Ir. Geogr.* **6**, pp. 30–50.

BOAL, F. W., 1970, 'Social space in the Belfast urban area' in Stephens, N. and Glasscock, R. E. (eds), *Irish Geographical Studies*, Department of Geography, Queen's University, Belfast.

BOAL, F. W., 1971, 'Territoriality and class: a study of two residential areas in Belfast', *Ir. Geogr.* **6/1**, pp. 229–48.

Board of Trade, Report 1964, *Census of Distribution and Other Services*, 14 parts.

BOWEN, E. G. (ed.), 1957, *Wales: a physical, historical and regional geography*, Methuen (London).

BOWEN, E. G., 1959, 'Le Pays de Galles,' *Trans. Inst. Br. Geogr.* **26**, pp. 1–23.

BOWMAN, I., 1921, 1923, 1924, 1928, *The New World*, World Book Co. (Yonkers-on-Hudson).

British Association for the Advancement of Science, Bradford 1873, *Reports, Notices and Abstracts*, pp. 156–7.

BROWN, R. N. RUDMOSE, 1914, 'The province of the geographer', *Scott. Geogr. Mag.* **30**, pp. 467–79.

BROWN, T. N. L., 1971, *The History of the Manchester Geographical Society 1884–1950*, Manchester University Press.

CARRÉ, F., 1978, 'Camille Vallaux,' *Geographers; biobibliographical studies* **2**, pp. 119–26, Mansell (London).

CARRUTHERS, I., 1957, 'A classification of service centres in England and Wales,' *Geogr. J.* **123**, pp. 371–85.

Census 1951, England and Wales, *General Report* (1958) HMSO.

Census 1951, England and Wales, *Report on Greater London and five other Conurbations* (1956) HMSO.

Census 1961: county reports.

CHORLEY, R, J., DUNN, A, J., and BECKINSALE, R. P., 1964, *The history of the study of landforms* **1**, Methuen (London).

CHRISTALLER, W., 1933, *Central places in Southern Germany* (translation of *Die Zentralen Orte in Suddeutschland* by C. W. Baskin), Prentice-Hall Inc. (Englewood Cliffs, N.J. 1946).

CLAPHAM, J. H., 1926–38, *An Economic History of Modern Britain* 3 vol., Cambridge University Press.

CLARK, J. G. D., 1932, *The Mesolitic Age in Britain*, Cambridge University Press.

CLARK, J. G. D., 1936, *The Mesolithic Age in Northern Europe*, Cambridge University Press.

CLOSE, C. F., 1911, 'The position of geography', *Geogr. J.* **38**, pp. 404–13.

COATES, B.E. and HUNT, A. J., 1965, 'Sheffield and the Don basin conurbation; an East Midland view', *E. Midld. Geogr.* **3**, pp. 358–72.

COLE, G. D. H. (ed.), 1929, *A Tour Thro' the Whole Island of Great Britain . . . by Daniel Defoe, Gent. 1727*, 2 vols with an introduction by G. D. H. Cole, printed for Peter Davies 1927 (London).

COLEMAN, A., 1961, 'The second Land Use Survey: progress and prospects', *Geogr. J.* **127**, pp. 168–86.

COOKE, R. U. and ROBSON, B. T., 1976, 'Geography in the United Kingdom. 1972–76', *Geogr. J.* **142**, pp. 81–100.

DARBY, H. C. (ed.), 1936, *An Historical Geography of England Before A.D. 1800*, Cambridge University Press.

DARBY, H. C., 1940(a), *The Drainage of the Fens*, Cambridge University Press.

DARBY, H. C., 1940(b), *The Medieval Fenland*, Cambridge University Press.

DARBY, H. C., 1951, 'The changing English landscape', *Geogr. J.* **117**, pp. 377–98.

DARBY, H. C., 1953, 'On the relations between geography and history', *Trans. Inst. Br. Geogr.* **19**, pp. 1–11.

DARWIN, L., 1911, presidential address, *Geogr. J.* **38**, pp. 1–7.

DAVIS, W. M., 1895, 'The development of certain English rivers', *Geogr. J.* **5**, pp. 127–46.

DAVIS, W. M., 1899, 'The geographical cycle', *Geogr. J.* **14**, pp. 481–504.

DEFOE *see* Cole.

Department of Economic Affairs: 1964 *The West Midlands: a regional study*; 1965(a), *The North West: a regional study*; 1965(b), *The East Midlands study*; 1966, *A survey of Yorkshire and Humberside*, HMSO.

DICKINSON, R. E., 1947, *City, Region and Regionalism*, Kegan Paul (London).

EAST, W. G. and MOODIE, A. E. (eds), 1956, *The Changing World*, Harrap (London).

EVANS, E. R. G. R., 1913, 'The British Antarctic expedition 1910–1913', *Geogr. J.* **42**, pp. 11–28.

FAWCETT, C. B., 1932, 'Distribution of the urban population in Great Britain 1931', *Geogr. J.* **79**, pp. 100–16.

FENTON, E. W., 1933, 'The vegetation of an upland area (Boghall Glen, Midlothian)', *Scott. Geogr. Mag.* **49**, pp. 331–54.

FISHER, C. A., 1954, 'The third generation', *Geographical Studies* **1**, p. 2.

FLEURE, H. J., 1919, 'Human regions', *Scott. Geogr. Mag.* **35**, pp. 94–105.

FLEURE, H. J., 1922, *The Peoples of Europe*, Oxford.

FLEURE, H. J., 1923, *The Races of England and Wales*, Humphrey Milford (London).

FLEURE, H. J., 1927, *The Races of Mankind*, Benn (London).

FLEURE, H. J., 1929, *An Introduction to Geography*, Benn (London).

FLEURE, H. J., 1932, *The Geographical Background of Modern Problems*, Longmans Green (London).

FLEURE, H. J., 1953, 'Sixty years of geography and education', *Geography* **38**, pp. 231–66 (esp. pp. 236–45).

FLEURE, H. J., *see* Peake, H. J. E.

FREEMAN, T. W., 1954, 'Early developments of geography at Manchester University', *Geogr. J.* **120**, pp. 118–19.

FREEMAN, T. W., 1958, 1964, 1967, 1974, *Geography and Planning*, Hutchinson (London).

FREEMAN, T. W., 1959, 'Two landscapes: southwest Scotland and northeast Ireland', in Miller, R. and Watson, J. W. (eds), *Geographical Essays in Memory of A. G. Ogilvie*, Nelson (London).

FREEMAN, T. W., 1967, *The Geographer's Craft*, Manchester University Press.

FREEMAN, T. W., and RODGERS, H. B., 1966, *Lancashire, Cheshire and the Isle of Man*, Nelson (London).

FREEMAN, T. W., 1976, 'The 'Scottish Geographical Magazine': its first thirty years,' *Scott. Geogr. Mag.* **92**, pp. 92–100.

GALTON, F., 1855, 'Notes on modern geography' in *Cambridge Essays; contributed by members of the University*, John W. Parker and Son (London).

GARNETT, A., 1935, 'Insolation, topography and settlement in the Alps', *Geogr. Rev.* **25**, pp. 601–17.

GARNETT, A., 1937, *Insolation and relief* (monograph) *Publs. Inst. Br. Geogr.* 5.

GEDDES, A., 1937, 'The population of Bengal: its distribution and changes – a contribution to geographical method', *Geogr. J.* **89**, pp. 344–68.

GEDDES, A., 1941, 'Half a century of population trends in India: a regional study of net change and variability', *Geogr. J.* **98**, pp. 228–53.

GEDDES, P., 1898, 'The influence of geographical conditions on social development', *Geogr. J.* **12**, pp. 580–7.

Geography Through a Century of Congresses 1972, International Geographical Union (Montreal).

GILBERT, E. W., 1932, 'What is historical geography?', *Scott. Geogr. Mag.* **48**, pp. 129–36.

GILBERT, E. W., 1939, 'Practical regionalism in England and Wales', *Geogr. J.* **94**, pp. 29–44.

GILBERT, E. W., 1947, 'The industrialization of Oxford', *Geogr. J.* **109**, pp. 1–25.

GILBERT, E. W., 1948, 'The boundaries of local government areas', *Geogr. J.* **111**, pp. 172–206.

GILBERT, E. W., 1951, 'Seven lamps of geography', *Geography* **37**, pp. 21–43.

GILBERT, E. W., 1954, *Brighton: old ocean's bauble*, Methuen (London).

GILBERT, E. W., 1957, 'Geography at Oxford and Cambridge', *Oxford Magazine* 14 Feb.

GILBERT, E. W., 1971, 'The RGS and geographical education', *Geogr. J.* **137**, pp. 200–02.

GOLDIE, G, T., 1906, 'Twenty-five years of geographical progress', *Geogr. J.* **28**, pp. 377–85.

GOSKAR, K. and TRUEMAN, A. E., 1934, 'The coastal plateaux of South Wales', *Geol. Mag.* **71**, pp. 468–77.

GOUDIE, A., 1972, 'Vaughan Cornish: geographer', *Trans. Inst. Br. Geogr.* **55**, pp. 1–16.

GREEN, F. H. W., 1950, 'Urban hinterlands in England and Wales: an analysis of bus services', *Geogr. J.* **116**, pp. 64–88.

GREEN, F. H. W., 1951, 'Bus services in the British Isles', *Geogr. Rev.* **41**, pp. 645–55.

GREEN, J. R., *The making of England*, London. 1882, 1897, 2 vols.

GRESSWELL, R. K., 1937, 'The sandy shores of the southwest Lancashire coastline', *Geogr. J.* **90**, pp. 335–49.

GRESSWELL, R. K., 1953, *Sandy Shores in South Lancashire*, Liverpool University Press.

HARE, F. K., 1967, in *Trans. Inst. Br. Geogr.* **42**, pp. 184–5.

HAVILAND, A., 1892 (2nd edn), *The Geographical Distribution of Disease in Great Britain*, Swan Sonneschien and Co. (London).

HERBERTSON, A. J., 1905, 'The major natural regions', *Geogr. J.* **25**, pp. 300–12.

HERBERTSON, A. J., 1913–14, 'Natural regions', *Geogr. Teach.*, **7**, pp. 158–63.

HERBERTSON, A. J., 1915–16, 'Regional environment, heredity and consciousness', *Geogr. Teach.* **8**, pp. 147–53.

HOSKINS, W. G., 1959, *Local History in England*, Longman (London).

HOUSE, J. W., 1952, *Bellingham and Wark; Population Structure and Employment Conditions; Migration Among Children and Young Adults*, North Tyne Survey committee.

HOUSE, J. W., 1954, *North-eastern England: population movements and the landscape since the early 19th century*, King's College, Newcastle-upon-Tyne, Research series no 1.

HOUSE, J. W., 1969, *The North East*, David and Charles (Newton Abbot).

HOUSE, J. W. (ed.), 1973, *The UK Space: resources, environment and the future*, Weidenfeld and Nicolson (London).

HUMPHRYS, G., 1972, *South Wales*, David and Charles (Newton Abbot).

HUTTON, A. W. (ed.), 1892, *Arthur Young's Tour in Ireland*, George Bell (London).

JOHNS, E., 1965, *British Townscapes*, Arnold (London).

JOHNSTON, R. J., 1971, *Urban Residential Patterns*, Bell (London).

JONES, E., 1960, *A Social Geography of Belfast*, Oxford University Press (London).

JUKES, J. B., 1862, 'On the formation of some river valleys in the south of Ireland', *Q. J. Geol. Soc.* **18**, pp. 378–403.

KELTIE, J. SCOTT, 1915, 'A half-century of geographical progress', *Scott. Geogr. Mag.* **31**, pp. 617–36.

LEWIS, F. J., 1904, 'Geographical distribution of vegetation of the basins of the rivers Eden, Tees, Wear and Tyne', *Geogr. J.* **23**, pp. 313–31.

LEWIS, P. and JONES, P. N., 1970, *The Humberside Region*, David and Charles (Newton Abbot).

LEWIS, W. V., 1931, 'Effect of wave incidence on the configuration of a shingle beach', *Geogr. J.* **78**, pp. 129–48.

LEWIS, W. V., 1932, 'The formation of Dungeness foreland', *Geogr. J.* **80**, pp. 258–85.

LEWIS, W. V. and BALCHIN, W. G. V., 1940, 'Past sea-levels at Dungeness', *Geogr. J.* **96**, pp. 258–85.

LINTON, D. L., 1933, 'The origin of the Tweed drainage system', *Scott. Geogr. Mag.* **49**, pp. 162–75.

LINTON, D. L., 1934, 'On the former connection between the Clyde and the Tweed', *Scott. Geogr. Mag.* **50**, pp. 82–92.

LINTON, D. L., 1940, 'Some aspects of the evolution of the rivers Earn and Tay', *Scott. Geogr. Mag.* **56**, pp. 1–11, 69–79.

LINTON, D. L., 1968, 'The assessment of scenery as a natural resource', *Scott. Geogr. Mag.* **84**, pp. 219–38.

LOWENTHAL, D. and PRINCE, H. C., 1964, 'The English landscape', *Geogr. Rev.* **54**, pp. 309–46.

LOWENTHAL, D. and PRINCE, H. C., 1965, 'English landscape tastes', *Geogr. Rev.* **55**, pp. 186–22.

LOWENTHAL, D. and BOWDEN, M. J. (eds), 1976, *Geographies of the Mind*, Oxford University Press (New York).

LUCAS, C. P., 1914, 'Man as a geographical agency', *Geogr. J.* **44**, pp. 477–92.

LYDE, L. W., 1915, 'Types of political frontiers in Europe', *Geogr. J.* **45**, pp. 126–45.

MACKINDER, H. J., 1887, 'One the scope and methods of geography', *Proc. R. Geogr. Soc.* New Series **8**, pp. 698–714 (discussion 714–18).

MACKINDER, H. J., 1895, 'Modern geography, German and English,' *Geogr. J.* **6**, pp. 376–79.

MACKINDER, H. J., 1902, *Britain and the British seas*, Clarendon Press (Oxford): 2 edn ('with acknowledgements to G. G. Chisholm, H. N. Dickson, A. J. Herbertson, H. R. Mill, J. L. Myres') 1907, also 1911, 1915, 1922, 1925, 1930.

MACKINDER, H. J., 1904, 'The geographical pivot of history', *Geogr. J.* **23**, pp. 421–37.

MACKINDER, H. J., 1919, *Democratic Ideals and Reality*, London; also Holt (New York) 1942.

MARKHAM, C. R., 1879, 'The Arctic explorations of 1878', *Proc. R. Geogr. Soc.* New Series **1**, pp. 16–22.

MARKHAM, C. R., 1880, 'Geographical knowledge in 1830 and 1880 with a notice of the work that remains to be done', *J. R. Geogr. Soc.* **50**, pp. 11–26.

MARKHAM, C. R., 1900, *Geogr. J.* **16**, pp. 8–10.

MARKHAM, C. R., 1905, *Geogr. J.* **26**, pp. 6–7 (Presidential Address pp. 1–28).

MIDDLETON, D., 1965, *Victorian Lady Travellers*, Routledge and Kegan Paul (London).

MILL, H. R., 1892a, 'The principles of geography', *Scott. Geogr. Mag.* **8**, pp. 87–93.

MILL, H. R., 1892b and 1897, 'The Clyde Sea area', *Trans. R. Soc. Edinburgh* **36**, pp. 641–729 and **38**, pp. 1–61.

MILL, H. R., 1895a, 'The Challenger publications', *Geogr. J.* **5**, pp. 360–8.

MILL, H. R., 1895b, 'The geographical work of the future', *Scott. Geogr. Mag.* **11**, pp. 49–56.

MILL, H. R. (ed.), 1899, *The International Geography by Seventy Authors*, Newnes (London) also 1911.

MILL, H. R., 1896, 'Proposed geographical description of the British Islands based on the Ordnance Survey', *Geogr. J.* **7**, pp. 345–65.

MILL, H. R., 1900a, 'A fragment of the geography of England: south-west Sussex', *Geogr. J.* **15**, pp. 205–27, 353–78.

MILL, H. R., 1900b, 'The development of habitable lands: an essay in anthropogeography', *Scott. Geogr. Mag.* **16**, pp. 121–38.

MILL, H. R., 1904, 'England and Wales viewed geographically', *Geogr. J.* **24**, pp. 621–36.

MILL, H. R., 1905, *The Siege of the South Pole*, Alston Rivers (London).

MILL, H. R., 1909, 'Lieut. Shackleton's achievement', *Geogr. J.* **33**, pp. 569–73.

MILL, H. R., 1930, *The Record of the Royal Geographical Society*, Royal Geographical Society (London).

MILL, H. R., 1934, 'Recollections of the Society's Early Years', *Scott. Geogr. Mag.* **50**, pp. 269–280.

MILL, H. R., 1951, *An Autobiography*, Longman (London).

MILLER, A. A., 1937, 'The 600 ft. surface in Pembrokeshire and Cardiganshire', *Geogr. J.* **90**, pp. 148–59.

MILLER, A. A., 1939, 'River development in southern Ireland', *Proc. R. Ir. Acad.* **45**, B 14, pp. 321–54.

Ministry of Housing and Local Government, 1964, *The South East Study*, HMSO.

Ministry of Town and Country Planning, 1947, (Hobhouse Report) National Parks Committee, England and Wales, HMSO.

MITCHELL, J. B., 1962, *Great Britain: geographical essays*, Cambridge University Press.

MURPHY, R. E., 1972, *The Central Business District*, Longman (London). (Earlier papers from 1954.)

NEWBIGIN, M. I., 1907, 'The Swiss Valais: a regional study', *Scott. Geogr. Mag.* **23**, pp. 169–91, 238–39.

NEWBIGIN, M. I., 1915a, *Geographical Aspects of Balkan Problems*, London (see also *Scott. Geogr. Mag.* **31**, (1915)b, pp. 281–303, 636–51.

NEWBIGIN, M. I., 1934, editorial, *Scott. Geogr. Mag.* **50**, pp. 257–69.

OGILVIE, A. G., 1922, *Some Aspects of Boundary Settlement at the Peace Conference*, no. 49 of 'Helps for Students of history', S.P.C.K. (London).

OGILVIE, A. G. (ed.), 1928, *Great Britain: essays in regional geography*, Cambridge University Press.

OSBORNE, R. H., 1965, 'Sheffield and the economic planning region: an East Midland view', *E. Midld. Geogr.* **3**, pp. 419–23.

PATON, J. and WILSON, C. T. R., 1954, 'The Ben Nevis Observatory', *Weather* **6**, pp. 290–311.

PEAKE, H. J. E. and FLEURE, H. J., *Corridors of Time* series. *Apes and Men; Hunters and Artists; Peasants and Potters; Priests and Kings* (all 1927): *The Steppe and the Sown* (1928): *The Way of the Sea* (1929): *Merchant Venturers in Bronze* (1931): *The Horse and the Sword* (1933): *The Law and the Prophets* (1936): *Times and Places* (1956), Clarendon Press (Oxford).

Report of the Committee on Land Utilisation in Rural Areas (1942) – the Scott Report.

ROBSON, B. T., 1969, *Urban Analysis: a study of city structure*, Cambridge University Press.

ROSING, K. E. and WOOD, P. A., 1971, *Character of a Conurbation*, University of London Press (London).

ROXBY, P. M., 1919–20, 'The Far East question in its geographical setting', *Geogr. Teach.* **10**, pp. 82–90, 142–50, 253–69.

ROXBY, P. M., 1925, 'The distribution of population in China', *Geogr. Rev.* **15**, pp. 1–24.

ROXBY, P. M., 1930, 'The scope and aims of human geography', *Scott. Geogr. Mag.* **46**, pp. 276–90.

ROXBY, P. M., 1934, 'China as an entity', *Geography* **19**, pp. 1–20.

Royal Commission on the Distribution of the Industrial Population, 1940 (Barlow), Cmnd. 6153, HMSO.

Royal Commission on Local Government in Greater London, report 1961, Cmnd. 1164, esp. pp. 295–305, 341–53, HMSO.

Royal Commission on Local Government in England 1966–1969 (Redcliffe-Maud), Cmnd. 4040: articles on the report include Thomas, D. *et al.*, *Area*, No. 4 (1969), pp. 1–20 and by James, J. R., House, J. W. and Hall, P., *Geogr. J.* **136**, (1970), pp. 1–23.

Royal Geographical Society, 1854, 1861, 1871 and later to 1938, *Hints for Travellers*.

RUSSELL, E. J., 1907, 'The relations between the geographical position and the productive capacity of the land', *J. Manchr Geogr. Soc.* **23**, pp. 28–42.

SARGENT, A. J., 1912, 'The Tyne', *Geogr. J.* **40**, pp. 469–86.

SAUER, C. O., 1941, 'Foreword to historical geography', *Ann. Ass. Am. Geogr.* **31**, pp. 1–24.

SCARGILL, D. I., 1976, 'The RGS and the foundation of geography at Oxford', *Geogr. J.* **141**, pp. 216–39.

Scott Report, 1942, *Report of the Committee on Land Utilisation in Rural Areas* Cmnd. 6378, HMSO.

SHEAIL, J., 1975, 'The concept of National Parks in Great Britain 1900–1950', *Trans. Inst. Br. Geogr.* **66**, pp. 41–56.

SMAILES, A. E., 1953, *The Geography of Towns*, Hutchinson (London).

SMAILES, A. E. and HARTLEY, G., 1961, 'Shopping centres in the Greater London area', *Trans. Inst. Br. Geogr.* **29**, pp. 201–13.

SMITH, D. M., 1969, *The North West*, David and Charles (Newton Abbot).

SMITH, W. (ed.), 1953, *A Scientific Study of Merseyside*, Liverpool University Press (for British Association for the Advancement of Science).

SMITH, W. G. and MOSS, C. E., 1903a, 'Geographical distribution of vegetation in Yorkshire: Part 1, Leeds and Halifax district', *Geogr. J.* **21**, pp. 375–401.

SMITH, W. G. and RANKIN, W. M., 1903b, 'Geographical distribution of vegetation in Yorkshire: Part 2, Harrogate and Skipton district,' *Geogr. J.* **22**, pp. 149–78.

SNODGRASS, C. P., 1941, 'The density of agricultural population in Scotland with English and European comparisons', *Geogr. J.* **97**, pp. 236–45.

STAMP, L. D., 1947a, 'Wartime changes in British agriculture', *Geogr. J.* **109**, pp. 39–57.

STAMP, L. D., 1947b, *The Land of Britain: its use and misuse*, Longman (London).

STAMP, L. D., 1950, *Our Developing World*, Faber and Faber (London).

STAMP, L. D. and HOSKINS, W. G., 1963, *The Common Lands of England and Wales*, Collins (London).

STEEL, R. W. and WATSON, J. W., 1972, 'Geography in the United Kingdom 1968–72,' *Geogr. J.* **138**, pp. 139–53.

STEERS, J. A., 1927, 'The East Anglian coast', *Geogr. J.* **69**, pp. 24–48.

STEERS, J. A. (ed.), 1934, *Scolt Head Island*, Heffer (Cambridge).

STEERS, J. A., 1937, 'The Culbin Sands and Burghead Bay', *Geogr. J.* **90**, pp. 498–528.

STEVENS, A., 1939, 'The natural geographical region', *Scott. Geogr. Mag.* **55**, pp. 305–17.

STEVENS, A., 1946, 'The distribution of the rural population of Great Britain', *Trans. Inst. Br. Geogr.* **11**, pp. 21–53.

STODDART, D. R., 1975a, 'That Victorian science: Huxley's *Physiography* and its impact on geography', *Trans. Inst. Br. Geogr.* **66**, pp. 17–40.

STODDART, D. R., 1975b, 'The RGS and the foundation of geography at Cambridge', *Geogr. J.* **141**, pp. 216–39.

TANSLEY, A. G. (ed.), 1911, *Types of British Vegetation*, Cambridge University Press.

TANSLEY, A. G., 1939, *The British Islands and Their Vegetation*, Cambridge University Press.

TAYLOR, E. G. R., 1930, *Tudor Geography 1485–1583*, Methuen (London).

TAYLOR, E. G. R., 1934, *Late Tudor and Early Stuart Geography*, Methuen (London).

TAYLOR, E. G. R., 1947, 'Geography in war and peace', *Advancement of Science* **4**, pp. 187–94: also in *Geogr. Rev.* **38**, (1948), pp. 132–41 and in *Scott. Geogr. Mag.* **63** (1947), pp. 97–108.

University College of South Wales and Monmouthshire (for Board of Trade) 1932, *An Industrial Survey of South Wales*.

University College of Swansea. *Social and Economic Survey of Swansea and District*. Six pamphlets, including George, T. N., *The Geology, Physical Features and Natural Resources of the Swansea District*, 1939; Williams, D. T., *The Economic Development of Swansea and the Swansea District to 1921*, 1940; Hare, A. E. C., *The Anthracite Coal Industry of the Swansea District*, 1940; Lloyd, W. Ll., *Trade and Transport: an account of the trade of the port of Swansea and the transport facilities and industry in the district*, 1940.

University of Manchester, Economics Research Section, 1932, *An Industrial Survey of the Lancashire Area.*

University of Manchester, Economics Research Section, 1936, *Readjustment in Lancashire.*

UNSTEAD, J. F., 1912, 'The climatic limits of wheat cultivation, with special reference to North America', *Geogr. J.* **39**, pp. 347–66: also **42** (1913) pp. 165–81, 254–76.

UNSTEAD, J. F., 1933, 'A system of regional geography', *Geography* **18**, pp. 175–87.

UNSTEAD, J. F., 1949, 'H. J. Mackinder and the new geography', *Geogr. J.* **113**, pp. 47–57.

Vidal de la Blache in *Revue de Paris*, 15 decembre 1910.

VINCE, S. W. E., 1953, 'Reflections on the structure and distribution of the rural population in England and Wales', *Trans. Inst. Br. Geogr.* **18**, pp. 53–76.

WANKLYN, H. G., 1948, 'The Middle People: resettlement in Czechoslovakia', *Geogr. J.* **112**, pp. 28–42.

WANKLYN, H. G., 1954, *Czechoslovakia*, Philip (London).

WATSON, J. W. and SISSONS, J. B., 1964, *The British Isles: a systematic study*, Nelson (London).

West Midlands Group, 1948, *Conurbation: a planning scheme of Birmingham and the Black Country*, London.

WHITE, A. SILVA, 1913, 'The dominion of Canada: a study in regional geography,' *Scott. Geogr. Mag.* **29**, pp. 524–47.

WILLATTS, E. C., 1937, 'Middlesex and the London region', Part 79 of Stamp, L. D. (ed.), *The Land of Britain*, Geographical Publications (London).

WILLATTS, E. C. and NEWSON, M. G. C., 1953, 'The geographical pattern of population changes in England and Wales 1921–1951', *Geogr. J.* **119**, pp. 431–54.

WILSON, L. S., 1946, 'Some observations on wartime geography in England', *Geogr. Rev.* **36**, pp. 597–612.

WISE, M. J., 1949, 'On the evolution of the jewellery and gun quarters in Birmingham', *Trans. Inst. Br. Geogr.* **15**, pp. 59–72.

WOOLDRIDGE, S. W. and SMETHAM, D. J., 1931, 'The glacial drifts of Essex and Hertfordshire and their bearing upon the agricultural and historical geography of the region', *Geogr. J.* **78**, pp. 253–69.

WOOLDRIDGE, S. W. and LINTON, D. L., 1933, 'The loam-terrains of southeast England and their relation to early history', *Antiquity* **7**, pp. 297–310, 473–5.

WOOLDRIDGE, S. W., and LINTON, D. L., 1935, 'Some aspects of the Saxon settlement in southeast England considered in relation to the geographical background', *Geography* **20**, pp. 204–22.

WOOLDRIDGE, S. W. and BEAVER, S. H., 1950, 'The working of sand and gravel: a problem in land use', *Geogr. J.* **115**, pp. 42–57.

YOUNG, A., 1770, *Six Months' Tour Through the North of England*, 4 vols, printed for W. Strahan; W. Nicholl, no. 51 St Paul's Churchyard; B. Collins at Salisbury; and J. Balfour at Edinburgh.

YOUNG, A., *see* Hutton.

Index of persons

Index of subjects